MANAGING THE GREAT LAKES SHORELINE:

Experiences and Opportunities

edited by

P.L. Lawrence and J.G. Nelson

Proceedings of a Workshop held at the
University of Waterloo
October 22-23, 1992

Occasional Paper 21
Heritage Resources Centre,
University of Waterloo

Co-sponsored with
Saugeen Valley Conservation Authority and the
Ontario Ministry of Natural Resources
(Lands and Water Policy Section)

Heritage Resources Centre

University of Waterloo

Occasional Papers Series

ISSN 0830-1115

ISBN 0-921245-66-1

Published by:

Heritage Resources Centre
University of Waterloo
Waterloo, Ontario N2L 3G1
© 1993

Canadian Cataloguing in Publication Data

Managing the Great Lakes shoreline : experiences
 and opportunities

(Occasional paper, ISSN 0830-1115 ; 21)
Proceedings of a workshop held at the University
of Waterloo, October 22-23, 1992.
Includes bibliographical references.
ISBN 0-921245-66-1

1. Great Lakes - Shorelines - Conservation -
Congresses. 2. Coastal zone management - Great
Lakes - Congresses. I. Lawrence, P. L. (Patrick
Lloyd). II. Nelson, J. G. (James Gordon), 1932-
III. Heritage Resources Centre. IV. Series:
Occasional paper (Heritage Resources Centre) ; #21.

HT395.C32054 1993   333.91'7'0977   C93-094172-1

Table of Contents

Session III: Concepts, Roles and Institutions

Session IV: Ontario Shoreline Management Program

Session V: Setting the Agenda: Group Sessions

Appendices

WORKSHOP INTRODUCTION

Wetland at the mouth of the Goulais River, Lake Superior, recognized as a
provincial area of natural and scientific interest, provides important habitat for
shorebirds, waterfowl and fish
(photo provided by Peter Burtch, Sault Ste Marie MNR)

Motivation for and Direction of Shore Planning and Management in Ontario

J.G. NELSON and *P.L. LAWRENCE*
Heritage Resources Centre, University of Waterloo
Waterloo, Ontario

"Managing the Great Lakes Shoreline: Experiences and Opportunities" was the focus of a workshop sponsored by the University of Waterloo Heritage Resources Centre, the Saugeen Valley Conservation Authority and the Ontario Ministry of Natural Resources (Lands and Water Policy Section) on October 22-23, 1992.

The motivation for the workshop was a growing interest in planning and managing the Great Lakes shoreline as a result of high lake levels, pollution problems and conflicts among residential, industrial, recreational and conservational users in recent years. Planning and management has been ineffective in dealing with these conflicts and with the rising costs of flooding, erosion and other hazards throughout the Great Lakes system. This situation led to a Great Lakes water levels reference to the International Joint Commission (IJC) in 1985 aimed at trying to arrive at a long term solution. It also led to a provincial review of planning along the Great Lakes shore. The Ontario provincial government decided to make the Ministry of Natural Resources responsible for developing a shoreline management program and the Ontario Conservation Authorities responsible for preparing and implementing shoreline management plans in association with municipalities and other responsible bodies as well as landowners. The surge of interest in resolving land use conflicts and development impacts also led to the report of the Crombie Commission and the creation of the Toronto Waterfront Regeneration Trust which is responsible for implementing a more environmentally sensitive and sustainable approach to the Toronto Waterfront from a broad bioregional perspective.

Problems like those arising in Ontario have been experienced on the American side of the Great Lakes and also along other North American coasts. In many of these areas development pressures are becoming very widespread and acute, threatening loss of citizen access to the shore as well as loss of wetlands and other habitats which support bird, fish and other resources valued by many groups and individuals. Spills of oil and other toxic materials are threats to the shore globally and are also generally not adequately managed.

United Nations agencies and major political bodies such as the European Community have begun to develop coastal policies and directions for states having responsibilities for coastal health. The United States has led in the development and implementation of coastal legislation and policies at the federal, state and local level, notably with the passage of the 1972 federal Coastal Zone Management Act. In Canada attempts to create a more effective planning and management system to respond to increasing coastal stresses have not been very effective except perhaps on a limited local basis.

Our immediate focus of concern is the Great Lakes shore, although we do have a strong interest in developing more effective policy and practice throughout Ontario and Canada. It was in this context that we organized this workshop.

We have summarized the presentations and discussions at the workshop in several sections or sessions. The first *sets the stage* and is intended to provide an opportunity to learn from the experience of others as a basis for improving policy and practice in the Canadian Great Lakes area and particularly in regard to the current preparation of shoreline plans by the Conservation Authorities as part of the new Ontario Shoreline policy. The first paper by Larry Hildebrand is a review of the history of coastal thinking, policy and practice in Canada. He pays special attention to the east coast and to a recent promising resurgence of interest in the coastal zone management idea at the national level. The second paper by Chad Day and colleagues, focuses on experience on the west coast. The paper is basically a comparison of policy and practice between Canada and U.S., and especially Washington state and the province of B.C. This review shows that we have much to learn from the U.S. in terms of developing an effective legal and policy basis for coastal planning as well as in other respects such as resources inventory, implementation and enforcement, cost-sharing, impact assessment, agency co-ordination, public participation, education and private stewardship.

The third paper by Penny Holt and Cathie Cunningham reviews Michigan's experience with coastal zone planning and management. Michigan is a close neighbour to Ontario and a U.S. state that had an early concern for its coast. Michigan is a leader in coastal zone practice in the U.S. Michigan offers lessons to Ontario on the co-ordination of government agencies at the state, local and federal levels. In this regard the *consistency provision* which requires that federal activities be in line with state and local plans is of special interest. Canadian federal and provincial activities proceed independently of any such consideration, leading to conflicts and lost opportunities for co-operation on an ecosystem or other broad basis. Michigan also has lessons for Canada in terms of its level and array of professional staffing and resource commitment and in terms of the way the agencies work closely with people living along the coast.

The next two sections of papers deals with Alternative Approaches and Concepts, Roles and Institutions which could make a difference for Ontario Great Lakes shores. The papers consider: a human ecological approach to management (Lawrence and Nelson); the idea of a biosphere reserve for the Great Lakes as a whole (Francis); the role and importance of biodiversity (Serafin); the applicability of a sustainable development approach (Mckenzie); progress of the IJC reference study on Great Lakes water levels (Stewart); Canada's Great Lakes clean-up fund (Sherbin); climatic change (Sanderson); and, A Green Plan initiative (Koshida and Mortsch).

All of these initiatives and challenges bear on the use and conservation of the Great Lakes area as a whole, but they have especially strong implications for coastal management. The human ecological and the sustainability approaches mean we must think about planning and management in a more comprehensive, interactive and adaptive way. More cross-departmental and multi-disciplinary thinking is needed as well as greater stress on the long term effects and implications of proposals in contrast to the short term focus generally pursued now. The biosphere reserve idea reinforces the ecosystem approach to management which has been stressed in water quality and other challenges over the last ten years or so. A strength of the biosphere reserves idea is its stress on interrelating conservation, use, monitoring, and research in coastal areas. Biodiversity is a major challenge to Canada and other countries as a result of the acceptance of a Global Biodiversity Convention at the Earth Summit in Rio in June, 1992. To date however, biodiversity has been neglected in coastal planning in Ontario. The IJC challenge lies in its rejection of structural control of fluctuating lake levels as too costly economically and environmentally in favour of alternatives such as more stringent land use controls. The nature of climatic change and its effects are still uncertain. Analysis using current models suggests a drop of a metre or more in lake levels which will certainly have effects on shipping, power production, cottaging and recreational and other activities and interests, justifying the Great Lakes - St. Lawrence Basin study now getting underway.

The next section of papers focuses on the strengths and weaknesses of the new Ontario shoreline management program being conducted by the Conservation Authorities under the general guidance of Ontario Ministry of Natural Resources. The first paper outlines the current direction of Ontario coastal planning, which is mainly concerned with better responses to flooding and erosion hazards through for example, improved computerized information systems (GIS), and a broader hazards policy stressing hazard prevention and protection, environmental concern, and research and information as well as more effective use of setbacks and other tools (McKeen). The second paper is a review of Ontario Conservation Authority shore regulations to date (Kreutzwiser and Slaats) based on an assessment of Essex County and Toronto Region Conservation Authorities. The review indicates unevenness in implementation of the regulations, lack of clarity and comprehensiveness in the Conservation Authorities Act with regard to regulations and penalties, understaffing and limited budgets, and lack of knowledge of the reasons for regulations among citizens, this in turn, reducing support for the regulations and associated management measures.

Four case studies are then presented on the development of shoreline management plans by Conservation Authorities in Ontario; Kettle Creek (McCoob), Sault Ste. Marie District (Burtch), Ausable - Bayfield (Donnelly) and Saugeen Conservation Authority (Peach). The approaches to and nature of the planning differs in some ways among the four cases. However some common elements are apparent including a concern for a wider approach to shoreline or coastal planning in the ecosystem or sustainability senses. Other common elements are a strong interest in involving the public at all stages in planning and the use of innovative monitoring and management systems such as videos of the shore and GIS information systems. Another common element is the need for better co-ordination and integration among concerned provincial and local agencies and groups. A related issue is how shoreline planning and management by the Conservation Authorities can be linked with a provincial policy or law which would make planning and management more effective.

The Ontario Planning Act is seen as important in this regard, through its provisions for provincial policies and guidelines on special concerns such as the shoreline. The Planning Act also provides an opportunity for municipalities to build shoreline concerns into official plans and other basic planning and management tools. In this sense the work of the Sewell Commission on the reform of land use planning in Ontario is seen to be potentially very important. There is also considerable interest in a stronger role for environmental impact assessment in screening structural and other proposals for dealing with hazards and other projects in the shore or coastal zone.

On the evening of October 22, a presentation was made on the Waterfront Regeneration Trust (Symmes: Appendix). This presentation stimulated thinking about a watershed, and/or a bioregional approach to planning and management. One fundamental result of the work of the Crombie Commission — and the subsequent creation of the Regeneration Trust — is that the Waterfront approach is before us as an alternative way to plan and manage the water/land interfaces in Ontario, especially in urban areas.

Summaries of questions, discussion and small groups reports are included in these proceedings. These indicate considerable interest among Ontario planners and managers in how the U.S. system works in detail. Many questions were directed to the Michigan people about how they work with setbacks, with zoning, monitoring and local people.

The small group summaries and indeed the entire workshop, highlight the following *major concerns* and the need for government agencies and private groups and individuals to work on them.

1. Shore policies and activities are too focused on flooding and erosion and other hazards in Ontario although the new plans suggest more attention is now being paid to land use conflicts and environmental effects.
2. Hazard policy and practice is still too focused on engineering or structural responses such as breakwalls and groins rather than land use or other behavioural approaches.
3. Scientific and evaluation research is beginning to develop although it is still insignificant in terms of the efforts by governments, the private sector and the universities in the U.S.
4. Broader approaches such as human ecology, ecosystems, and sustainable development are increasingly being advocated and to a lesser extent used in coastal and related planning. Interest in biodiversity and innovative management systems such as biosphere reserves is growing but slowly.
5. Although broad comprehensive ideas or approaches are helping to bring things together, much fragmentation still exists among the various governments and private agencies and groups concerned with the Great Lakes coast. Concern is frequently expressed about the need for clearer and stronger legal and policy bases for responsibility and action. Some of this concern is attitudinal and historic and is lessened to some extent by gains that seem achievable through the participatory information exchange and co-operation which may be developing as part of current shore planning.

6. Much more attention is needed in building awareness and providing information and communication on shore or coastal processes. Many professionals, politicians, and private citizens simply do not understand the shore and how it works and mistakes are frequently repeated. Better information and learning systems are urgently needed.

7. Monitoring and assessment has been and continues to be weak not only in shore but also in land use planning and management generally in Ontario. Some improvements are being made in this regard in the current planning, for example in developing GIS and other information systems — although the old question of the degree to which these should be centralized or dispersed to localities is still before us. Periodic assessments or reviews of progress and problems are seen as useful to ordinary people as well as responsible government agencies and politicians. State of the Coast or other reports seem desirable in this regard, it being possible to discuss and respond to these on a community or regional basis.

8. The very serious matter of shore or coastal planning and management is still not really on the public agenda in Ontario and Canada. However, the new surge of interest internationally, nationally and regionally suggests its time may be coming. Many people feel more advocacy is needed in this direction by government and especially by private groups in the Great Lakes area. Current shore planning is an opportunity and a challenge in this regard.

9. Stress needs to be placed on defining management in terms of coastal ecosystems rather than more narrowly, as shorelines. The provincial program of shoreline management appears to be too narrowly focused. Coastal zone implies a larger area, perhaps defined on an ecosystem basis, and encompasses a range of issues and concerns (such as water quality and land use conflicts) fundamental to our understanding of the Great Lakes. In this context some people have suggested thinking more generally in terms of waterfront in the sense used by the Crombie Commission.

10. Our management and planning mechanisms need to be adaptable. Concerns about climate change, ecosystem health and water levels imply a degree of uncertainty. Shoreline management on the Great Lakes requires an ability to adapt to change and plan for rapid shifts in environmental factors or in scientific understanding of natural or human influenced processes.

ACKNOWLEDGEMENTS

Funding to support the workshop and preparation of these proceedings was provided by the Ontario Ministry of Natural Resources (Lands and Waters Policy Branch), the Saugeen Valley Conservation Authority, the Canadian National Parks Service and the Social Sciences and Humanities Research Council of Canada.   All the authors are thanked for their time and effort in the presentation and preparation of the papers. The help of the session moderators and group leaders; Geoff Peach, Reid Kreutzwiser, Rafal Serafin, Ron Stenson, Chris Stewart and Andy Skibicki is greatly appreciated. The editors wish to thank Joanne Hoffman for her assistance in typing and editing of the draft papers. Lisa Weber administered the workshop organization and final publication of these proceedings.

Session I

SETTING THE STAGE: LEARNING FROM THE EXPERIENCE OF OTHERS

Horseshoe Bay on the West Coast of British Columbia
Important port facility for ferry transport across to Vancouver Island
and a centre for recreation and tourism
(photo provided by Patrick Lawrence, University of Waterloo)

Coastal Zone Management in Canada: The Next Generation

LAWRENCE P. HILDEBRAND
Environment Canada, Dartmouth, Nova Scotia

Introduction

These are exciting times for Coastal Zone Management (CZM) in Canada! Momentum for the development of a national approach to the coordinated planning and management of the extensive Canadian coastal zone is once again on the rise. The federal government is leading the development of a national policy and strategy for CZM, various provinces are expressing interest in, and seriously considering their relationships to their coastal environments, and two key international commitments are providing the political motivation for us to take a concerted and coordinated approach to the management of the Canadian coastal zone.

But this hasn't always been the case. Over the past twenty years, support for the concept of Coastal Zone Management in Canada has waxed and waned in bureaucratic and political circles. It was a great struggle - ultimately lost throughout the 1970s and 1980s - to translate an identified and documented concern for coastal zone problems into a national approach to the comprehensive management of our coastal and shoreline areas. The essential political support, which would secure the issue a place on the Canadian public policy agenda, could not be maintained. From heady highs in the late 1970s when the Canadian Council of Resource and Environment Ministers convened a national Shore Zone symposium, to the lows of the early 1980s when Coastal Zone Management became a term not to be spoken in mixed company, the concept has remained alive in practice, albeit under several aliases.

This paper will review the history of national CZM policy development in Canada, highlight the practice in its present-day manifestations, place the issue in the current international context, and make recommendations to advance CZM in Canada over the coming decades.

Canada as a Coastal Nation

A Mari usque ad Mare. For over a century, Canada's motto "From Sea to Sea" has symbolized this country's relationship to the marine environment. Surrounded by the Atlantic ocean in the east, the Pacific to the west, the Arctic ocean in the north, and the Great Lakes to the south, the coastal environment figures prominently in our geography, history, commerce and way of life. It is only politically it seems, that the coastal zone has not been afforded a place on the Canadian public policy agenda.

Canada has always been proud to promote itself as a coastal nation in terms of its prominence in areas such as shipping, fisheries, recreation, and scientific research. With the longest marine coastline in the world (244,000 km), an immense Exclusive Fisheries Zone (4,925,000 km2), and a land mass that fronts on three oceans and the world's largest lake system, our claim to coastal nation status is certainly merited in geographical terms.

Yet Canadian coastal zones are a paradox. While undeveloped and remote stretches may well constitute the largest portion of the coast, the intensively used and more densely settled coastal urban centres and their hinterlands portray all of the resource management problems which can possibly be expected in similar urban coastal areas around the world. Prime locations for a variety of different activities may be in abundance in northern Labrador for instance, but in the southern mainland of British Columbia or along the north shore of Lake Ontario, such locations are scarce. As a result, the management of much of the undeveloped coastal zone of Canada may simply require the care to preserve or enhance; but in more populated regions, it implies the solving of extensive and pervasive conflicts and even the creation of new institutional arrangements.

One of the realities of Canadian politics is that if an issue cannot be made to seem significant as far as central Canada is concerned, it rarely makes headway on the national public agenda. The political indifference to the Canadian coastal zone may be tied to a number of factors, but key among them has been the inherent uncertainty over our orientation to the coastal zone. The question, "is Canada a coastal nation?" has never been adequately debated or resolved in this country, thus leaving us unclear where our priorities lie.

Politics

The Need for CZM in Canada

By world standards, large areas of the Canadian marine environment are relatively untouched and uncontaminated by human activities and support a diverse and flourishing biota and many commercial, recreational and cultural uses (Wells and Rolston, 1991). But we do have serious problems - especially in many harbours, estuaries and nearshore waters. Even distant offshore waters are threatened by humankind's activities. Rapidly increasing demands for urbanization, industrialization, transportation and recreation, and many unplanned and locally-taken decisions on coastal use are made without full consideration of environmental impacts or resource foreclosure options. Even remote parts of the Arctic are beginning to experience effects similar to those along other coasts. There are early warning signs that show a decline in marine environmental quality in many areas.

Growing problems of harbour pollution, fisheries declines, loss of wetlands, oil spills, threats to unique and fragile ecosystems from oil exploration and transportation (such as in the ice-laden Arctic), and the highly industrialized and pollution issues of the Great Lakes basin, all demonstrate the deficiencies in current management arrangements.

Pollution of some coasts has led to social and economic problems such as shellfish contamination resulting in the closure of thousands of square kilometers of estuarine areas to harvesting. Poorly planned coastal developments in other areas have degraded and continue to threaten vulnerable marshlands, wetland habitats, and estuarine ecosystems, leading to adverse effects on the fishing resource, economics, and recreational opportunities. At the same time, inappropriate development siting has proceeded without adequate accounting of the risks from coastal-related natural hazards such as storms, flooding and erosion. No one level of government can act independently to resolve coastal-related problems; yet many coastal zone conflicts develop from the unilateral exercise of specific mandates by a single level of government or by a single agency within a government.

All of these developments, taken in conjunction with other uses and abuses, suggest that Canada should carefully weigh, not just the environmental problems and resource use conflicts associated with each activity, but the combined consequences of such developments. When both the cumulative effects of small- scale modifications of the coastal zone and major impacts of massive developments are considered, the need for overall planning and coordination in the coastal zone - the need for Coastal Zone Management - becomes more urgent.

Institutional Development for CZM in Canada

The planning and management of coastal areas in Canada have been largely an ad hoc process. There have been a number of steps taken by both federal and provincial governments toward management including: the control of pollution from some urban and industrial areas; the reservation of some critical habitats for particular purposes in recognition of their special values, and investigations, through the environmental assessment processes at both the federal and provincial levels, to determine the probable effects of some proposed developments. However, an overall framework has never been developed.

By the late 1970s, it was becoming increasingly evident that such ad hoc responses to specific problems were inadequate. Further, in the absence of a more comprehensive policy, important ecological, cultural, historic and aesthetic values; would continue to be degraded in small increments through a number of individual abusive actions, none of which are regarded in themselves as contributing a serious threat. It is not surprising then, that concern over the use and abuse of such a valuable resource as the coastal zone has grown in recent years. What is surprising, is that despite twenty years of discussion on the subject, and some degree of inter-agency cooperation in coastal resource management, existing management activities related to coastal resources are still largely ad hoc, narrowly conceived and poorly coordinated, and Canada does not have a national policy or framework for the management of its immense coastal zone.

There has been no legislative focus through a national CZM Act as in the U.S. and many other coastal nations, nor specific policy objectives or an overall management framework for the coastal zone. Neither are there clear or well- defined provincial or territorial coastal zone programs. There have been no coordinated programs to link the myriad coastal activities, regulations or policies, nor a common vision to guide us.

Instead, policies and institutions have evolved from the existing legislative framework, responding to opportunities and needs as they have arisen. Unfortunately, there has been little agreement as to what the objectives of a national program should be, how they should be enunciated, and who should promote their realization. Not surprisingly, many conclude that there is no CZM in Canada.

The main problem with proposals to create specific coastal management agencies is convincing policy makers that the coastal zone is somehow more worthy of specific institutions than other integrated environmental systems. It must be remembered that CZM is only one of many competing demands for public funds, and accrued benefits must be weighed against investments in other activities. Although considerable human and financial resources have already been invested in certain coastal zone problems, the need for greater coordination, improved communication, and teamwork to manage coastal resources more effectively clearly exists.

History of CZM Policy Development in Canada

In 1972, when our American neighbours passed their Coastal Zone Management Act and began to implement their federal-state partnership for the cooperative management of their extensive coastal zone, Canada looked south and was inspired to consider a similar approach for our own coastal zone.

Whereas the U.S. program was developed in response to the dramatic and growing issues of environmental degradation, habitat loss and expensive and socially disruptive resource use conflicts, these same problems in Canada were not of an order of equivalent magnitude. While we could readily cite similar problems in various locations about our four coasts - in the Fraser Estuary in British Columbia, the St. Lawrence River, various industrialized harbours in Atlantic Canada and on the Ontario shores of the Great Lakes - the overriding need for a comprehensive, coast-wide response could not be successfully elevated on to the political agenda.

Throughout the 1970s and early 1980s, numerous meetings, workshops, symposia and planning meetings were held to scope out the problems and develop the basis for a concerted response. These meetings emphasized that if concerns about the use and misuse of coastal zone resources were to be resolved, some mechanism was required to enable the jurisdictions concerned to work cooperatively to resolve coastal zone resource problems.

The most significant event in terms of elevating the level of discussion about a national approach to Coastal Zone Management in Canada, was a major Shore Zone Symposium, sponsored by the Canadian Council of Resource and Environment Ministers (CCREM), held in Victoria, B.C. in October, 1978 (14 years ago to this month). This symposium marked the highest level of political recognition that CZM had received to date. It was attended by senior level representatives of both the federal and provincial governments, and the academic community. An important product of the Victoria symposium was a set of ten principles for coastal management which, it was purported, if pursued by agencies at both federal and provincial levels, could lead to much more coordinated and thereby effective planning and management frameworks (Table 1). It seemed as though the momentum for establishing a coordinated approach to CZM in Canada had reached a peak.

It is noteworthy that the term "Shore Zone" was used deliberately at this Symposium in an effort to convince the central provinces that they too had problems and management needs at the land-water interface. The term "shore zone", as opposed to "coastal zone" continued to appear throughout discussions of the subject in Canada.

While the event was convened under the auspices of the CCREM, and attended by senior bureaucrats at both the federal and provincial levels and leading academics in the field, the true measure of the importance of this issue on the Canadian scene was in the lack of response to the call for moving the issue of CZM forward in Canada.

Nevertheless, with these principles in hand, the federal government did establish a 'Shore Zone' program in 1980. The objective of the program was to develop and implement policies that would ensure coordination of federal activities and to participate with provinces in the planning of shore zone areas where significant federal responsibilities are involved. Unfortunately, the federal program was poorly supported and the provinces were not particularly inspired to pursue the development of their own coastal programs. Despite the broad recognition for the need for CZM, the essential federal and provincial roles, and the development of general principles, little had changed in terms of institutional development for CZM in Canada (Table 2).

It became apparent that the federal government was unwilling to fully support the concept. So, while the concept of shore zone planning was recognized and endorsed, resources were not forthcoming to support a more ambitious shore zone program that would include new federal-provincial shore zone planning agreements. Ultimately, both political and financial factors were impediments to the federal government's response to the CCREM recommendations and the Federal Shore Zone Program had faded away within three years.

After more than ten years of effort, and with no concrete policy in hand or even in sight, CZM had become a 'bad word' in government circles, and most people were convinced that national policy development had, in fact, finally died. In administrative terms, perhaps it had. It was now obvious that the goal to develop and implement a formal CZM plan, or nationwide coastal resource use policy, would not be realized in the political and temporal contexts of the 1980s. Coastal Zone Management, as a formally identified intersectoral component of federal and most provincial government activities in Canada, was considered dead by 1983.

Table 1. Principles of Shoreline Management

Each shore management policy should be based on, but need not be limited to, the following principles:

(1) "The recognition of the importance of shore areas"
All levels of government recognize the critical environmental, economic, and social importance of shores and actively promote the sensitive and orderly management of shores and shore resources in the long term.

(2) "A cooperative approach to management"
Where interests of governments and/or agencies coincide, a cooperative approach to the management of shores should be undertaken. A lead agency should be identified within each jurisdiction to provide the leadership to develop and integrate intra-and inter-jurisdictional policy. This does not preclude direct cooperation between and among individual agencies in relation to specific issues.

(3) "Policy and program coordination"
All levels and agencies of government must strive to coordinate their policies and programs so that integrated management of shores and shore resources can be achieved. To accomplish this, interjurisdictional coordinative mechanisms could be adopted to embrace the numerous and diverse interests associated with shore management.

(4) "The recognition of the role of local governments"
The key role of local governments in shore management planning and implementation must be recognized. Senior governments could support these efforts by providing technical and financial assistance.

(5) "The contribution of industry"
The potential contribution and cooperation of industry in the development and implementation of shore management practices must be actively encouraged.

(6) "The interrelationship of shore activities"
All shore users must take into account the consequences of their actions on shore systems and on other activities. Development siting criteria sensitive to the physical, biological and social characteristics of shores must be included within each policy.

(7) "The protection of sensitive, unique, and significant areas"
Sensitive, unique, and significant shore areas, including biotic habitats, should be identified and protected. Government could provide incentives to private individuals and groups who manage, protect, and restore sensitive shore areas.

(8) "The right of public access"
Rights of public access to shore areas must be ensured. In those areas where shore access is in short supply, efforts should be made to restore public rights-of-way.

(9) "Information systems"
Cooperative information systems must be structured so that information obtained is readily applicable to shore management decision-making and planning. Interjurisdictional information centres to coordinate the collection, collation, and dissemination of shore management information could be established for this purpose.

(10) "Public awareness"
All levels of government must undertake programs designed to increase public awareness and appreciation of the dynamic and sensitive nature of shores. Public concerns should be incorporated into the objectives of shore management policies.

(From Hildebrand, 1989)

Table 2. Problems Experienced with Canadian Efforts to Develop a
National Coastal Zone Management Policy

1. Lack of agreement on a satisfactory definition of the coastal zone
2. Political boundaries vs. ecological boundaries
3. Coastal zone treated as a common property resource
4. Lack of awareness of coastal zone problems
5. No clear motivation for CZM
6. Administrative fragmentation
7. Lack of clearly state goals
8. Dominance of short-term management over long-range planning
9. Inadequate information on which to base decisions
10. Attitudinal problems
11. Ran against political and economic grain of the time

(From Hildebrand, 1989)

If we step back from the immediacy of the coastal issues that face
each of us every day, and step into the shoes of our most senior bureaucrats and politicians of the day, we too might see not a compelling and
coast-wide emergency that demanded a comprehensive national
response, but rather a vast expanse of largely untouched and unoccu-
pied coast in the Arctic, northern B.C. and the Atlantic provinces, that
was not demanding an immediate and urgent national institutional
response. Many other issues were demanding attention on the public
policy agenda, and a full and coordinated policy response to the coastal
zone did not rank very high. Many of those who were championing the
cause became discouraged and the momentum that had been building
for a comprehensive policy and strategy to address this issue was lost.
By 1983, even the most ardent visionaries had finally accepted that
development of a national CZM approach had been aborted.

Present Day Context

Although CZM failed to materialize in official terms in Canada over the
past twenty years, a number of regional and estuary-specific initiatives
have emerged throughout this period. Although not formally resulting
from the Victoria symposium, a comparison of their fundamental goals
and principles to those which came out of Victoria in 1978 (Hildebrand,
1989) reveals that they are in fact following those basic principles, yet
adapting them to reflect local needs and circumstances despite the
absence of a national program.

British Columbia

Perhaps our most prominent example has been in the Fraser River estuary in British Columbia. In the late 1970s, extensive studies were undertaken on the Fraser to define the problems it was encountering and to recommend appropriate actions. In 1985, the five-year Fraser River Estuary Management Program (FREMP) was established under a federal-provincial agreement to "provide the means for accommodating a growing population and economy, while maintaining the quality and productivity of the Fraser estuary's natural environment". From its inception, FREMP has successfully fostered a cooperative atmosphere, coordinating the efforts and activities of more than 30 agencies representing all levels of government, First Nations and other official groups. The Agreement has since been extended to 1993.

The FREMP experience to date has provided some valuable lessons for CZM in Canada. While improvements could be made to the process (see article by Chad Day in this volume), the experience gained through FREMP over the past seven years has been invaluable to the development of a Canadian approach to CZM. One significant realization has been, that to properly manage the Fraser as a system, a much broader approach, which included the entire Fraser River and Basin, would be required.

In 1991, significant new resources under Canada's Green Plan brought the establishment of the Fraser River Action Plan (FRAP) - a $100-million program jointly administered by Environment Canada and Fisheries and Oceans Canada to clean up the Fraser River, restore sockeye salmon populations to historical levels of abundance, and restore the river to environmental health.

In May, 1992, the planning perspective was further broadened with the signing of a five-year Agreement Respecting the Fraser Basin Management Program (FBMP) between the Government of Canada (DFO, DOE), the province of British Columbia (Ministries of Environment, Lands & Parks and Economic Development, Small Business and Trade) and the Municipalities and Regional Districts. The Agreement was reached in recognition that the individual efforts of the parties will not achieve sustainable development in the Fraser Basin on their own, and that integration of the social, economic and environmental components would require the coordination of their activities with each other and with other stakeholders. The need for collective and coordinated action has been reflected in the development of this Agreement.

The FBMP features a 19-member management board with representatives from three levels of government, aboriginal peoples, environmental groups, industry, labour and other interested parties, to assist in developing and implementing an integrated management program for long-term sustainability in the Basin. An initial focus of the program will be on cleaning up and preventing pollution, restoring productivity of the natural environment, conserving natural areas, returning salmon stocks to historic levels, and monitoring and reporting on the state of the river.

Together, the three levels of government will spend in excess of $1 billion over the five-year life of the Fraser Basin Management Program Agreement. Provincial initiatives, which will be carried out in cooperation with the local governments involved, will focus on sewage treatment upgrading, integrated resource management, solid waste management, air emissions control, groundwater quality monitoring and control, and elimination of toxics from pulp and paper mills.

With the signing of the Agreement, the three levels of government have made the commitment to share information and coordinate all of their programs involving the Fraser River, and to work with the regional districts and municipal governments towards achieving sustainable development in the entire Fraser basin.

Canadian Arctic

The need for a coordinated planning and management response to the immense Arctic coastal zone, has perhaps been least apparent from the view from Ottawa. Largely remote and untouched, the urgency for a coordinated course of action has never been clearly recognized. However, there is growing national and international appreciation of the importance of Arctic ecosystems and an increasing knowledge of global pollution and resulting environmental threats. The Arctic is highly sensitive to pollution and much of its human population and culture is directly dependent on the health of the region's ecosystems. This vulnerability of the Arctic to pollution requires that action be taken now, before degradation becomes irreversible.

In recent years, the federal and territorial governments have worked cooperatively to develop conservation and sustainable development strategies for land, marine and heritage resources in the Canadian north. It became clear, however, that much more needed to be done if the Arctic environment was to be protected and the sustainable use of its resources ensured.

On a broader scale, the governments of the eight Arctic countries have become increasingly aware of the need and responsibility to combat these threats to the Arctic ecosystem. The Arctic countries (Canada,

Denmark, Finland, Iceland, Norway, Sweden, the (former) USSR, and the United States) have recently prepared a comprehensive Environmental Protection strategy for the Arctic environment. These circumpolar countries realize that the pollution problems of today do not respect national boundaries and that no state alone will be able to act effectively against environmental threats to the Arctic. The Strategy is designed to be compatible with nature and to guide development in a way that will safeguard the Arctic environment for future generations.

For its role in the partnership, Canada has developed its own Arctic Environmental Strategy under the Green Plan. The goal of this six-year, $100-million program is to preserve and enhance the integrity, health, biodiversity, and productivity of our Arctic ecosystems for the benefit of present and future generations. The Strategy is based on the need for a comprehensive approach to maintaining the integrity of the Arctic environment - one which takes into consideration the entire ecosystem.

The Canadian Strategy includes actions to: reduce and whenever possible eliminate contaminants in country foods; eliminate unsafe, hazardous and unsightly waste; establish an enhanced water resource management regime; promote economic opportunities for northern communities based on the development and use of traditional values, knowledge and resources; and achieve better decision making by using both scientific and traditional knowledge.

In terms of ongoing challenges, the Canadian Strategy must deal with the changing political and constitutional environment of the Arctic as land claims and devolution of federal powers proceed and new jurisdictions evolve. With respect to possible management models, it has been suggested that a United Nations Environment Program (UNEP) Regional Seas approach might be appropriate for the joint management of the Arctic ocean.

St. Lawrence River

The St. Lawrence is eastern Canada's most majestic and significant river. It has long been an important transportation route to the heart of the continent, and an essential factor in establishing and developing important economic activity. Over 80 percent of Quebec's population is concentrated on the banks of the river, and nearly 50 percent of the population takes its drinking water from the St. Lawrence. Yet the river has been suffering great abuse over the years and the signs of neglect have become starkly apparent.

During the last decade, the Quebec and federal governments have been pursuing a series of measures aimed at solving problems related to the poor quality of the St. Lawrence river. In 1988, both levels of government reached agreement on an ambitious action plan to protect and clean up the St. Lawrence. The St. Lawrence Action Plan (SLAP) provides $110 million and $63 million from the Federal and Quebec governments respectively, to reduce by 90 percent the liquid toxic waste being discharged into the river by 50 industrial plants recognized to the biggest polluters, develop environmental technologies, ensure the conservation of flora, fauna and ecosystems, and achieve the enhancement of increased individual and collective respect for the environment.

A Steering Committee made up of representatives from Environment Canada, the ministre de l'Environnement du Quebec and the ministre du Loisir de la Chasse et de la Pêche du Quebec, oversees the work of coordinating committees responsible for the Conservation, Protection, State-of-the-Environment and Restoration components of the Action Plan.

Significant progress toward these goals has been made to date and the federal government is now looking to extend the SLAP to 1998. The overall vision will be to restore and protect the St. Lawrence ecosystem to give the River back to the people in the context of sustainable development. The ongoing objective will be to work cooperatively with federal and provincial departments and agencies, university and research centres, non-governmental organizations, industrial associations, private sector enterprises and public and citizens' groups, to extend the significant accomplishments to date and to continue with the management of the River as an ecosystem, involving the full set of stakeholders.

Atlantic Canada

Efforts to realize the integrated management of various watersheds/estuaries throughout Atlantic Canada have been underway, in an informal sense, for several years. Under an ad hoc consortium of federal, provincial and university interests, the Atlantic Estuaries Cooperative Venture (AECV) undertook to identify and select a number of critical estuaries in the Region which could benefit from a cooperative approach to planning, remediation and management.

These efforts were significantly enhanced in 1991 with the establishment of the Atlantic Coastal Action Program (ACAP) - a six-year, $10-million program under the Green Plan - targeted at the development of comprehensive environmental management plans and concerted actions in 13 harbours and estuaries throughout the four Atlantic provinces.

Like most initiatives 'down east', the solutions to the problems people face are home grown. ACAP embodies the principles of managing on an ecosystem basis, and stands out in particular, in the degree of community ownership it employs. In each of the thirteen sites, locally formed and incorporated groups assume the ownership to develop the strategies required to achieve their desired objectives. Federal, provincial and municipal governments, business and industry, non-governmental groups, and interested citizens, all participate as equal partners in the development of this process at the local level.

The level of enthusiasm with this approach to date is reflected in the rapid start up of the initiatives in each of the sites, the pace at which they are developing and the number of stakeholders, and thus, additional resources, which are being brought to bear. Environment Canada signs letters of Agreement with the local groups and contributes up to $50,000 per year to help the groups get started. DOE then participates as one of many stakeholders and works to bring the attention and resources of other partners to the table.

Another, broader ecosystem management approach in the Atlantic region, is underway in the Bay of Fundy/Gulf of Maine. In 1989, the Premiers of the provinces of Nova Scotia and New Brunswick and the Governors of the states of Maine, New Hampshire and Massachusetts, signed an Agreement for the cooperative management of the Gulf of Maine (which includes the Bay of Fundy) as a shared ecosystem. This formed the Gulf of Maine Council on the Marine Environment. Cooperative efforts are now underway in support of a ten-year Action Plan which targets coastal and marine pollution, monitoring and research, habitat protection, education and participation, and the protection of public health.

No specific block of funds are earmarked for this program, but each jurisdiction and the federal governments from both sides of the border, work in support of the jointly developed objectives by focusing existing programs and resources in support of the Action Plan. The experience of cooperative international management being gained in the Gulf of Maine program may provide useful lessons in other shared ecosystems, such as the Arctic or in the waters shared by British Columbia and the State of Washington.

Great Lakes

The Great Lakes are the largest system of fresh, surface water on earth, holding 20 percent of the world's fresh water. Home to more than 40 million Canadian and American citizens; one out of every three Canadians draw their drinking water from the Great Lakes. Over the years, particularly in the last half of this century, there has been a slow deterioration of the Great Lakes ecosystem as a result of various forms of pollution. Problems of toxic chemical pollution, habitat deterioration and shoreline erosion and flooding due to fluctuating lake levels, have challenged management agencies on both sides of the border.

There are a number of cooperative initiatives underway in the Great Lakes basin which are working toward the resolution of these problems. In 1987, Canada and the United States updated the 1978 Great Lakes Water Quality Agreement (GLWQA) to strengthen existing pollution controls and pursue joint management on an ecosystem basis.

The overall purpose of the GLWQA is to restore and maintain the chemical, physical and biological integrity of the Great Lakes Basin ecosystem. It is recognized that to clean up the Great Lakes it is necessary for existing programs to be extended and new programs to be added. It expresses a renewed commitment to pursuing the objective of virtual elimination of persistent toxic substances from the ecosystem. With the amendments to the 1978 Agreement, the emphasis has shifted to implementation with the development of Remedial Action Plans in 43 Areas of Concern and Lake-wide management plans.

Remedial Action Plans (RAPs) and Lake-wide Management Plans embody a systematic and comprehensive ecosystem approach to restoring and protecting beneficial uses in Areas of Concern and in open lake waters. They are to serve as an important step toward virtual elimination of persistent toxic substances and restoring and maintaining the chemical, physical and biological integrity of the Great Lakes Basin Ecosystem.

Under the Canada-Ontario Agreement Respecting Great Lakes Water Quality, RAPs are being prepared for the 17 Canadian Areas of Concern. The principle of an ecosystem approach and local community involvement is being pursued. In addition to the area-specific RAPs, Lake-wide Management Plans will be developed and implemented as a means of reducing the levels of pollutants in open lake waters.

In further support of the GLWQA, the Canadian government's Great Lakes Action Plan (GLAP) has committed $125 million over a five-year period designed to accelerate the cleanup of contaminated areas and prevent future pollution. The GLAP represents one part of a comprehensive strategy for the Great Lakes which includes remediation, conservation, environmental technology and preservation.

In terms of shoreline erosion and flooding, the Ontario Shoreline Management Program has been in development since 1986. As this program is the subject of today's conference, no further explanation will be attempted. However, it is suggested that consideration should be given to the benefits of linking these Great Lakes initiatives (i.e. RAPs, Lake-wide Management Plans and Shoreline Management) into a truly comprehensive Basin-wide management approach.

International Motivation

One of the major stumbling blocks to the establishment of a national policy and program for Coastal Zone Management in Canada in the 1970s and 80s, was the lack of political motivation. The problems of the Canadian coastal zone, while significant on an area-specific basis, were not seen as significant enough to warrant a coordinated national response. Equally, there was little call from the provinces for the federal government to take on this responsibility. However, 1992 has been a turning point for CZM in terms of international expectations for Canada and other coastal nations.

Organization for Economic Cooperation and Development (OECD)

In 1989, the OECD initiated a three-year study on the integration of environmental considerations into CZM. Canada participated in the seventeen country comparative review of CZM practices in which policies, programs, legislation and approaches were reviewed and contrasted to derive the common lessons and to develop recommendations for improving the practice in member countries.

The recommendations which were developed from this project, and adopted by the OECD Council in the summer of 1992, call on member countries, among other things, to develop coordinated and comprehensive national approaches to CZM. While many of the participating nations already have such approaches in place, Canada stands out as particularly lacking in this regard. While our area-specific approach to CZM in practice was viewed as progressive and valuable to other nations, our lack of a coordinated national policy and process, leaves us behind the international community.

Canada has participated in many international studies in the past on a range of subjects, including CZM, where it was identified as falling short of recommendations that were developed. In most of these collegial exercises, each country is left to consider the non-binding recommendations developed and to decide for itself the degree to which it will put them into practice. For recommendations on CZM made in the past, Canada has obviously chosen to ignore them.

The challenge with this OECD study and its significance to Canada, is that as part of the recommendations adopted by the OECD Council, a follow-up evaluation of the progress and performance of member countries in implementing CZM, will be conducted within two years of the adoption of the recommendations (i.e. in 1994). With a pending evaluation of progress in implementation, Canada wants to avoid any international embarrassment that a further lack of action would bring among its peers. This 'morally-binding' arrangement has finally inspired the political motivation within Canada to undertake the development of a national policy on CZM. The federal government is currently initiating the development of a national CZM policy and will be discussing the basis for the essential federal-provincial partnerships with the provinces in 1993.

United Nations Conference on Environment and Development (UNCED)

Clearly, the most significant event of the year, if not the past two decades, in terms of elevating the discussion of and moving the world closer to the achievement of sustainable development, was the United Nations Conference on Environment and Development (UNCED) in Rio de Janeiro in June, 1992. World leaders from across the globe gathered to discuss environment and development issues and to finalize agreements to move all nations closer to a sustainable future.

At UNCED, two global conventions were signed (Biodiversity and Climate Change), a broad statement of general principles on environment and development was agreed to (the Rio declaration) and Agenda 21 - an 800-page Action Plan for the 21st century — was developed, covering everything from protection of the atmosphere, and forests to sustainable agriculture and protection of the oceans and coastal areas.

Significant in the Oceans chapter of Agenda 21 is a commitment, similar to that in the OECD study — not surprisingly as the OECD study fed into the development of the Agenda 21 text — for nations to pursue integrated management and sustainable development of coastal and marine areas under their national jurisdiction. To this end, it is stated that nations should "provide for an integrated policy and decision-making process (for their coastal zones), including all involved sectors, to promote compatibility and a balance of uses". It calls on each coastal state "to consider establishing, or where necessary strengthening, appropriate coordinating mechanisms (such as a high-level policy planning body) for integrated management and sustainable development of coastal and marine areas and their resources, at both the local and national levels".

While Canada is demonstrating considerable progress in pursuing these objectives at the local level, and a high-level ocean policy body exists at the federal level in the Interdepartmental Committee on Oceans (ICO), an integrated approach to CZM at the national level is still lacking. In terms of follow-up by the international community, Canada is expected to participate in a global conference on CZM to be held in the Netherlands in the fall of 1994, at which we are to table our response to this call. If the OECD recommendations provided the political incentive to work toward meeting our international obligations for a national approach to CZM, then the United Nations Conference and its follow-up mechanisms must truly inspire us to work toward this goal with due haste. After all, 1994 is not that far away.

Conclusions/Recommendations

Canada is one of the few industrialized coastal nations that does not have a comprehensive policy or approach to its coastal zone. While we have assumed in the past that we could address our growing problems within existing institutional and policy arrangements, evidence is clearly demonstrating that we are losing ground with this approach and that we have no vision for the future.

It has been demonstrated throughout this discussion and through the brief examples of regional initiatives provided, that the practice of CZM is alive and well in Canada. What we are lacking is the coordinating mechanism which would allow us to share the experiences that are building on the west coast, in the Arctic, in the Atlantic region and on the Great Lakes - to make CZM in Canada more than the sum of its parts.

Most of the thinking on CZM to date has focused on our three marine coasts, but the commonality of the issues that are being tackled, and the approaches that are being employed, argue clearly for inclusion of the Great Lakes as Canada's fourth coastal zone. There is now every intention to include the Great Lakes as an integral part of a national policy and program for the comprehensive planning and management of the Canadian coastal zone.

Recent experience in other coastal nations suggests that a comprehensive national approach to CZM be developed with a number of key components. These include: Federal leadership, nationally consistent guidelines for coastal zone practices, comprehensive provincial and/or regional coast-wide policies, and local-level delivery mechanisms in full partnership with federal, provincial and municipal governments and other stakeholders.

If Canada is to maintain the right to call itself one of the great coastal nations of the world, it must continue with the momentum that we have generated for CZM and ensure that a fully comprehensive and coordinated approach to the planning and management of our coastal zone is implemented.

REFERENCES

Hildebrand, L.P. 1989. Canada's Experience with Coastal Zone Management. Oceans Institute of Canada. Halifax. 118 p.

Wells, P.G. and S.J. Rolston. 1991. Health of Our Oceans. A Status Report on Canadian Marine Environmental Quality. Environment Canada, Conservation & Protection. Ottawa and Dartmouth. 186 p.

Coastal Management on the West Coast of Canada and the United States: Lessons for the Great Lakes

J.C. DAY, J. PAUL GEORGISON, and SANDRA P. TIPPETT
School of Resource and Environmental Management
Simon Fraser University, Burnaby, B.C.

Introduction

As the decade of the 1990s begins, it is instructive to reflect back on trends and accomplishments in coastal management on the west coast of North America and to reflect on the question of fundamental relevance to this conference: What can coastal managers in the Great Lakes learn from the experience in California , Oregon, Washington states and British Columbia? To do so, a brief evaluation is presented of institutional arrangements adopted to manage the coastal zone and their comparative effectiveness. Institutional arrangements are defined broadly here to include legislation, agencies, planning strategies, decision making systems, and stakeholders which society has created or uses to formulate public policy with which to manage the coastal environment. The federal, provincial-state, regional, and urban planning and management systems within British Columbia are compared to related systems in the three United States Pacific states.

The analysis begins with a brief review of the general institutional approach to coastal management within British Columbia vis-a-vis other jurisdictions. Then particular attention is focused on the lessons from comparative analysis of water quality management and urban harbor management in British Columbia and Washington State. Some recent developments within provincial, federal, and combined federal-provincial planning systems are noted in the next section. The paper concludes with some recommendations on the kinds of lessons which Great Lakes managers might consider from the west coast experience.

Coastal Zone Institutions

The states of California, Oregon, and Washington adopted dramatically different institutional approaches to manage coastal environments than British Columbia (Day and Gamble 1990). In the United States, most requirements for comprehensive coastal zone management are legislated; responsible bureaucrats and politicians attempt to implement an integrated system of federal, state, county, and municipal goals and policies. In Canada, there are comparatively few management actions that are required by any government level beyond the mandates of individual ministries and departments. The British Columbia coastal management system can best be characterized as many individual agencies, each of which operates with a specific mission. But an overriding set of federal and provincial legislation, lead agencies, goals, and objectives has not been established. In comparison to the United States, this approach has produced an unstructured, reactive, and ineffective system of coastal governance on Canada's west coast. Specific components of this approach are discussed next.

Ecological Protection

All of the U.S. jurisdictions have invested heavily in inventory systems to define and protect valuable coastal wetlands. However, the Canadian Wildlife Service and British Columbia Ministry of Environment have been comparatively ineffective in developing political support for inventorying, designating, enhancing, and protecting wildlife management areas (Table 1). Coastal inventory initiatives were belatedly initiated in recent years and the Canadian Wildlife Service recently completed a review of wetlands in the Fraser lowland, the most important overwintering habitat for waterfowl on Canada's west coast (Dunn 1992).

Public Access and Esthetics

A requirement of the U.S. federal and state coastal zone protection acts is to assure public access to the coast. This is a requirement in all jurisdictions. Indeed in Washington, a movement is underway to reclaim for public use foreshore areas which were alienated over the past century to private interests using the public trust doctrine. In British Columbia there is no requirement to assure public access in any provincial legislation although municipalities, acting on their own, have a strong record of doing so.

Table 1. Coastal Institutional Arrangements: California, Oregon, Washington, and British Columbia

Issues	California	Oregon	Washington	British Columbia
Ecological protection	wetland inventories, restoration, acquisition	estuary classification; habitat banking, mitigation	wetland designation for fisheries and wildlife protection	beginning coastal inventories, recent mitigation, limited acquisition
Public access and aesthetics	dedicated corridors, preferential assessments, acquire development rights	fees, easements, cluster developments	dedicated corridors, height limitations on coastal structures	discretionary provincial land-tenure requirements; no local construction standards or regulations
Natural hazards	geological and flood setbacks; construction design standards to ensure geotechnical stability and slope integrity	geological and flood setbacks; land use regulations to prohibit development in hazardous areas	geological and flood setbacks; prohibits development that could have adverse effects on shoreline	no geological setbacks; coastal flood management based on riverine criteria
Water dependency criterion	yes	yes	yes	no
Public involvement	mandatory	mandatory	mandatory	discretionary
Consistency	yes	yes	yes	no

Natural Hazards

Each of the U.S. jurisdictions has adopted construction design standards, land use regulations, and impact assessment requirements in an effort to ensure geotechnical stability and slope integrity. The BC approach to protecting against natural hazards is haphazard and fails to ensure that new developments will not expose the publics to unwarranted risk. Little effort has been devoted to inventorying hazardous terrain and there is no institutional system to protect the public from undesirable and potentially hazardous coastal development outside of urban areas (Van Osch 1990).

Water Dependency

Federal and state legislation in the United States require that proposed new developments have a need to be located in the coastal zone. Unless such a requirement can be demonstrated, it is difficult to gain permission to locate a structure or land use in a coastal location. In contrast, there are no similar federal and provincial requirements in British Columbia. Indeed, if such a policy were to be adopted it would have to be at the regional district or municipal level of government for settled areas but to date that has not happened.

Public Involvement

The administration of coastal management in the United States is based on legislated public participation requirements. Indeed, it is difficult to find a program or project that does not ensure widespread, continuing, public consultation. In contrast, the senior governments in British Columbia have been inconsistent and generally weak in their efforts to involved interested publics in the coastal management process. The strongest and most consistent policies have been associated with the Federal Environmental Impact Assessment Review Office in a variety of coastal projects. But otherwise, both Environment Canada and BC Environment only release information to the publics when crises occur such as leaked scientific reports or shellfish bed closures. Such incidents have always been catch-up exercises to inform the affected publics about a deteriorated state of the environment. Even the flagship of federal-provincial cooperation and integrated management, the Fraser River Estuary Management Program, did little during the 1980's to involve interested publics in controversial areas such as water quality and its management committee.

Consistency

In 1972, the United States Congress enacted the Coastal Zone Management Act (CZMA) because of the need for increased protection of the natural, biological, and physical resources of the coast (Chasis 1985:21). Based on a federal-state partnership, it established a national coastal management framework that encourages states to address the purposes of the national program. The act emphasized the need to protect important ecological, cultural, historical, and aesthetic values of the coastal zone (U.S.1982: s.1452(2)), recognizing that living marine resources, wildlife, wetlands, and open spaces had been seriously impaired by development pressures and threatened by burgeoning shoreline development (U.S. 1982: s. 1451(C)). The National Oceanic and Atmospheric Administration, Department of Commerce, is the lead agency charged with managing the program. The federal government assumes legal responsibility to ensure that federal activities directly affecting the coastal zone are consistent with state programs (U.S. 1982:s. 1456(c)(1). In comparison, neither Canada nor British Columbia have adopted legislation to manage the coastal environment nor have lead agencies been created to coordinate such work. As a consequence, there are a large number of individual agencies, each of which pursues its individual mandate in the absence of overriding goals and objectives.

Selected Accomplishments in British Columbia

In spite of these institutional shortcomings, there were nevertheless a number of achievements in British Columbia coastal management during the 1970s and 1980s. In general, resource assessment and planning studies were undertaken by the provincial environment and lands ministries in areas of growing conflict including Sooke Harbour as well as the estuaries of the Cowichan, the Squamish, the Campbell, and the Fraser River. Although none of them solved all of the existing problems, they presented an opportunity for competing developmental interests to exchange views and to become familiar with the goals and aspirations of other publics.

A more positive development has been the use of formal impact assessments associated with major new projects. This has been particularly true when federal interests and the Federal Environmental Impact Assessment Office (FEARO) were involved. For example, the Roberts Bank Coal Terminal, the new docks and rail facilities at Ridley Island port expansion, West Coast offshore exploration, the North Fraser Fuel Terminal, and the parallel runway at Vancouver International Airport are all examples of more open environmental assessment processes where interested publics were allowed to participate in a major way.

Another positive development was the shoreline mapping program introduced by Environment Canada. This provided valuable planning and management information to a variety of agencies and publics. Unfortunately, the program was canceled as part of an austerity program in the mid-1980s. It has not been replaced. And a variety of provincial agencies began to undertake assessments of the shoreline potential for different uses. Forests completed an initial draft of resource potentials in the inside passage from the north end of Vancouver Island to Prince Rupert. However, this study was made without the cooperation of all other relevant agencies and interest groups in the affected area as the Ministry of Forests attempted unsuccessfully to capture control of all coastal planning in this vast region. Agriculture and Aquaculture surveyed selected sections of the British Columbia shoreline from the perspective of aquaculture potential, although this information was not available in report form to the public. And Crown Lands surveyed the suitability of shorelines for a variety of uses. The most important characteristic of all of these studies was that they were single-agency initiatives, undertaken without the contribution of all other affected federal, provincial, regional, and local governments and affected publics.

In summary, Canadian actions to manage the coastal zone in British Columbia over the past 20 years have largely been reactionary, sporadic, secretive, and uncoordinated in comparison to programs adopted in the United States. In no instance was the planning for individual projects preceded by planning processes in which goals and objectives for a region to be affected by a project were subjected to widespread discussion before deciding on the merits of a specific project. Indeed, when the province canceled all planning by regional districts in 1983, it effectively ensured that all projects would be considered on a case-by-case basis. By doing so, the provincial government missed a major opportunity to merge new development into sustainable patterns of resource management. This change locked the province into a system of project-by-project planning based on secret referral processes among provincial and federal agencies. In this manner, municipalities, regions, and interested publics were largely bypassed in terms of contributing to integrated coastal resource management decision making.

The following two sections elaborate in greater detail the experience in two significant areas, water quality and urban harbor management, in terms of the institutions, policies, and practices developed in Washington and British Columbia to manage these concerns.

Water Quality

By the mid-1970s it had become apparent that the approach in both British Columbia and Washington to managing marine water quality was ineffective. Elevated levels of metals, PCBs, and other organic substances were found in Seattle's harbor and river and deterioration was noted in the vicinity of Vancouver. In response, dramatically different systems of planning and institutional arrangements were adopted in both countries in an effort to correct the deficiencies and protect the aquatic environment.

Institutions and Planning Focus

British Columbia

Much of the management effort focused on the Fraser River estuary, and indeed only the wetted area between the flood-control dikes (Figure 1).

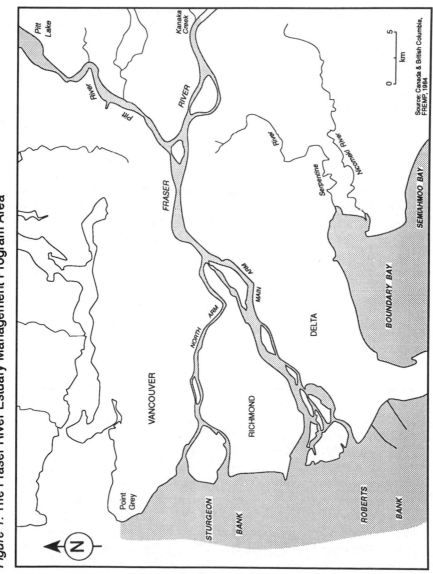

Figure 1. The Fraser River Estuary Management Program Area

Comparatively little special attention was paid to the Strait of Georgia. Existing federal and provincial agencies created a new institution, which was retained under their control. Studies undertaken between 1977 and 1984 culminated in a federal-provincial agreement to create the Fraser River Estuary Management Program in 1985, and its subsequent reauthorization until 1994. It is comprised of the federal departments of fisheries and environment, the BC Ministry of Environment, and the north Fraser and Fraser harbor commissions. Under the Green Plan, the federal government created the Fraser River Action Plan (FRAP) in 1992 with a commitment of $100 million over a 6-year period to develop a management plan for the rest of the Fraser basin. It is unclear to what extent FREMP and FRAP will be linked (Tippett 1992).

FREMP's goal (Canada and British Columbia 1986) is to provide the means for accommodating a growing population and economy, and at the same time maintaining the quality and productivity of the Fraser estuary's natural environment. These objectives and goals are to be achieved through a linked management system, a public participation process, a coordinated referrals and assessment process, and the Fraser estuary information system. It is estimated that more than 70 municipalities, other planning and management units, and public interest groups have an interest in managing the estuary. The planning process was to be implemented by a management committee through five FREMP-facilitated initiatives: a project review process; a water-quality plan; various activity programs related to port and industrial development, navigation and dredging, log management, waste management, habitat, recreation, and environmental emergencies; area plans; and area designations.

Washington State

Elevated levels of metals, PCBs, and other organic substances were found in Seattle's harbor and associated river following a large spill of PCBs in the mid-1970s. Research revealed that bottom fish had a variety of liver diseases in 1975. Rising bacterial levels in the early 1980s led to advisories to limit recreational fish consumption in urban areas and commercial shellfish closures in rural areas. The ensuing public concern over these events led to the creation of a citizens coalition in 1983 that resulted in the creation of the Puget Sound Water Quality Authority (PSWQA) in 1985 (Washington chpt. 90-70 RCW) (Figure 2). Its area of concern was the marine water body and all of the watersheds that drain into it. The authority prepared and then revised a plan in December 1986, 1988, and 1990. Its duties were extended to oversee the plan application and enforcement. In addition, selected federal programs were used to increase

Figure 2. Puget Sound Water Quality Planning Area.

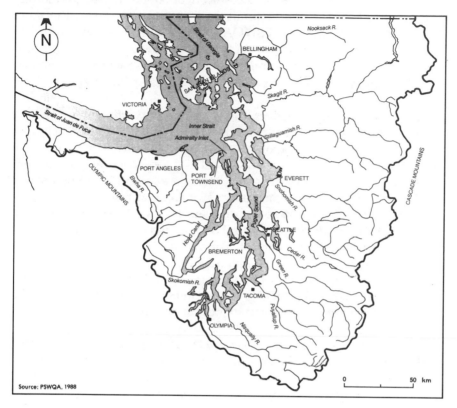

Source: PSWQA, 1988

the capacity for sensitive resource management in the area. A national estuary program (NEP) was created in Puget Sound in 1985 and jointly administered by the Environmental Protection Agency, the state Department of Ecology, and PSWQA. The authority was invited to join this program because it was developing a comprehensive management plan for the sound. Subsequently, the Sound was designated an estuary of national significance under section 320 of the Clean Water Act and NEP in 1988 (Tippett 1992).

In pursuing these objectives a PSWQ Authority action plan was prepared that initially embraced fourteen components. These included: monitoring, research, education and public involvement, nonpoint source pollution, shellfish protection, municipal and industrial discharges, contaminated sediments and dredging, storm water and combined sewer overflows, wetland protection, spill prevention and response, laboratory support, household hazardous wastes, and legal and personnel support. An unfinished agenda was presented of other issues which require study when the first 13 are under control. For each issue discussed, the agencies responsible for the work were identified, timetables and deadlines for completion were specified, and budgets and who would pay were listed.

The goal of the authority is to restore and protect the biological health and diversity of Puget Sound and to prevent pollution (Washington 1987). The restoration goal is much more ambitious than FREMP's maintenance goal. To do so, it is beginning to characterize the condition of the water, sediments, plants, animals, and habitats in Puget Sound and its watersheds (Washington *Soundwaves* May 1990). To achieve these goals the plan aims to protect and enhance three resources: water and sediment quality, fish and shellfish, and wetlands.

PSWQA deals with a complex institutional environment in all the waters and lands draining into Puget Sound and the Strait of Georgia south of the Canadian border and the Strait of Juan de Fuca. More than 450 governmental bodies—federal, state, local, and tribal—play a role in regulating water quality (Washington 1987). These include 6 federal agencies, 5 state agencies, 12 counties, 10 cities, 14 tribes, 40 ports, 13 sewer districts, 15 flood control districts, 121 soil and water districts, 14 park and recreation districts, and 9 public utility districts. About 400 industries and sewage treatment plants have permits to discharge effluent in the Sound while urban development, agriculture, forestry, and roads also contribute to surface water degradation.

In summary, the Americans recognized that their existing institutions were incapable of improving water quality in their section of the shared international water body within a reasonable period. In response, they created a new institution to create a plan and oversee its implementation.

In contrast, federal and provincial institutions in British Columbia simply assembled a body, which they completely controlled, composed of existing managers (Table 2). The study area adopted for Puget Sound water quality management was the entire Puget Sound basin; in British Columbia, the Fraser River estuary was investigated in detail while the Fraser River basin and the Strait of Georgia received comparatively little attention.

Water Quality Standards

British Columbia

The approach by the two senior Canadian governments to protect marine aquatic ecosystems in west coast waters has been inadequate. The federal government has not yet set marine water quality standards although our American neighbors did so 20 years ago; they subsequently revised those standards on two occasions. Ten years ago the BC Ministry of the Environment began to develop water quality objectives and criteria; by July 1992 the province had adopted criteria for 15 substances and objectives for 33 areas (Buchanan 1992). However, coastal areas for which objectives have been established—Boundary Bay, Pender Harbour,

Table 2. Water Quality Management in the Strait of Georgia and Puget Sound: 1985-91

	FREMP, BC	PSWQA, WA
independent planning and oversight body created	no	yes
watershed focus	no: limited to river dikes and estuary foreshore	yes: all fresh water drainage basins and marine bodies
water quality standards	no legally enforceable federal or provincial marine water quality standards; few provincial criteria and objectives; starting to set guidelines for marine water	integrated federal and state enforceable standards; protect against adverse effects to public health, land wildlife, vegetation, aquatic resources, and fresh and marine water
public involvement	weak	strong
staff	3	20
planning and nonstructural funding since 1985	weak ($1.1 million)	inadequate but 100X more ($119 million)
political support	weak	strong

Burrard Inlet—embrace less than 0.1% of the provincial shoreline (BC MOE 1992, 1991). Moreover, these limits are merely suggestions; they are not enforceable standards. The process by which objectives and criteria are established is secret and the public has not been allowed to comment during the deliberations, although relevant industries are often consulted late in the process. The time needed to complete this process throughout British Columbia is estimated to be decades rather than years.

The federal role in protecting the marine aquatic environment is unclear at present. The federal Canadian Environmental Protection Act of 1988 has not yet led to a noticeable improvement in coastal water quality although the Canadian Council of Ministers of Environment belatedly began setting quality guidelines for the marine environment in 1990 (CCME 1992). Environment Canada continues to disagree with its provincial counterpart concerning an appropriate size for the initial dilution zone within which wastes are assimilated prior to water quality testing, insisting on a smaller area, or more rigid standard, than the province wishes to adopt. Affected stakeholders have not been given the opportunity to comment on this issue and, generally, there is a high degree of animosity between some federal and provincial water quality managers in the province.

Environmental monitoring has been minimal so that it is unknown whether ambient conditions generally meet the existing water quality objectives, except in heavily populated areas where recent water quality studies have been completed. The program addressed the chemical and physical environments separately and independently in the belief that they could be integrated at the end of the process. This assumption is still to be tested.

Washington State

The United States Environmental Protection Agency set water quality standards for fresh and marine waters in 1972 which have been revised on two occasions. States and lower level governments had to meet these standards within specified periods and financial incentives were created to promote these policies. This approach led to 100% secondary treatment of all pulp mill effluents entering Puget Sound, and more than 95% of municipal wastes by 1992. In comparison, only one pulp mill and none of the coastal municipalities in British Columbia have installed secondary treatment.

Public Participation

British Columbia

Public participation has been weak in all phases of FREMP. The first five years of study had virtually no public input and were generally perceived to be unproductive from a citizens perspective. Since that time the public involvement strategy has remained conservative. All participants must be approved by the chairperson of the FREMP Management Committee, and there is still no involvement in the waste management and water quality programs. However, the extreme level of secrecy which has surrounded the activities of both the federal and provincial environment agencies has been, and continues to be, a major impediment to improving public understanding of, and support for, water quality management improvements.

Washington State

It was public concern which resulted in the impetus to create PSWQA in 1985. Since that time there has been a continuing high level of public involvement in virtually all phases of program development and monitoring. The authority has operated with a full-time staff of 20, 4 of whom were seconded from the state water quality management agency , the Department of Ecology, and 4 from the Environmental Protection Agency. It also has numerous part-time personnel. Initially, approximately half of the staff were devoted to public outreach activities; later, these professionals were replaced by technical staff who were partly chosen on the basis of their effectiveness in dealing with the public. Indeed, current staff are required to spend 40 to 60% of their time in public consultation. A special fund was created to improve public involvement and education (PIE) Fund. It underwrites innovative citizens' initiatives to improve water quality in the sound. The most innovative of these projects are published as examples for other public groups who may wish to help improve water quality in their local areas.

Funding and Staff

British Columbia

FREMP and institutional predecessors have been seriously underfunded throughout the lives of these programs. As a consequence, it has been difficult for agency personnel to accomplish their planning tasks in a timely manner. Until 1992, the program office was located in a difficult-to-find site in New Westminster which few people visited. The inventory of current projects in the estuary was in a chaotic state and difficult for potentially interested users to access easily. Moreover few publications were available to the public and newsletters were infrequent. However, a recent budget increase, which has allowed a doubling of staff to 3 and relocation to a more central location, should help alleviate some of these problems.

Washington

Funding for PSWQA activities and plan implementation comes from a variety of sources. An 8 cent tax is paid on every package of cigarettes sold in the state and placed in the Centennial Clean Water Account. In addition, state capital funds, discharge permit fees, the toxins account, the Puget Sound grants program, and the motor vehicle fund all contribute (Washington *Soundwaves* Aug., Oct.1990). Although there have been insufficient funds to do all the work which the authority requested, it received a cumulative amount of $119 million (FREMP $1.1 million) over its first 6 years. Its 1991 budget , $3 million, was roughly triple that of FREMP's. This is one of many reasons that it has achieved much more in terms of coordinated planning and in the creation of a long-term strategy to combat water quality degradation.

Political Support

A major international difference in the approach to water quality management has been the degree to which politicians at various levels have been involved in, and have supported the creation and effectiveness of, FREMP and PSWQA. In British Columbia there has been little direct involvement of federal and provincial politicians except for signing the program agreement and its extensions. This lack of political awareness and commitment has been a major weakness. In contrast, American politicians have been comparatively active in attending meetings related to PSWQA and in supporting the creation of a strong and effective agency. This same pattern of agency involvement was apparent when Canadian and provincial agencies undertook most of the FREMP planning without the affected regional and municipal governments. In contrast, all levels of government were much more fully involved in planning and implementing a strategy to combat water quality deterioration in Puget Sound.

Summary

British Columbia

Strengths. It is clear that for a variety of reasons FREMP has been a major step forward for water quality management in British Columbia.. It is the most ambitious attempt at coordinated estuarine management on the west coast. The area designation process and action plan give FREMP the potential to influence upland activities outside its narrow boundaries. Sequential development permitted adjustments to be made to the program as experience accumulated. Furthermore, the vision statement related to "a living river" helped create an acceptance of a variety of uses and subsidiary agreements among the management agencies (Tippett 1992).

Weaknesses. There have been major problems, many of which are related to the weak political commitments made to FREMP, and inadequate funding and personnel. These led to inadequate monitoring programs, insufficient surveillance, and weak enforcement (Hagen and Langford 1989; Dorcey 1990). There has been insufficient research on both biophysical and socioeconomic issues, particularly the latter. Federal and provincial politicians have had little direct involvement except for signing the program agreement and its extensions. This lack of political commitment has been a major weakness. The entire process developed without involvement of the regional government or the affected municipalities. In the area designation process, the Greater Vancouver Regional District (GVRD) boycotted the deliberations because it was not clear what effect would be on its planning process, or whether the designations could be changed. Moreover, municipalities were not involved in creating the original designation maps despite the fact that they control land uses landward of the dikes. Understandably they have had little interest in supporting use of the maps. However, this situation improved over the past year when GVRD and some municipalities were requested by FREMP to adopt the land designations. Finally, the Department of Fisheries and Oceans (DFO) felt that industrialists and developers had dominated the planning process and that habitat destruction would be experienced in areas designated for industrial use. Thus, the 1982 area designation map will be updated in the 1990's to protect against this possibility.

Urban Port Administration

A significant component of coastal management is the diverse array of developments located in urban ports. Urban harbors are a focal point for human activity, commerce, and habitation in the coastal zone, Traditionally, the public port authority is in charge of marine commercial development within urban harbors to ensure efficient movement of goods and people to maximize business for the economic benefit of its constituency. However, port authorities now face broader pressures from municipal waterfront developers, recreationists, environmentalists, and residents of contiguous communities who lobby for preservation and enhancement of their quality of living conditions. Indeed, a broadened approach to planning, assessment, and implementation which accounts for, and responds to, these modern public pressures is required to manage this highly valued coastal resource, to anticipate and resolve development conflicts, public disputes, unnecessary environmental degradation, and costly operational delays.

The port planning and decision making processes adopted in Vancouver are compared here to another large North American port administered according to a fundamentally different institutional system: the Port of Seattle in Washington State. Both these facilities face similar circumstances. Vancouver and Seattle are situated within 200 kilometers of each other, and they share the responsibility of being North American gateways with Pacific Rim nations, particularly the Asian community. Furthermore, both are located in urban milieux characterized by prized natural environments, rapid population growth, and residents with similar lifestyle objectives.

Four basic components of port decision making are assessed to evaluate the effectiveness of these institutions for supporting the goals of urban coastal zone management. First, the mandates and administrative structures established to govern port development and operation in Vancouver and Seattle are compared to identify where public port decision-making power resides and to whom these decision makers are responsible. Then, the two institutions are assessed for their accountability to all stakeholders, including adjacent jurisdictions and their residents. Third, the planning approaches adopted by the two port authorities are evaluated for their capabilities to improve overall port effectiveness through the development of long-term, comprehensive, development strategies. Finally, the coastal resource and environmental policies, plans, and programs adopted to assess and regulate port developments in both jurisdictions are analyzed.

Port Management

Vancouver

The Port of Vancouver comprises the federally owned seabed and fore-shore of Burrard Inlet, Indian Arm, and a parcel of federal seabed on Roberts Bank (Figure 3). These lands are surrounded by Vancouver Harbour over which the port authority has the right to regulate navigation. It is the largest port in Canada and consistently ranks among the top three foreign tonnage ports in North America (Vancouver Port Corporation 1992). The Vancouver Port Corporation (VPC) was established in 1983 to administer, manage, and control federal Port of Vancouver lands in accordance with National Ports Policy as set out in the Canada Ports Corporation Act (CPCA) (Canada 1985). All developments and use proposals on Port of Vancouver lands must be approved by the corporation. VPC is governed by a 7-member board of directors appointed by federal cabinet. Its major goal is " . . . to facilitate the efficient movement of maritime imports and exports . . . in the best interests of Canadian trade objectives" (Vancouver Port Corporation 1990:1). In doing so it can acquire, sell, and lease property, develop port facilities and infrastructure, and manage port uses in its harbor.

Seattle

In contrast to the strong Canadian federal role, the United States (U.S.) has no central agency with any direct administrative or financial review function, administrative law, or national development policy over port organizations (Hershman and Kory 1988). Instead, state and local governments are responsible for port administration. The power to form a port district rests solely with local county governments and their constituencies through the electoral process. Once established, port districts have the power of eminent domain and the authority to acquire, develop, and regulate lands, facilities, and services within there boundaries (Washington 1989a). They also have the right to levy a yearly property tax on citizens of port districts to finance property acquisition and capital improvements which benefit the community. A board of elected port commissioners governs these facilities with port district elections held in conjunction with county elections. Consequently, local taxpayers control the port decision making process as they elect port policy makers and form the port development financial base.

Established in 1911, the Port of Seattle did not inherit a large area of government-owned land. Instead, it must compete with private interests

Figure 3. The Port of Vancouver

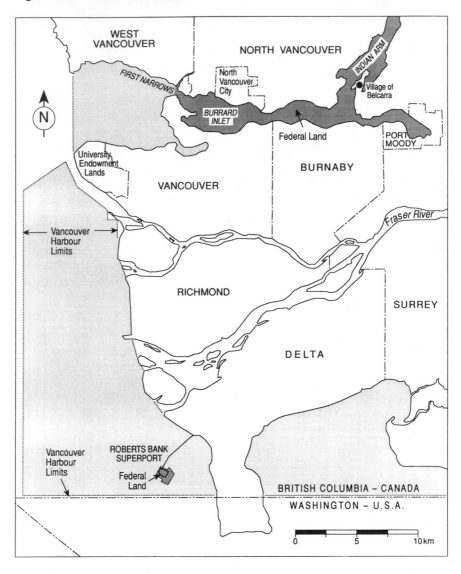

in purchasing waterfront property with public funds (Historical Society of Seattle and King County 1986). Five locally elected commissioners are responsible for ratifying port policy and they have authority over development proposals (Washington 1990). The port mandate is much broader than that of Vancouver: It is " . . .to be a leader providing services and facilities to accommodate the transportation of cargo and passengers . . . to foster regional economic vitality and a quality life for King County citizens" (Port of Seattle 1990b, p. 1).

Accountability

Vancouver

VPC is the most prominent federal landlord and industrial developer in a largely municipally and regionally governed area. It is an "island" of federal territory surrounded by eight municipalities and the Greater Vancouver Regional District (GVRD). The governments and residents of these jurisdictions abutting Port of Vancouver property are not interested exclusively in federal trade objectives or marine industrial development. However, activities on port property may have direct economic and environmental impacts on surrounding communities (GVRD 1990). On one hand, VPC has a responsibility to account for the concerns of, and the impacts on, these stakeholders. On the other hand, as a federal authority VPC has prominent decision making power over provincial, regional, and municipal policy.

The National Ports Policy and (CPCA) establish a decision making framework which ensures federal trade objectives take precedence over provincial, regional, and local interests without providing consistently appropriate means for these stakeholders to be heard. By having only federally appointed directors to VPC, the representation of nonfederal objectives are not guaranteed. This secretive appointment process means that stakeholders outside of federal cabinet and Ports Canada have no opportunity to influence the selection of those empowered to made decisions on corporate policy. Indeed, VPC's Port-Municipal Liaison Committee, appointed in 1990, fails to effectively represent all stakeholders in decision making. Moreover, the commission's legal foundations and policy enable the corporation to conduct its business in a secretive manner. Its board meetings are held in camera, it is not required to allow for public participation in any of its planning and decision making processes (Kimpton 1990), and interested publics have no reliable means for contacting corporate directors. As a consequence, Port of Vancouver

administration lacks balanced accountability as local publics and municipal, regional, and provincial stakeholders are not provided with consistent and effective opportunities to participate in decision making.

Seattle

The legal and institutional framework for Port of Seattle (Figure 4) governance is diametrically opposed to the approach in Vancouver. It requires
broadly based participation in virtually all phases of decision making. A
comparison of these strategies is presented in Table 3.

The Port of Seattle is mandated to foster both regional economic vitality and a quality life for King Country constituents, and its institutional
structure provides these citizens with the power to promote these goals
To do so, King County taxpayers elect port district commissioners so local
citizens control who establishes Port of Seattle policy. Port commissioners
can be contacted directly by any member of the public. In contrast, VPC
will not disclose its director's phone numbers of addresses to the general
public. The Port of Seattle must comply with local land-use regulations
(Port of Seattle 1989). The Washington State Open Public Meetings Act
requires that all official commission meetings, including all development
decisions, be held in open public forums (Washington 1989b). In addition,
all commission decisions are subject to public review and comment prior
to adoption (Port of Seattle 1989). Citizens can become involved in every
major decision-making step by attending meetings, serving on committees, or submitting written comments. Public disclosure laws require that
all port district records by made available to interested publics upon
request, except in rare cases (Washington 1990). The Port of Seattle

Table 3. Port Authority Accountability: A Comparative Evaluation

Vancouver	Seattle
can override local land-use policies	must comply with local land-use policies
decision makers secretly appointed by federal cabinet	decision makers elected by local taxpayers
support of nonfederal objectives discretionary	mandated to support local objectives
advisory and liaison committees have no direct role in planning	advisory committees broadly represented; involved directly in planning
administration comparatively secretive	administration comparatively open
public access to information discretionary, selective	public access to information required, more consistent
public meetings discretionary, occasional	public meetings required, often

Figure 4. The Port of Seattle

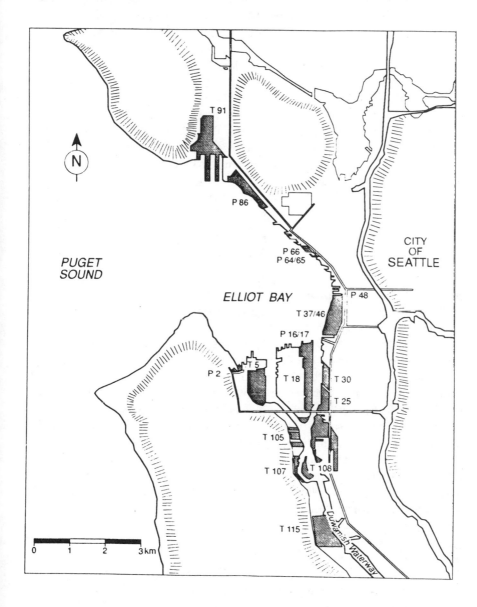

encourages port district constituents to join a mailing list to receive information on impending projects. And obligations to open administration compel the port authority to establish external advisory committees to aid stakeholder consultations during major development planning and construction. Unlike Vancouver, these committees ensure broad representation and are involved directly in port planning.

Strategic Planning

A systemic process is required to ensure that all stakeholders have direct input into the formulation of long-term goals for maximizing cost effectiveness and harmonizing development objectives of the modern port with its surrounding region.

Vancouver

PVC has a poor image for development planning, mainly because it is not required to design long-term, comprehensive plans. Nor does CPCA contain provisions requiring such ports to resolve harbor-use and development issues. This is surprising in light of the fact that the corporation is surrounded by highly populated municipalities with long histories of land-use planning.

In 1983 the port unsuccessfully attempted a master planning exercise which failed because of poor coordination among the consultants, VPC, and stakeholders (Canada 1983; Jordan 1991). Under new leadership, it initiated a new open process to formulate long-term, land-management policies for its property in 1990 which is expected to be completed in 1992. The plan is a response to corporate perceptions that it is increasingly obligated to confront environmental, urban growth, and public process issues associated with Port of Vancouver land-use competition and controversies (Vancouver Port Corporation 1991). This 20-year comprehensive land-use and land-management plan is intended to avoid major controversy with surrounding municipalities.

Seattle

In contrast to the discretion granted to VPC, the Port of Seattle is mandated to plan comprehensively for its development (Table 4). Its long-range development policies are organized under its Harbor Development Strategy (HDS). The strategy directs Port of Seattle marine cargo facility development and use through the year 2000. The strategy is crucial for ensuring the port authority responds rapidly to business opportunities and community objectives. HDS formulation relied heavily on a year-

Table 4. Strategic Planning: Comparative Evaluation

Vancouver	Seattle
secret, three-year financial plans required; other planning initiatives discretionary	legally required to plan comprehensively
traditionally, development based on short-term financial or project-specific plans	development based on long-term, comprehensive plan
poor reputation for collaborative, multifaceted, development planning; strained relationship with adjacent municipal land-use planners	open strategic planning since 1911; coordinated with local land and water use planning
1990 initiation of Port 2010, VPC's latest and most successful planning effort to date	systematic organization and implementation of long-range port development policies under HDS
stakeholder consultation facilitated, but on a one-time basis	HDS formulation based on year-long, iterative process between port staff and broadly based advisory committee, in addition to public meetings
no proposed plan review and update program	annual HDS review and update, with public meetings

long process of consultations between port staff, consultants, and the broadly resented Harbor Development Advisory Committee (HDAC)(Port of Seattle 1986). This 30-member committee was composed of representatives from all Port of Seattle stakeholder groups, including business, industry, local government, and labor, civic, and environmental organizations. It was subject to public review and several open commission hearings prior to ratification. Then the port conducted an environmental assessment and an annual public review and update to the plan.

Thus, there is a major difference in the requirement to conduct comprehensive and open strategic planning in the two ports. Vancouver has belatedly admitted the potential benefits of this kind of planning process. However, VPC had the discretion to avoid such an exercise until crises were encountered and there is no assurance that the process will be updated annually or open to all stakeholders.

Regulatory Frameworks

Vancouver

This evaluation is based on the principle that the port development decision-making process must be controlled by appropriate legislation and programs to effectively, equitably, and efficiently regulate and assess land and water uses according to coastal management objectives.

Land and Water Use. VPC has never adopted harbor-use bylaws under CPCA to control all development and uses on its federal port lands and waterways. Instead, it loosely follows the land-use policies of adjacent municipalities when administering new developments (Yeoman 1990) although it is free to ignore these regulations if they conflict with federal trade objectives. Although VPC's recently initiated Port 2010 plan would designate permitted harbor uses according to existing uses and port site-selection criteria, VPC maintains complete discretion over its application and enforcement. Further, the effectiveness of the comprehensive objectives ultimately depends on the federal legislation and decision-making processes already in place.

Environmental Assessment. VPC is exempt from the federal Environmental Impact Assessment and Review Process (EARP) guidelines and the requirements of the Canadian Environmental Assessment (CEA) Act (Canada 1984,1992). Despite this exemption, VPC has established an environmental services office to administer it own Environmental Appraisal Procedure (EPA), the first such port to do so in Canada (Jordan 1991). While VPC appraisal guidelines parallel EARP in many ways, it is internally administered, there is no public scoping, and public involvement is discretionary.

Habitat Conservation. The only legislation capable of protecting coastal habitat on Port of Vancouver lands is the federal Fisheries Act (Canada 1985). The federal Department of Fisheries and Oceans (DFO) administers a comprehensive fish habitat management policy intended to achieve a new habitat gain for Canada's fishery (Canada 1986) although it is not legally binding on VPC. Nevertheless, the commission joined a potentially effective program for preserving and enhancing environmental quality in the Port of Vancouver, the Burrard Inlet Environmental Action Program (BIEAP) in 1991. This 5-year strategy is intended to coordinate agency responsibilities and improve protection and remediation programs for water, habitat, and sediment quality in the inlet and Indian Arm.

Public Access and Esthetics. VPC is not mandated to protect public waterfront access from upland sites. Consequently, Port 2010 and EAP contain no policies for protecting or enhancing public access opportunities nor are others administered by other government agencies with the authority to regulate VPC. Similarly, the port is not required to ensure developments maintain or enhance harbor views (Jordan 1991). Neither the port corporation nor applicable regulatory agencies administer policies that specify use requirements or design standards for protecting views from designated upland areas.

Seattle

Land and Water Use. In contrast, the Port of Seattle has been governed for over 15 years according to a systematic land and water use regulatory framework based on coordinated federal, state, and local government legislation (Table 5). All port shoreline developments must comply with zoning ordinances administered according to the federal coastal zone management program.

According to the federally approved Washington State Coastal zone Management Program, the state Shoreline Management Act (SMA) requires local governments to prepare and administer comprehensive shoreline master programs (SMP's) under state supervision. The Seattle

Table 5. Regulatory Frameworks: A Comparative Evaluation

Issue	Vancouver	Seattle
land and water use regulation	VPC-controlled; discretionary; can override municipal bylaws; Port 2010 will impose harbor-use districts; VPC exempt from EARP; enforces own internal, discretionary, procedure; occasional public involvement opportunities	locally administered according to federal, state, and local policy; legally binding, comprehensive coastal management policies enforced by permitting process; legally required to submit plans to externally enforced EIA process; public involvement mandatory
habitat conservation	habitat protection discretionary; VPC mapping and inventory under BIEAP; no specific protective designation	legally required to prevent or minimize harmful impacts to fish, wildlife, and their habitats; protective designation for important wetlands and shorelines
public access and esthetics	VPC not required to protect or enhance public access to its harbor; mandate promotes alienation of such corridors; no land-use design standards to protect views from upland vistas	legally required to provide, maintain, or improve physical access by publics to and along the waterfront; comprehensive public access plan implemented; legally binding height limitations and view corridor requirements; NAC monitors compliance to specific development agreement to mitigate esthetic impacts

SMP was endorsed by the state after widespread public consultation in 1977 (Hildreth and Johnson 1985). It establishes overlay districts which specify uses to: protect shoreline ecosystems; encourage water-dependent uses; provide for maximum public use and enjoyment of the city's shoreline; and preserve, enhance, and increase views of the water and access to the water (Seattle 1988). All Port of Seattle coastal projects must meet Seattle SMP zoning requirements and receive state approval (Port of Seattle 1989). Proposals must conform to city land-use regulations if situated outside SMP jurisdiction. Port development is forbidden on areas designated for conservation and public enjoyment. Similar guarantees are not provided in the Port of Vancouver, as VPC has complete discretion over the enforcement of port 2010 land-use policies.

Environmental Assessment. In contrast to VPC, the Port of Seattle is subject to applicable EIA and review legislation. All development policies, plans, and projects are subject to a set of codified rules for implementing and enforcing the State Environmental Policy Act (SEPA)(Washington 1983). The City of Seattle is empowered to administer the SEPA review process for Port of Seattle development proposals. This legislation requires public review of all proposals, with the level of public involvement relating to project size.

Habitat Conservation. In comparison, the externally administered, legally binding, coastal zone management framework applied in the Port of Seattle appears to be a more effective tool for preventing development on sensitive habitats. Under SMA, the state designates and protects wetland and shoreline habitats of vital importance to fish and wildlife (Washington 1986). Seattle SMP prohibit construction in designated specifically for conservation (Seattle 1988). These rules and regulations are enforced by the city through its shoreline development permit and SEPA review process which require opportunities for public review and comment. Furthermore federal legislation, particularly the U.S. Clean Water Act, establish mandatory permitting procedures which require proponents to mitigate harmful impacts to fish, wildlife, and their habitats (United States 1977).

Public Access and Esthetics. The Port of Seattle must conform to physical and visual access requirements established in coastal zone management legislation. The Seattle SMP contains specific regulations for preserving , enhancing, and increasing views of the water and access to the water which include maximum building heights and view corridor requirements. In addition, all publicly owned and controlled waterfront development, including all Port of Seattle projects in the coastal zone, must meet specific criteria for providing, maintaining, or improving public access to and along the waterfront. And port planners must accommodate the concerns of adjacent communities in all their developments. A Neighborhood Advisory Committee (NAC) was established to monitor proponent compliance to an agreement pledging protection and enhancement of living conditions in the area (Port of Seattle 1989).

Summary and Conclusions

Jurisdictions in the Great Lakes would not be advised to follow many aspects of the coastal management experience in British Columbia. This situation is basically the result of an inadequate set of legislation and institutional arrangements to coordinate and implement an integrated system of coastal governance. On the other hand, the states of California, Oregon, and Washington, working in cooperation with the U.S. federal government have adopted innovative legislation and policies over the past 20 years which are worthy of careful study and potential adaptation to the special needs of the Great Lakes.

Institutional innovations under the federal Green Plan in 1992 in the Fraser River Basin and estuary as well as Burrard Inlet hold considerable promise. Perhaps in five to ten years sufficient experience will have accumulated to determine if the experience just beginning in British Columbia coastal governance will be of use to other jurisdictions.

REFERENCES

B.C. Ministry of Environment (1992) *Schedule for Reports on Water Quality Objectives and Criteria* Lands and Parks, Water Management Division, Water Quality Branch, Victoria, B.C.

B.C. Ministry of Environment (1991)*Approved and Working Criteria for Water Quality* Water Management Division, Victoria, B.C.

Buchanan, R.J. (1992) *Water Quality Management in British Columbia: A Summary* Ministry of Environment, Lands and Parks, Water Management Division, Water Quality Branch,Victoria, B.C.

Canada and British Columbia Fraser River Estuary Study Steering Committee (1978) *Fraser River Estuary Study Summary: Proposals for the Development of an Estuary Management Plan.* Victoria, B.C.

Canadian Council of Ministers of the Environment (1992)*Water Quality Guidelines Task Group: 1993-94 Workplan* Environmental Protection Committee, Task Force on Water Quality Guidelines, Ottawa, Ontario.

Chasis, S. (1985) "The Coastal Zone Management Act: A Protective Mandate," *Natural Resources Journal* , 25:21-30.

City of Seattle (1988) *Seattle Shoreline Master Program* SMC Ch. 23.56, 23.60., Seattle, WA.

Day, J.C. and Don B. Gamble (1990) "Coastal Zone Management in British Columbia: An Institutional Comparison with Washington, Oregon, and California," *Coastal Management,* 18:115-41.

Dorcey, A.H.J. (1990) *Sustainable Development of the Fraser River Estuary: Success amidst Failure.* Second draft of paper prepared for a meeting of the Environmental Directorate, OECD, 12-14 March 1990. Paris, France.

Dunn, M. (1992) "Wetlands of the Fraser Lowland: An Inventory," *Littoral,* Issue No.4, CC-SEA, Ottawa, Ontario.

Federal Government of Canada (1984) Environmental Assessment and Review Process Guidelines Order Canada Gazette SOR/84-467, Ottawa, Ontario.

_____ (1985c) *Fisheries Act* RSC F-14., Ottawa, Ontario.

_____ (1988) *Canadian Environmental Protection Act,* RSC chpt. 16, 4th supp., Ottawa, Canada.

Fisheries and Oceans Canada (1986) *Summary: Fish Habitat Management Policy,* Ottawa, Ontario.

Greater Vancouver Regional District (1990) *Memorandum from GVRD Development Services to Port (VPC)/Municipal Liaison Committee: Consolidated List of Municipal Issues,* Burnaby, BC: Greater Vancouver Regional District.

Hershman, M.J., and M. Kory (1988) "Federal port policy: Retrenchment in the 1980s," in *Urban Ports and Harbor Management*, (ed. M.J. Hershman) Taylor & Francis, Washington, DC:

Hildreth, R.G., and R.W. Johnson (1985) "CZM in California, Oregon, and Washington," *Natural Resources Journal*, 25(Jan): 103-65.

Historical Society of Seattle and King County (1986) *Portage: The Port of Seattle Celebrates 75 Years of Service*, Seattle, WA.

House of Commons (1992) *Bill C-13: Canadian Environmental Assessment Act*, Third session, 34th Parliament, 40-41 Elizabeth II Supply and Services Canada, Ottawa, Ontario.

Jordan, A.J. (1991) Personal communications with manager, Environmental Services, Port Development Department, Vancouver Port Corporation, Vancouver, B.C.

Kimpton, R. (1990) Personal communications with internal legal counsel, Vancouver Port Corporation, Vancouver, B.C.

Port of Seattle (1985) *Comprehensive Public Access Plan for the Duwamish Waterway*, Seattle, WA.

_____ (1989) *Our Doors are Open: A Citizen's Guide to Public Participation in Port of Seattle Development*, Seattle, WA.

_____ (1990b) *Port of Seattle: Mission and Goals Statement*, Seattle, WA.

Puget Sound Water Quality Authority (1987) *1987 Puget Sound Water Quality Management Plan*, Seattle, WA.

State of Washington (1983) *State Environmental Policy Act*, RCW Ch. 43.21C.

_____ (1986) *Adoption of Designation of Wetlands Associated with Shorelines of the State*, WAC Ch. 173-22.

_____ (1989a) *Port District Act*, RCW Ch. 53.04 et seq.

_____ (1989b) *Open Public Meetings Act*, RCW Ch. 42.30.

United States Congress (1972) *Coastal Zone Management Act of 1972*, Title 16 United Stated Code Annoted. Secs. 1451-1464. St. Paul, MN.

_____ (1977) *Clean Water Act*, USPL 95-217., Washington, D.C.

Vancouver Port Corporation (1989) *1988 Statistics*, Vancouver Port Corporation, Vancouver, BC.

_____ (1990) *Port 2010-Phase I: A Framework for Consultation*, Vancouver Port Corporation, Vancouver, B.C.

_____ (1991b) *Port of Vancouver International Port Handbook 1991-92*, Charter International, Norfolk, VA.

_____ (1992a) *The Port and You*, Vancouver Port Corporation Vancouver, B.C.

Washington Research Council (1990) *Washington's Public Ports*, Washington Research Council, Olympia, WA:

Yeoman, G. (1990) Personal communication with planner, Planning Department, City of Vancouver, B.C.

Coastal Zone Management in the United States Great Lakes with Special Reference to Lake Michigan

PENNY HOLT and *CATHIE CUNNINGHAM*
Land and Water Management Division
Michigan Department of Natural Resources, Lansing, Michigan

Introduction

Coastal zone management in the United States involves a cooperative effort from government agencies at each level: Federal, state, and local. Federal law provides financial incentives, technical assistance and oversight of participating states. States choosing to participate have the responsibility of developing and administering their own programs designed to address the specific issues facing their shorelines. The role of local governments varies depending on the state program. This paper will discuss the roles of federal, state, and local agencies in coastal zone management; briefly review the programs developed by the participating Great Lakes states, and present a detailed overview of Michigan's Coastal Management Program.

The Federal Coastal Zone Management Act

In 1972, Congress enacted the Federal Coastal Zone Management Act (CZMA) as the result of increasingly intense development pressures facing the country's coastal areas. Many shorelines were being permanently altered by poorly planned development, resulting in habitat loss, increased erosion and increased development in high risk areas. This increased conflicts between various users of the resource and decreased public access. Passage of the CZMA demonstrated a national interest in improving control over use and development of coastal resources. The purpose of the legislation is "to restore or enhance the resources of the nation's coastal zone for this and succeeding generations."

The federal agency responsible for administration of the CZMA is the National Oceanic and Atmospheric Administration (NOAA) which is part of the Department of Commerce. States are not required to participate in the program, however, 29 of the 36 eligible states are currently participating and five others are in the process of developing programs.

Through the CZMA, funding is provided to requesting states to develop Coastal Management Programs. These development grants are provided by federal contributions in a 4/1 ratio of Federal/State dollars. Funding for development grants is limited to $200,000 per year and each state is eligible to receive only two development grants. Second-year development funding is granted only if progress has been made toward program development. Once a program has been approved, "match" requirements gradually increase from 4:1 the first year, to 2.3:1 for the second year, 1.5:1 for the third year, and 1:1 each year thereafter.

Federal approval of a state Coastal Management Program is granted if the state demonstrates that it has sufficient statutory authority to protect sensitive coastal resources and sufficient organizational capacity within its jurisdiction to implement, coordinate, and ensure compliance with the program. States are also required to identify and map coastal boundaries, identify sensitive coastal resources, and identify specific activities and geographic areas that will be subject to the management program.

NOAA has the responsibility of reviewing and approving state management programs. After a state's program is approved, NOAA provides technical and financial assistance to the state but the states have the responsibility of administering their own programs.

Benefits of Participation

One of the primary incentives of participation in the Federal Coastal Management Program is the financial assistance that is provided annually to implement state programs. Grants are allocated to the states by a formula that considers the extent and nature of the shoreline and area covered by the program, the population of the area and other relevant factors. Due to Michigan's extensive shoreline and the population concentrations along the coast, we receive the maximum amount of funding that is available, approximately $2,140,000 in federal funds per year.

Another important incentive for participation is the authority extended to states with approved programs to review activities of federal agencies for consistency with the state's approved Coastal Management Program. The CZMA requires federal agencies issuing permits or licenses or providing financial assistance within the coastal zone to be consistent with the state's coastal program. Direct federal activities must be consistent to the maximum extent practicable. If a state finds that a federal activity, license, permit or loan is inconsistent with the state's program, the federal agency is prohibited from proceeding. Federal agencies and applicants for federal permits or licenses have the right to appeal the state's finding of inconsistency to the U.S. Secretary of Commerce.

The federal consistency provisions of the CZMA strengthen the authority of state Coastal Management Programs by requiring federal agencies to coordinate their activities with state programs and to be held accountable to the same standards and statutory requirements as any other agency, group, or individual.

Great Lakes States Coastal Zone Management Program

Of the eight states bordering the Great Lakes, four have approved Coastal Management Programs and are participating in the federal program. These states are New York, Pennsylvania, Michigan, and Wisconsin. Minnesota and Ohio are in the process of developing coastal management plans.

Under the CZMA, each state has the ability to adopt a program that best suits its particular needs. Subsequently, there is a great deal of variety in the way state programs are structured. Michigan has a centralized program in which the administrative and regulatory functions are housed in the same division. Some states such as New York and Wisconsin are "networked", i.e.: the administrative and regulatory responsibilities are housed in separate branches of state government. This organizational structure requires a great deal of coordination and cooperation. Other states have developed programs that provide for adoption of the coastal programs by local governments. The local programs are developed, approved and monitored by the state's coastal program agency.

The six states bordering the Great Lakes are of particular interest as each has a different organizational structure to their programs.

Wisconsin

Administration and implementation of the coastal management program is shared by a number of Wisconsin state agencies. The lead agency is the Coastal Management Section, which is housed in the Department of Administration, the state's executive agency. Regulatory responsibilities are divided among the Department of Natural Resources, the Department of Transportation, the Public Service Commission, and county governments who are responsible for shoreline zoning. Wisconsin's coastal boundary includes all 15 counties bordering on Lake Michigan. Wisconsin does not have a statute requiring setbacks in erosion hazard areas. However, they have calculated bluff and recession rates. These data, along with a model zoning ordinance were supplied to the coastal counties for possible adoption. Five of the 15 coastal counties have incorporated erosion setbacks into zoning ordinances.

Pennsylvania

In addition to 63 miles of Lake Erie shoreline, Pennsylvania's coastal zone includes frontage on the Delaware River and the nationally designated Delaware Bay National Estuary. The Department of Environmental Resources is the lead state agency for implementing, administering and enforcing the program. The Division of Coastal Zone Management is responsible for monitoring and evaluating activities related to coastal zone management and ensuring compliance with the program's enforceable policies. An Executive Order and Memorandum of Understanding provide the basis for state agency compliance with enforceable policies.

The major coastal management issues addressed by Pennsylvania are: coastal hazards, dredging and spoil disposal, fisheries management, wetlands, public access for recreation, historic sites and structures, port activities, energy facility siting, and intergovernmental coordination and public involvement. The Pennsylvania program was established from several state laws: the Dam Safety and Encroachment Act, the Floodplain Management Act, the Bluff Recession and Setback Act, the Clean Streams Act, and the Air Pollution Control Act. The Bluff Recession and Setback Act provides a long-term regulatory approach to reducing property losses from bluff recession. The Act requires municipalities in hazard areas to develop, adopt and administer bluff setback ordinances. The Pennsylvania Coastal Program provides free site analysis, on-site inspections and technical assistance on bluff stabilization.

New York

In addition to lake frontage on Lakes Erie and Ontario, New York's coastal boundary also includes the St. Lawrence and Niagara Rivers, the Hudson River estuary, the Atlantic Ocean and Long Island Sound. The Department of State, through its Division of Coastal Resources and Waterfront Revitalization, administers the New York Coastal

Management Program. The New York Program is based primarily on the Waterfront Revitalization and Coastal Resources Act which gives the State the legal authority to establish a coastal program, and provides an option for municipalities to establish local Waterfront Revitalization Programs, which meet or exceed State policies. Approximately half of the 250 eligible communities have adopted local programs, which cover about 60% of the shoreline, where 90% of the state's population lives. State coastal environmental protection statutes include the State Environmental Quality Review Act, which is the mechanism by which state agency actions are coordinated, the Coastal Erosion Hazards Areas Act, which provides for uniform setback requirements in coastal high hazard areas, and the Tidal Wetlands Act.

Ohio and Minnesota

Minnesota, bordering on Lake Superior, and Ohio, located along Lake Erie, have both received federal grants for the development of coastal programs. Although neither state has submitted final programs for federal approval, both states have environmental statutes in place which provide protection to coastal resources, and organizational structures which coordinate state coastal management efforts.

Michigan's Coastal Zone Management Program

Michigan was one of the first states to join the Federal Coastal Zone Management Program. Initial application was made in 1974 with approval granted in 1978. Michigan's commitment to coastal management actually predates the state's inclusion into the federal program, as several of the state's protective coastal statutes were adopted before the CZMA was enacted in 1972.

Michigan's Coastal Management Program is housed in the Land and Water Management Division of the Department of Natural Resources (Figure 1). The Land and Water Management Division is one of the regulatory arms of the Department, and the Division administers a number of environmental protection statutes. In a recently completed report assessing problems facing the state of Michigan, the authors strongly recommended that land management agencies adopt a more integrated ecosystem approach in their decision making.

Geographically, Michigan's coastal boundary, the area subject to State review under the Coastal Program, generally runs 305 meters (or 1,000 feet) landward from the water's edge (Figure 2). This boundary, however, may exceed 305 meters based on specific geographic features

Figure 1. Michigan Department of Natural Resources Organization Chart

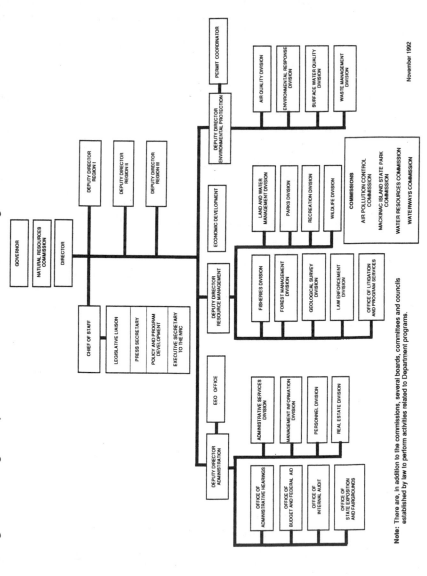

November 1992

Note: There are, in addition to the commissions, several boards, committees and councils established by law to perform activities related to Department programs.

Figure 2. Schematic Diagram of the Michigan Coastal Management Program Boundary

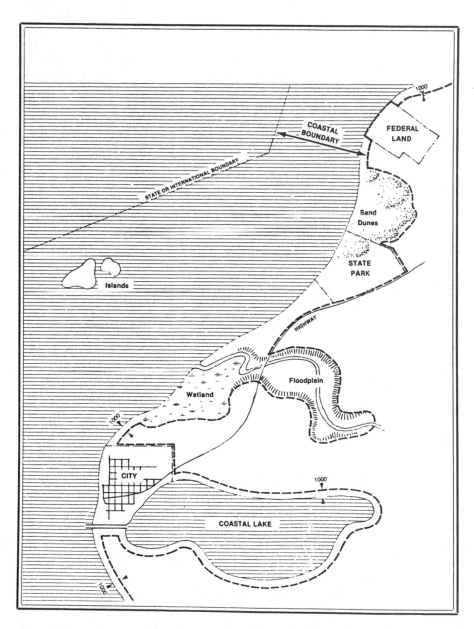

such as critical sand dunes, coastal wetlands and floodplains, coastal lakes and drowned river mouths, and state parks and recreation areas. The coastal boundary also includes all Great Lakes islands and submerged bottomlands. Approximately 40% of Michigan's land area is submerged beneath the Great Lakes. These bottomlands are held in public trust for the people of the State of Michigan. Michigan's bottomlands comprise an area that is greater than thirteen of the United States.

Since Michigan's program was approved, the state has been a leader both in the number of local projects funded and in the amount of funds from the state's federal grant that are passed through to local governments to implement local projects. Approximately one third of Michigan's annual allocation of federal funds is passed-through to communities for planning, design or low-cost construction projects. Every year, "Invitations to Apply" for Coastal Management funds are mailed to coastal communities, planning agencies, universities and other public and non-profit agencies. Funds are provided on a matching, dollar-for-dollar basis. Projects must be open to the public and grant funds cannot exceed $50,000.

To be eligible for funding, projects must further the objectives of the CZMA. These objectives include creation or enhancement of public access to the coast, protection of sensitive coastal resources, restoration of urban or industrial waterfronts and ports, preservation of historic coastal structures, educational efforts, and control of development in erosion or flood hazard areas. Provided objectives of the CZMA are met, coastal management programs have a great deal of flexibility in the types of projects that are funded. Pass-through grants are divided into two categories: planning and design, and low-cost construction. Planning and design grants can include local master planning, waterfront redevelopment plans, zoning ordinance revisions, site design, recreational planning, research and development, feasibility studies, facility relocation studies and engineering for recreational sites or coastal structures.

In 1988, Michigan became the first and only demonstration state to determine the effectiveness of using Coastal Management funds for low-cost construction projects. Due to Michigan's success during the demonstration period, the CZMA was amended to include funding for low-cost construction projects such as boardwalks, scenic overlooks, nature trails, lighthouse restoration, maritime museum exhibits and other resource protection, public access and historic preservation projects. Michigan has used pass-through grants as the primary tool to involve communities in coastal management. The combination of planning and implementation grants has assisted in the redevelopment of numerous waterfronts. In the late seventies and early eighties the Michigan

Coastal Management Program gave the City of Detroit consecutive planning grants to design and develop a series of linear riverfront parks which would be connected by pathways and which would reflect the importance of the river to the city. That investment has resulted in $37 million of additional federal, state and local government funds. In turn, those dollars have stimulated $210 million of private investment in housing and in office and commercial development, creating a total of 1,200 new jobs. While not all CZM funded projects have been this ambitious or fiscally successful, several projects have been the catalyst for comprehensive planning and more appropriate shoreline development.

In addition to the pass-through grants, the Coastal Program has assisted communities on several coastal protection initiatives. As an example, the Saginaw Bay Watershed Initiative has included local, state and multi-agency federal coordination and funding for the protection of the watershed and its extensive coastal wetlands. The Saginaw Bay Initiative is innovative in that it was the first time a specific region on a watershed basis was targeted for concentrated planning and implementation which attempted to balance economic development with a strong environmental protection ethic.

Michigan's Regulatory Statutes

One of the requirements for federal approval of a state CZM program is that there be regulatory authority over activities which affect the coastal area. Over the years, both before and after program approval, the Michigan Legislature enacted the following 7 statutes, which form the regulatory core of Michigan's Coastal Management Program(Figure 3):

- 1955 PA 247, the Submerged Lands Act
- 1970 PA 245 as amended, The Shorelands Protection and Management Act
- 1972 PA 346, The Inland Lakes and Streams Act
- 1976 PA 222 as amended by 1989 PA 146 and PA 147, The Sand Dunes Protection and Management Act
- 1979 PA 203, The Goemaere-Anderson Wetland Protection Act
- 1988 PA 452, The Great Lakes Underwater Salvage and Preserve Act
- 1913 PA 326, The St. Clair Flats Act

The goal of these statutes is to protect and manage coastal resources in a consistent and responsible manner, and to help resolve the increas-

Figure 3. Michigan Coastal Statutes

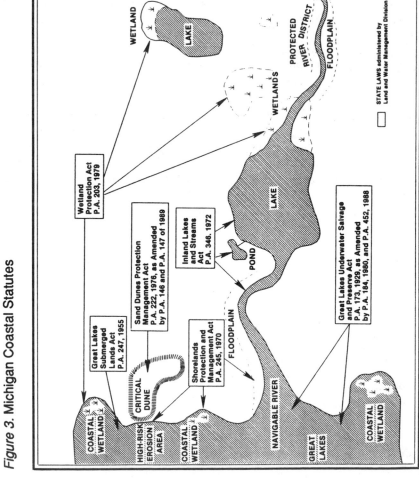

ing number of conflicts arising from multiple-use demands on the resource.

The Shorelands Protection and Management Act 1970 PA 245, as amended. This statute regulates activities within three types of coastal areas; Environmental Areas, Flood Risk Areas, and High Risk Erosion Areas. Regulations and permit requirements for construction and alteration activities are established in these designated areas. Communities may assume permitting authority under this statute by passing zoning ordinances which meet or exceed the States minimum standards. Administrative rule amendments went into effect May 1, 1992 which resulted in numerous changes in the High Risk Erosion and Flood Risk Programs.

Environmental Areas (Figure 4) are coastal wetlands that have high value as fish and wildlife habitat. Regulated activities include dredging, filling, alteration of drainage or vegetation, and construction within a designated area. No community has taken over Environmental Area permitting authority. Shorelines found to be eroding at a rate of one foot per year or greater are designated as High Risk Erosion Areas (Figure 5). Within these areas, setback requirements, calculated from the rate of erosion are established for new construction. Permits are required for construction of any permanent structure within a High Risk Erosion Area. There are special conditions which may allow construction lakeward of the established setback. Of the 119 communities which have designated High Risk Erosion Areas within their boundaries, nine currently are administering the permitting program.

Construction standards within the 100 year floodplain of designated Flood Risk Areas are designed to reduce water damage resulting from a 100-year flood event. Lowest floors must be built with the bottom of the floor joists at least one foot above the 100 year flood elevation. Basements are prohibited in floodplains. Floodplain construction standards are also found in building codes and in the National Flood Insurance Program. The National Flood Insurance Program, another national program which is administered by the Federal Emergency Management Agency, provides otherwise unavailable insurance against flood damage. In 1987, in response to extreme high water levels on the Great Lakes which resulted in a number of claims related to erosion damage, Congress expanded coverage under the National Flood Insurance Program to include prepayment to relocate homes imminently threatened with erosion damage. This authority, established in the Upton/Jones amendment, increased federal involvement in coastal management issues and overlaps with many state setback programs.

The Sand Dunes Protection and Management Act, PA 222, as amended by PA 146 and 147 of 1989. In its original form, this statute was limited to

Figure 4. Sensitive Areas Regulated Under Michigan's Coastal Management Program.

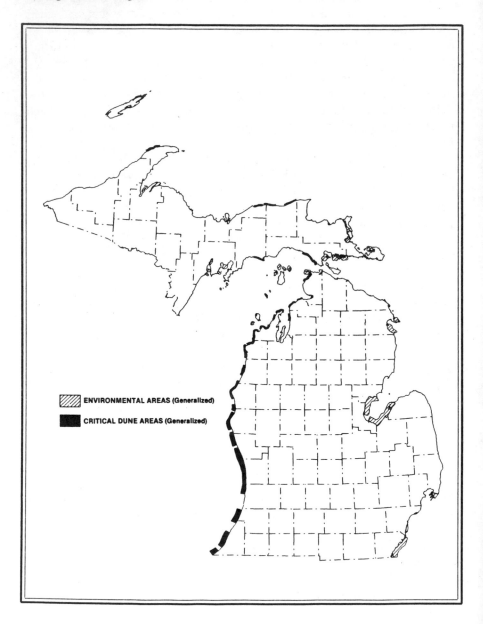

Figure 5. Hazard Prone Areas Regulated Under Michigan's Coastal Management Program.

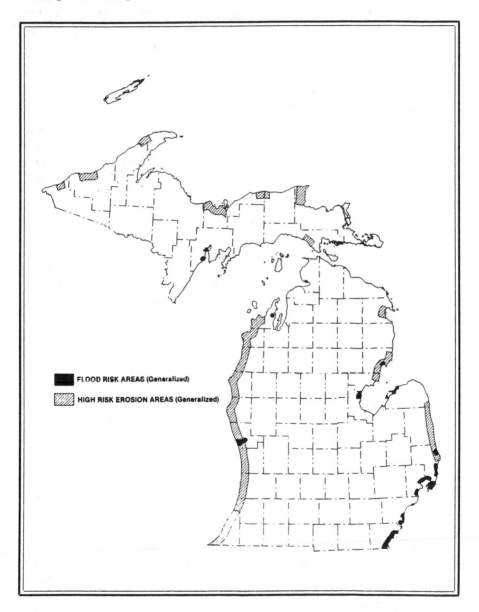

the regulation of sand mining in designated areas of the state. In 1989, amendments were enacted which expanded the state's regulatory authority to include all development proposed within designated Critical Dune Areas, i.e. those dunes which are the most sensitive to alteration or change. A permit is required for construction within designated critical sand dune areas. No construction is permitted on dunes with slopes greater than 25%. Structures must also be located behind the crest of the first landward ridge that is not a foredune. This statute also includes provisions for adoption at the local level. Of 72 eligible communities, 6 have assumed administrative authority. Over 70,000 acres of Critical Sand Dunes, the majority of which are publicly owned, are protected under this statute.

The Great Lakes Submerged Lands Act, PA 247 of 1955. This statute establishes the "ordinary high water mark" which is the landward boundary of state owned bottomlands. Michigan holds title to all Great Lake bottomlands within the state's boundaries. These submerged lands are held in public trust for the people of the state. This statute requires a permit for any filling, dredging, or construction of a permanent structure, such as a groin, seawall or dock, below the ordinary high water mark of any of the Great Lakes. Marinas and commercial piers are also regulated under this statute. The Submerged Lands Act allows "owners" of filled or occupied Great Lakes bottomlands to clear title by purchasing the State's equity through a deed or leasing agreements in regards to marinas or commercial piers.

The Goemaere-Anderson Wetland Protection Act, PA 203 of 1979. A permit is required for any dredging, filling, draining or construction in any wetland contiguous to a lake or stream, and in most isolated wetlands at least five acres in size (Figure 4). Regulations can be extended to parcels smaller than five acres in size if the Department determines the wetland is of substantial environmental significance. Michigan is the only state authorized by the U.S. Environmental Protection Agency to issue permits under Section 404 of the federal Clean Water Act of 1972. The U.S. Army Corps of Engineers and the Michigan Department of Natural Resources have joint jurisdiction over navigable waters in the state under the authority of the federal River and Harbor Act of 1989.

The Inland Lakes and Streams Act, PA 346 of 1972. A permit is required for dredging, filling, draining, or construction of permanent structures (and some seasonal structures below the ordinary high water mark) in any inland stream or lake greater than five acres in size and in coastal lakes and tributaries having a hydrologic or navigable connection to the Great Lakes. A permit is also required for dredging within 500 feet of the ordinary high water mark of a lake or stream. Marina development in coastal lakes and tributaries is regulated under this statute.

Michigan Underwater Salvage Act, PA 173, of 1929, as amended by PA 184, 1980 and PA 425, 1988. This statute provides for the designation of underwater preserves in areas that have a concentration of shipwrecks or significant geologic, historic, recreational, archaeological, or environmental features. There are currently nine designated Bottomland Preserves that provide protection for many of the estimated 6,000 shipwrecks that lie on the bottomlands of the Great Lakes. No salvage is permitted within a designated preserve.

St. Clair Flats Act, PA 326 of 1913, as amended. This act originally gave authority to lease platted lots in the St. Clair Flats, the delta at the mouth of the St. Clair River. Many of the lots were submerged or marsh when the original survey was completed in 1899. In 1981, the St. Clair Flats Management Plan was developed to control property transactions of leased lots. The plan allows for the assignment of leases and the issuance of deeds to only those parcels that are well maintained and to acquire the leasehold interests of private individuals in those lots that are submerged or marsh. The objective of the plan is to restore and protect the last remaining coastal marsh on the U.S. side of Lake St. Clair.

Future Directions of the federal Coastal Management Program

The Federal Coastal Zone Management Act was re-authorized by Congress in November, 1990. To make improvements to state and federal coastal management efforts, two new sections were added to the Act. Section 6217 requires that states develop and implement management measures for non-point source pollution. State coastal programs are to coordinate with other state and local water quality agencies to expand their non-point source pollution prevention programs.

Each state must identify land uses which may contribute to the degradation of coastal waters and identify critical coastal areas where new land uses or expansion of existing uses have the potential to increase non-point pollution. States are also required to implement management measures to achieve and maintain water quality standards and reduce non-point source pollution. Section 6217 contains provisions for technical assistance to local communities and opportunities for public participation in all aspects of the program, from development through implementation.

Section 309 is a voluntary program that provides funds to the states to address and prioritize several objectives for the purpose of enhancing and improving the nation's coastal resources. These objectives include: addressing cumulative and secondary imparts of coastal growth and development, protecting and restoring of coastal wetlands, managing coastal hazard areas, planning for management of Special Areas, increasing public access, reducing marine debris, siting of energy and governmental facilities and planning for the management of ocean resources. States are not required to participate in the enhancement grants process. However, to be eligible for future funding under this section, interested states are required to prepare an assessment of how they plan to address each issue and based upon the findings of the assessment, develop a strategy to implement or improve those efforts.

Future Directions for Michigan

Michigan spent considerable time assessing the enhancement issues and determined that the greatest challenges to coastal management are the cumulative and secondary impacts of development. Certain areas of the state, particularly northern and central lower Michigan along the Lake Michigan shoreline, are among the fastest growing areas on the Great Lakes.

Despite Michigan's comprehensive coastal protection statutes, the cumulative impact from both permitted and unregulated developments is resulting in the loss of prime farmland, open spaces, and sensitive coastal features such as wetlands and sand dunes. Waterfront development affects water quality, fragments fish and wildlife habitat and results in a loss of the biodiversity of coastal areas. Communities that were once small and rural are now experiencing traffic congestion, increased costs for public utilities and community services, and dramatic changes in land use.

Although zoning is authorized by State statute, Michigan does not have statewide zoning for land use. Zoning in Michigan is adopted and implemented at the county, township, village and/or city level. State zoning-enabling legislation was written in the 1940's and does not provide local governments much variety in the mechanisms they use to manage growth.

The Michigan Coastal Program has targeted cumulative impacts as a priority issue for the next two to four years and will be conducting a number of projects to assist communities by improving their planning capabilities, implementing innovative land use programs, and sponsoring studies which may support changes to current zoning legislation.

A package of growth management legislative bills has been written and is expected to be introduced into the next session of the Michigan Legislature. This legislation would greatly expand the techniques and authorities available to local units of government to manage growth and minimize development impacts. The package includes provisions for impact fees, transfer and/or purchase of development rights, developer agreements, and urban and general services districts.

In an effort to document the impacts of growth, the Coastal Management Program has requested federal funding to study the fiscal impacts of development. This information will be used to measure the benefits of increased growth against the costs to a community and will determine who actually pays the cost of the growth. This information will be used to educate legislators and local public officials on the need for expanded zoning and land use authorities.

Also proposed is a demonstration project for the purchase of development rights in one of the state's most important agricultural areas. The Old Mission Peninsula in northwest Michigan is a significant producer of specialty crops such as cherries, grapes and other fruits. This area is also experiencing unprecedented development pressure. Taxes which reflect the development potential of the land rather than its agricultural value are forcing farmers to sell small parcels of land to continue to support their farms. With financial and technical assistance provided by the Coastal Program in the Midwest for the purpose of preserving agricultural lands, Peninsula Township's program establishes zones where development is allowable, provides for buffer zones and designates areas where prime agricultural land should be preserved.

The Coastal Program will also be providing financial support to increase the Geographic Information System capabilities of the Northwest Michigan Regional Planning commission in order to provide land use information, zoning and master plan information, and identification of sensitive resource areas as overlays on property parcel maps. This will greatly expand the information available to communities as they update master plans and zoning ordinances and prepare for increased growth.

The Michigan Coastal Management Program looks forward to continuing its efforts to protect Michigan's shoreline from excessive and poorly managed coastal development. Future priorities for the program include expanding assistance to communities for planning and implementation of new programs that will protect coastal resources, preserve historic structures and restore urban waterfronts, while still providing for economic development.

REFERENCES

Michigan Department of Natural Resources (1990) *Michigan's Coastal Resources*, Land and Water Division, Lansing, Michigan.

U.S. Department of Commerce (1978) *State of Michigan Coastal Management Program and Final Environmental Impact Statement*, Office of Coastal Zone Management, National Ocean and Atmospheric Administration, Washington, D.C.

Panel Discussion

Panel: Penny Holt, Michigan Department of Natural Resources
Larry Hildebrand, Environment Canada
Chad Day, Simon Fraser University

Moderators: Patrick Lawrence
Gordon Nelson

(In Michigan) the municipality actually does the flood and erosion mapping ?

Holt: Well, the municipality can do either, can do any of them - the high risk erosion areas, floods, the environmental area...

So your role is in coordination ?

Holt: In communities which have taken over the program, that is our role. We meet with them periodically while they are developing or initiating their programs to make sure that their programs at least meet the minimum state requirements. After a community has assumed the program, then we meet periodically to make sure that they are following the process. So we have a lot of involvement in communities that have developed their programs.

My question is along the same lines. If the program does not devolve to local government, then what is your role, at that point? Do you conduct the necessary surveys?

Holt: Yes, there's an additional permit requirement, basically building permits cannot be issued until the state permit is received in the designated area. We've seen very good compliance state-wide. Certainly there are problems. Violations occur. But we try to maintain contact with building inspectors through periodic newsletters or correspondence, and it seems to have worked very well. A few communities have continual problems. But generally we feel that we're getting compliance.

What is the size of your staff, and how is it organized with respect to the particular functions you've described?

Holt: We have about eighteen professional staff. I am in the Land and Water Management Division. In the Great Lakes section, we have three units within the section. I have a colleague with me, Cathy Cunningham who works in the Coastal Management program. Its functions are basically grant application and administration. We try to make sure that what we are doing is what we said we would do to get our annual grant from the federal government. The Sand Dunes Act is also administered under the Coastal Management Program. Enforcement and the rest of the statutes are divided between my unit, the shorelands unit and the submerged lands unit.

I was interested in your comment with regard to erosion setback. In Ontario we're seeing the use of a hundred year setback and we're actually getting comments that it is not sufficient, that we are passing problems on to future generations.

Holt: Absolutely. We have amendments going into effect in May regarding the high risk erosion area program. Currently there is only a thirty year setback so whatever the rate of erosion is, say two feet per year — we multiply that by thirty and there is then a sixty foot setback from the eroding edge for all new structures. Basically that standard came about from the average life of a new mortgage, thirty years. We stress time and time again that these are minimum standards. If I were buying a house on the lake, or building a house on the lake, I would never, never build it at a thirty year setback, I don't care how wide the beach is. The federal government has been involved in reviewing our national flood insurance program and looking at the possibility of including erosion provisions within that act. Initially there was talk of fifty and seventy-five year setbacks at the federal level. But as you know, there's so much conflict when you talk about land use regulations that everybody backs down and says, well what's the minimum, what's the minimum, and basically thirty years is felt to be the accepted minimum.

You mentioned that federal funding is passed on to the states which participate in the program with the municipalities able to buy in to the earliest activities. Is there state funding that goes along with the federal dollars?

No.

So municipalities have their own particular reasons for participating?

Holt: Yes, they have their own particular reasons. Property owners have to work mainly with local government which works with and follows some state standards and guidelines, for the most part there may be some other state standards that they may have to work with in the state government. Generally our permitting review adds a month to two months or longer depending on the complexity of the project.

Does the state audit or monitor the programs?

Holt: Do we audit the local programs? Yes, we do. One of my jobs is to meet yearly with the locals administering the flood risk area programs to see how they're doing. I meet with about twelve communities a year on a rotating basis. The highest erosion area programs, we meet with less regularly, but we do have correspondence yearly.

My question concerns the difficulty we seem to have had in Canada in getting shoreline management on the political agenda. It strikes me that one thing that really helps is a crisis and I for one do not believe we would have a shoreline management program in Ontario today, if we had not had the big December 1985 storm. Nor would we have the IJC Reference Study either. When you look at the Michigan experience my recollection is that the first statutes of shoreline management protection act, 1970, did not seem to follow a crisis that I'm aware of. How were you able to elevate the shoreline management problem to that political level as early as 1970?

Holt: Well I wish we could say that we are a very forward thinking state, but it did indeed follow a high water period on the Great Lakes. It also was in response to a hazardous situation.

I wonder about that, because while the water was very high 1972, in the mid-60's record lows were in evidence. Yet still you were able to get the program started?

Holt: Perhaps some of our legislators had very good memories, and remember the effects of high waters previously. I can tell you it wasn't because they were trying to prevent future damage only. It was based on past damages.

Hildebrand: I think it's safe to say that there would be some underlying crisis that brought action. I mean certainly that's the Fraser River experience, recognition of the need for a response to dramatic problems, which couldn't be ignored any longer.

Nelson: Just a comment on your question Reid, I think that some of the people involved in the establishment of federal coastal legislation were working with Michigan and also the U.S. National Academy of Sciences at the time, and some of the discussions that led to the federal legislation occurred in association with the U.S. Academy of Sciences. Some people from Michigan were prominent in that. Crisis and long term and growing concern within the scientific and professional community about coastal zone management in the U.S. may have affected Michigan and other states.

Holt: Well certainly because of the length of our shoreline, our coastal area is widely recognized as very important to the state. I think that it is strongly part of the consciousness of Michigan citizens.

No one from the provincial land and water policy section is here to discuss their program but my sense is that in the development of an Ontario program there has been very little coordination with the federal government. I think that's very important because of successful Canada/Ontario cooperation in the past. I think of the Flood Damage Reduction Program and the Great Lakes Shore Damage Survey, and some other programs. Yet the federal government could have better coordination within federal programs as well as with the provinces. A number of activities in Environment Canada fit with provincial programs and that is something that we can get going at that level

Lawrence: I just want to clarify one thing so that people don't leave here with wrong impression. The Ontario Ministry of Natural Resources Lands and Water Policy Branch, which is co-sponsoring this event was slated to make a presentation tomorrow. They have a small staff to start with. There are only of two professionals who actually work on the program directly. Pearl McKeen who is the coordinator of the program is unfortunately recovering from a car accident two months ago, and is still not able to make a presentation. And the other staff member has another commitment. So their reason for being here isn't because of any other political issues or lack of interest. It is just circumstances, unfortunately.

I had one question for Penny Holt — but I'd also be interested in comments from the rest of the panel. One thing that bothers me here in Ontario is that defining the hazards of flood and erosion could perhaps be improved, for exam-

ple in regard to a dynamic beach could you give us some idea about how hazard areas are defined, whether they are based on geomorphology or setbacks?

Holt: The critical dune areas are defined as a geomorphic feature. The area has to be wind laid sand. We also looked at the terrain, the degree of relief in an area, and the vulnerability to development. So we do look at geomorphic features in areas with potential for development. We have units designated in the upper peninsula where development potential is much lower than along the lower peninsula. In regard to the dynamic beach - the actual beaches are not included in either the critical dune area designation or used to assess the high risk erosion area program - are you talking about both the high risk erosion programs and the sand dunes issues?

I am referring to both.

Holt: We look at beaches as very ephemeral features. In the high risk erosion area program, while we are doing our photogrammetric studies, we don't take the beach into account. We look for the edge of active upwind erosion and measure the rate of shoreline change. In doing field work and issuing permits, we again identify where the landward edge of active erosion is and the setback is measured from that point, regardless of the beach width and shore protection structures that may be there. Does that address your question?

Yes, I am just curious as to East coast/West coast and whether there are any similar regulations ?

Hildebrand: Yes, certainly in the east Nova Scotia, New Brunswick, and PEI, each have their own beach and dune regulations. Yet the boundaries vary. There is no consistency between them and there's nothing in the way of a system for defining setbacks for dunes.

Day: And we have no system, of course. The situation has been controlled by structural engineers for the last 20 years. What they did around the province was to build dykes everywhere. They didn't do any resource planning. So we don't have a system today for managing these areas.

Holt: I'd like to just add one observation. Often in working with local communities that are considering taking over the programs, one of the things that we quite frequently see when initial zoning ordinances come

in, is that communities will often begin with the idea that they will measure the setbacks from the water's edge. They think of the water's edge
as a benchmark. That's one of the things that we have to educate community officials on, that the beach is an ephemeral feature and not suitable for any development. In critical dune areas, development has to be
landward of the primary dunes. High risk erosion areas and sand dune
programs are two different statutes, really addressing different issues.
The high risk erosion area addresses the erosion hazards. The sand
dune act restricts development away from steep slopes. In Michigan
there are a lot of areas that are both critical dunes and high risk erosion
areas. But there are many other areas that are one or the other. If an
area is only a critical dune area, then there are no setback requirements
from the eroding edge, just the setback requirement from the primary
dune which varies and is based on the site conditions.

Do you require developers to do an environmental assessment before develop-
ment in or near hazardous areas ?

Holt: No, we really work on a case by case basis. In the sand dunes
program — and we have had a few instances in high risk erosion areas
— if developers know beforehand that the area is designated, they may
come in and say they are planning a development, can we come out and
review. The regulations are established in the statutes.

Therefore you don't have public consultation?

Holt: Public consultation was largely undertaken prior to passage of the
act. Public hearings were held. With our recent rule amendments we
held three sets of public hearings. We had a citizens ad hoc committee
that was formed to assist us in developing the changes to the regulations. Once the regulations are in place there is no longer public input in
regard to critical dune or high risk erosion area.

Hildebrand: We have an Ontario shoreline management program and
we have a US coastal zone management program operating in the Great
Lakes. Furthermore in the rest of Canada we talk of coasts not shores.
Is this a matter of semantics or should the Great Lakes in Canada operate differently from the other three coasts in the country? Perhaps you
could just maybe give your perspective on this matter.

Holt: Certainly there are a lot of different points of view. In Michigan
we have a wide variety of shoreline types and because of that, the

appropriate development techniques are different from region to region. One of the pluses is that the Federal Coastal Zone Management Act gives states guidelines under which they develop their programs. Within the state those issues can be addressed in the way that the state feels is most appropriate.

The same for Michigan, or Ohio, or South Carolina ?

Holt: The same objectives and guidelines are in place. But each state has its own authority, the setback programs are a good example of the resulting diversity. Our national coastal management program is being reassessed and in that context are looking at development of federal coastal setback or coastal erosion programs. A lot of difficulty lies in deciding on a national basis what is the best assessment methodology to use to calculate the rate of erosion. What's the appropriate setback. What feature should the setback be measured upon? There's just so much diversity nationwide that it's very challenging.

Any Ontario response or perspective ?

Reid Kreutzwiser: In Ontario, while the program is commonly known as a shoreline management program, in a way that is a bit of a misnomer because the focus is really on flood and erosion hazards. Which is fine, but it's not a shoreline management program in the broad sense of the coastal zone management act in the U.S. So we have to be careful with our terminology because we haven't really made an effort to try to integrate water quality concerns, recreational access, fisheries, these kinds of things into the Ontario program. There are some notable exceptions, for example the Toronto waterfront. Some individual Conservation Authorities may also be taking broader perspective in the preparation of shoreline management plans, but they are not expected to do so.

I have a question regarding the standards for setbacks. Is there any flexibility built into standards?

Holt: Yes there is. On lots that are substandard, that don't have the depth to meet that setback, the state has the authority to waive a portion of the setback. It's our policy to waive up to fifty percent. However, the home or structure must still be located as far landward as it possibly can be. Because of variances or special exceptions, we have very few actual denials of structure permits. I don't have the numbers off the top of my head, but they are very, minimal.

Is there not a requirement for removing structures?

Holt: Yes there is. It came about in the amendments this year. All small structures — those structures that are less than 3500 square feet — have to be moveable. Those that are built or proposed lakeward of the fifty year setback also have to be moveable. No slab foundations, no brick, stone, or block and we also look at accessibility on the site. Could moving equipment get to a house if it needed to be moved? We have found that it has worked. Generally we're comfortable in where homes are built.

Chad, The Governor of Washington and the Premier of British Columbia met in August to discuss cooperation through the two jurisdictions regarding Columbia River water quality and other inland waters. Is there any talk of an international agreement?

Day: I hope there is going to be cooperation and I think there will be more at the state and provincial levels than at the federal levels. Right now we're both under extreme growth pressure. People are flooding into the northwest corner of the U.S. and south end of British Columbia. We're going to start to develop a joint transportation system and I think we're going to start to look collaborating at water quality. Hopefully Environment Canada will be a part of that.

Hildebrand: Can I respond to that, and also give an east coast example. I mentioned the Gulf of Maine on the east coast. An agreement was signed in 1989 between the provinces of Nova Scotia, New Brunswick and the states of Maine, New Hampshire and Massachusetts. This agreement called for the cooperative management of marine environment in the Gulf of Maine, which extends from the Boston to lower Nova Scotia, including the Bay of Fundy and the Gulf of Maine. A couple of interesting things about this. One, it was not in response to a crisis. The Gulf of Maine is not in awful shape. But it's heading in that direction and there are some problems. It was recognized by the states and provinces that we needed to anticipate this. So we're taking initiatives in trying to respond to it. Perhaps we could learn from each other. The Gulf of Maine and its watershed are a large area, but perhaps we can make some progress. There have also been inquiries from B.C. and Washington State in terms of how does the model work in the Gulf of Maine.

This is an agreement signed between the two Premiers and the three State Governors. The federal governments are observers to the process;

Environment Canada, Fisheries and Oceans on the Canadian side and NOAA, EPA and Army Corps of Engineers on the U.S side. I think it's recognized that we still would not have signatures today if it had to be a federal agreement.

What is interesting about the process is that it hasn't been overly complicated or overly legalistic at all. Each jurisdiction, or each department, is undertaking something that it is particularly good at doing. The process brings others the table, perhaps to move differently or more quickly than they would have on their own with their efforts enhanced by the work and resources of other partners.

I wanted to ask Larry about the Canada-Ontario remedial action program. Whether you saw that as something leading to the process that you just described ?

Hildebrand: In the Gulf of Maine we take a broad ecosystem wide approach. Our Atlantic coastal action program is like the RAPs. We've selected 13 sites in the region, such as estuaries and harbours where we are taking about a remedial long-term planning approach. We need to respond to the coastal hazard. But there are many more issues. Again, there are pieces of legislation, and programs that are addressing those. But I don't think we're getting the wider effectiveness that we could in a context like the U.S. program.

Lawrence: To my knowledge with the exception of some Conservation Authorities and other agencies, involved with RAPs, the sorts of links you are talking about do not occur throughout the province.

The Crombie Commission has developed a model that can then be used in other areas. I would recommend the report Regeneration to all of you.

Lawrence: The Crombie Commission is an excellent example of a key initiative going on in the Province of Ontario that in many ways is very innovative, very ground breaking. It has the potential for developing some of the foregoing ideas and concepts within the context of shoreline management planning by the conservation authorities. The potential to learn about shoreline management initiatives in other areas on the Great Lakes and Ontario outside of the Toronto waterfronts is very great. There's a lot of initiative and a lot of political action continuing beyond the end of the Commission itself. So it's very timely opportunity for this.

The 1981 Great Lakes Shoreline Management Guide, took a very comprehensive approach to shoreline management planning. Due to a lack of funding, cooperation, promotion or whatever, it never really got off the ground. Agencies like the Ministry of Natural Resources focused on what their prime mandate was, erosion. But now with public concern about environmental issues and of course the Crombie Commission, the opportunity to again address this kind of broader approach is very good.

Session II

ALTERNATIVE APPROACHES

Beach and dune complex, Long Point spit, Lake Erie
Major staging area for migratory birds and habitat for rare or threatened species
(photo provided by Patrick Lawrence, University of Waterloo)

Developing a Human Ecological Approach to Coastal Management: Case Studies from the Great Lakes*

J.G. NELSON and P.L. LAWRENCE
Heritage Resources Centre, University of Waterloo
Waterloo, Ontario

Introduction

Coastal zone planning and management in Canada and other countries is plagued by difficulties and slow progress on a number of fronts (CCREM, 1978; Dorcey, 1983; Harrison and Parkes, 1983; Hildebrand, 1989). The very idea itself is subject to questions. What do we mean when we speak of the coast and the shore or shoreline, especially in terms of outlining scope and associated government and private responsibilities for planning and management? Many activities in the coastal area also continue to be dealt with ineffectively in terms of their economic, social and environmental impacts (Davidson-Arnott and Kreutzwiser, 1985; Day and Gamble, 1990). Examples include conflicts among competing land uses, loss of wetlands and other environmentally significant areas, pollution and decreasing water quality, and continuing flooding, erosion and other hazards (Day et al., 1977; Jessen et al., 1983).

Many reasons have been given for slow progress on coastal problems. These include lack of understanding of the dynamic processes at work on coastal areas, fragmentation of planning and management among many federal, provincial (state) and local agencies, lack of awareness of the importance of the coast economically, socially and environmentally, and failure to learn from historic experiences (Sorenson et al., 1984; Hildebrand, 1989; RCFTW, 1992). Of particular concern in regard to coastal management is the tendency to repeat maladjustments of the past, particularly in regard to flooding, erosion and hazards (Needham and Nelson, 1978; Kreutzwiser, 1987). Land use and economic policies and practices are closely related to flood and hazard damages, loss of wetlands, loss of citizen access to the beach and declines in water and environmental quality (Clark, 1983). Without careful assessment, residential or

* Amended version of paper presented at CAG'92, Vancouver, B.C., May 1992 and draft manuscript prepared for CAG Geography and Public Issues publication.

other developments push land use into wetlands, dunes, flood and other high risk areas and bring economic, social and environmental losses in their wake (Nelson et al., 1975; ; Kreutzwiser, 1988; Dilley and Rasid, 1990.

In this paper we wish to describe briefly, the attempts that a group, mainly of geographers' at the University of Waterloo Heritage Resources Centre, has been making to deal with shore or coastal zone problems more effectively in the Great Lakes area (Figure 1). The attempts are based on what we call a human ecological approach. By this we mean an approach that is comprehensive, interactive and adaptive (Nelson, 1991a). The approach stresses planning and management based on understanding the interrelationships among humans and the environment, in this case within the coastal zone. By comprehensive we mean inclusive of all activities, features and processes, including geologic and hydrologic (abiotic), plants and animals (biotic) and economic, technical, social and politi-

Figure 1. Great Lakes Basin and Study Sites

cal (cultural). By dynamic we mean keyed to understanding changes in processes and patterns through time. It is important to know the history of change. By interactive and adaptive we mean communicating and learning from as many sources as possible, including science as well as local knowledge.

For us, a human ecological approach therefore means providing information of the foregoing kinds for use by people of different backgrounds and interests in planning and managing the coastal zone. Our aim is to help prepare people to deal with coastal issues by collecting and analyzing information with and for them. It is our belief that planning and management will be made more effective if as many affected parties as possible learn about and deal with the situation together, on the basis of as comprehensive an information base as possible. This statement presents something of an ideal. It is of course not always attainable because of time or money constraints, political circumstances or other factors. Given these limitations it is important in our view, to be as open and co-operative as possible throughout each study or project in order that as much learning as possible is available to many interested groups and persons. We are actively working on this human ecological approach in the Great Lakes area and can briefly present the results of some recent studies to illustrate the nature of the work and its implications to date.

Frenchman's Bay, Lake Ontario

The first case is Frenchman's Bay in eastern Toronto (Figure 2). In this case we were asked by the Toronto Waterfront Commission's office for an assessment of the effects of proposed condominium and related developments on the Bay. We were asked also to provide views on the long term capacity of the Bay to accommodate such development. The project involved a report to the Commission's office based upon available reports and literature. The project did not provide support nor direction for public meetings and other citizen involvement, although it was understood that the results of our study would be published and so be widely available for public scrutiny. This project began on April 1, 1990 and was completed by a team consisting of 4 graduate students and a university professor by June 10, 1991 (Nelson et al, 1991).

The Frenchman's Bay case illustrates that a comprehensive array of information can be collected and analyzed quickly in terms of significance and constraints bearing on a public issue. The framework for analysis in Frenchman's Bay — and the other cases to be discussed later — is the ABC Resource Survey Method (Bastedo et al., 1984; Nelson et al., 1988,

Figure 2. Frenchman's Bay, Lake Ontario (from Nelson et al., 1991)

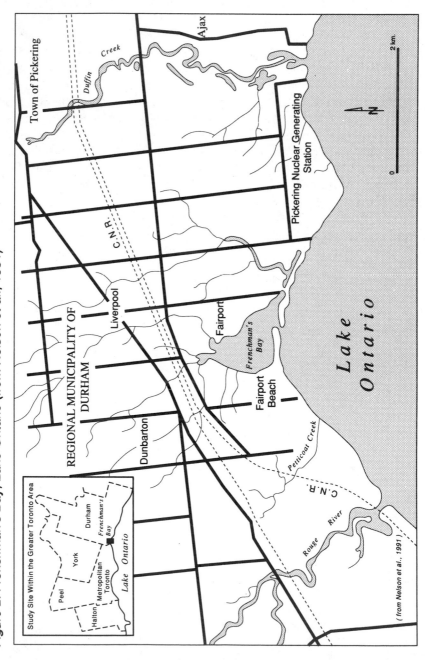

Nelson, 1991b). The technique involves the collection, analysis and inter-pretation of abiotic, biotic and cultural or human information in the sense described in the introduction to this paper (Figure 3).

Figures 4-7 are maps which provide some of the major results of the Frenchman's Bay study. The maps give important information on the geological, biological and human character of the Bay and on areas or places that are especially significant from the standpoint of environmental planning and management or sustainable development. The assessment found that development or urbanization in the area had led to stresses on shoreline erosion and geomorphic processes (Figure 4). Development during the past 40 years had also led to loss or decline of many valued

Figure 3. ABC Resource Survey Method

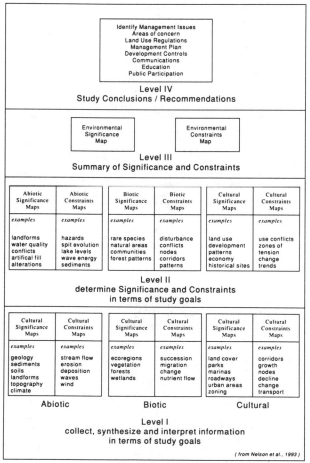

Figure 4. Abiotic Significant Processes and Stresses (from Nelson et al., 1991)

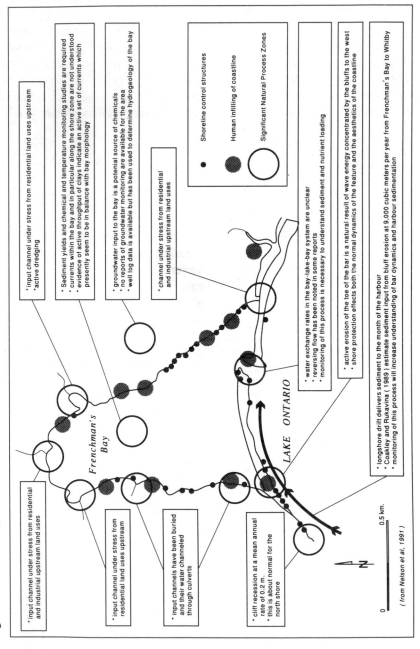

* input channel under stress from residential and industrial upstream land uses

* input channel under stress from residential land uses upstream
* active dredging

* Sediment yields and chemical and temperature monitoring studies are required
* currents within the bay and in particular along the shore zone are not understood
* evidence of active throughput of clays indicate an active set of currents which presently seem to be in balance with bay morphology

* groundwater input to the bay is a potential source of chemicals
* no reports of groundwater monitoring are available for the area
* well log data is available but has been used to determine hydrogeology of the bay

* channel under stress from residential and industrial upstream land uses

Shoreline control structures

Human infilling of coastline

Significant Natural Process Zones

* water exchange rates in the bay-lake-bay system are unclear
* reversing flow has been noted in some reports
* monitoring of this process is necessary to understand sediment and nutrient loading

* active erosion of the toe of the bar is a natural result of wave energy concentrated by the bluffs to the west
* shore protection effects both the normal dynamics of the feature and the aesthetics of the coastline

* longshore drift delivers sediment to the month of the harbour
* Coakley and Rukavina (1989) estimate sediment input from bluff erosion at 9,000 cubic meters per year from Frenchman's Bay to Whitby
* monitoring of this process will increase understanding of bar dynamics and harbour sedimentation

Frenchman's Bay

LAKE ONTARIO

* input channel under stress from residential land uses upstream

* input channels have been buried and their water channeled through culverts

* cliff recession at a mean annual rate of 0.2 m.
* this is about normal for the north shore

N

0   0.5 km.

(*from Nelson et al, 1991*)

opportunities, such as the natural, recreational and economic ones associated with wetlands which have become more and more fragmented over time (Figures 5 and 6). Historical or cultural values of the area, such as those associated with the old port and fishing history of the Bay, were likely to be modified by the proposed new residential and marina projects, along with the Bay's wetlands and other natural habitats (Figure 7).

With this in mind, the assessment recommended a moratorium on development for one year and called for further studies to consolidate and review information on natural and cultural values of the Bay in a more comprehensive, interactive coordinated manner. Since the completion of the study it has been used in discussion among provincial and municipal governments and other stakeholders leading to public purchase of several hectares of key bay wetlands.

Saugeen Watershed, Lake Huron

The second case study, of the Saugeen coast on Lake Huron, was conducted in partnership with the Saugeen Valley Conservation Authority (SVCA). In this case the SVCA had requested assistance in the preparation of a shoreline management plan. From the outset, it was possible to conduct the study in an open and interactive manner with concerned governments, agencies and citizens. Early discussions with SVCA and various agencies and citizens groups resulted in a decision to develop a background document to assist in preparing for planning rather than in preparing a plan itself. Subsequently a series of public meetings and numerous consultations were held with many government officials and people generally. The resulting information and views were used in completing a report over a period of about one year, from May 1991 to March 1992. The Saugeen project was also based on the ABC Resource Survey Method. One result of presentation of the material at public meetings was modification of the diagram illustrating the method in an attempt to make it clearer to the citizen (Figure 8).

Some of the major results are presented in Figures 9, 10, and 11. These maps show some of the major features and processes at work along the coast. Essential abiotic features and processes are noted such as sediment transport patterns, beach/dune complexes, and stream flow (Figure 9). Significant biotic areas (Figure 10) for rare and threatened species, forest corridors, dunes and wetlands are identified by using the criteria of representativeness, uniqueness, and productivity. Four main land use changes occurred with the study area from 1954 to 1990: forest fragmenta-

Figure 5. Human Impacts and Features (from Nelson et al., 1991)

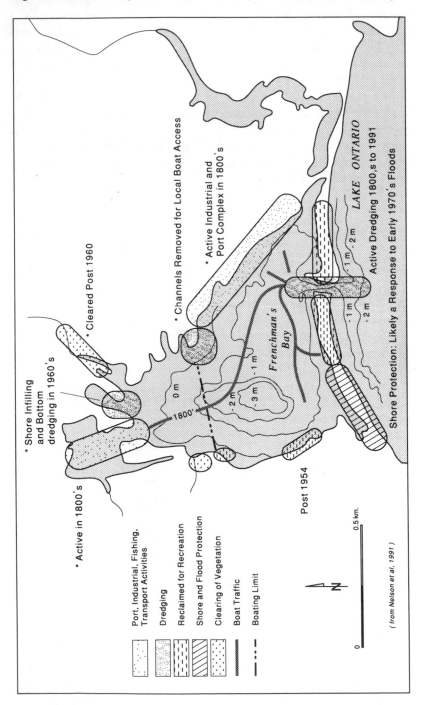

(from Nelson et al., 1991)

Figure 6. Biotic Structure and Function (from Nelson et al., 1991)

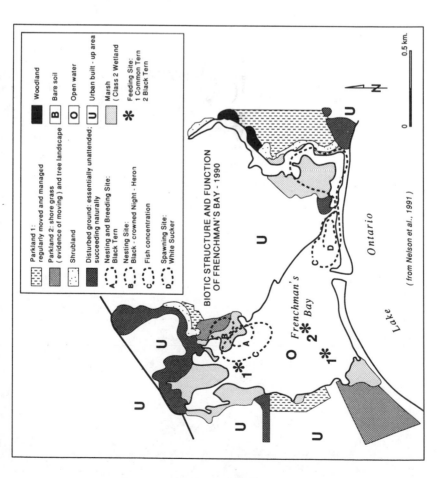

BIOTIC STRUCTURE AND FUNCTION
OF FRENCHMAN'S BAY - 1990

(from Nelson et al., 1991)

Parkland 1 :
regularly moved and managed

Parkland 2: shore grass
(evidence of moving) and tree landscape

Shrubland

Disturbed ground: essentially unattended:
succeeding naturally

A ⌀ Nesting and Breeding Site:
Black Tern

B ◯ Nesting Site:
Black - crowned Night - Heron

C ◯ Fish concentration

D ◯ Spawning Site:
White Sucker

Woodland

B Bare soil

O Open water

U Urban built - up area

Marsh
(Class 2 Wetland

＊ Feeding Site:
1 Common Tern
2 Black Tern

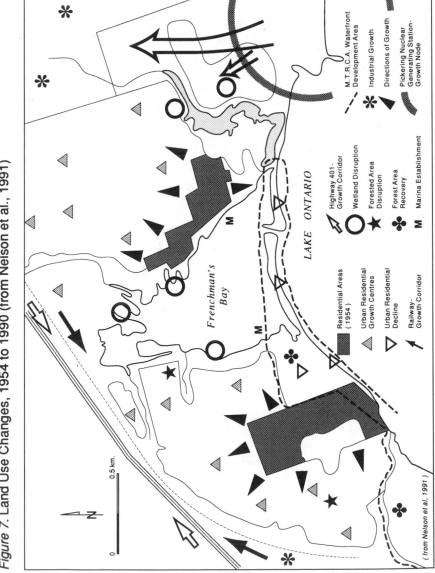

Figure 7. Land Use Changes, 1954 to 1990 (from Nelson et al., 1991)

(*from Nelson et al, 1991*)

Residential Areas (1954)

Urban Residential Growth Centres

Urban Residential Decline

Railway-Growth Corridor

Highway 401-Growth Corridor

Wetland Disruption

Forested Area Disruption

Forest Area Recovery

Marina Establishment   M

M.T.R.C.A. Waterfront Development Area

Industrial Growth

Directions of Growth

Pickering Nuclear Generating Station-Growth Node

LAKE ONTARIO

Frenchman's Bay

0.5 km.

N

Figure 8. Modified ABC Resource Survey Method (from Lawrence and Nelson, 1992)

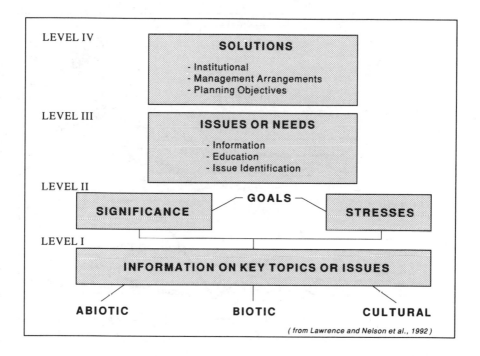

(from Lawrence and Nelson et al., 1992)

Figure 9. Significant Coastal Features and Processes (from Lawrence and Nelson, 1992)

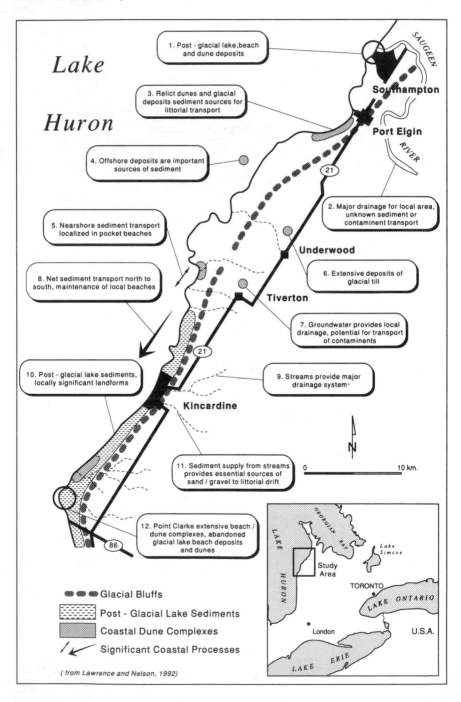

(from Lawrence and Nelson, 1992)

Figure 10. Areas of Biological Significance (from Lawrence and Nelson, 1992)

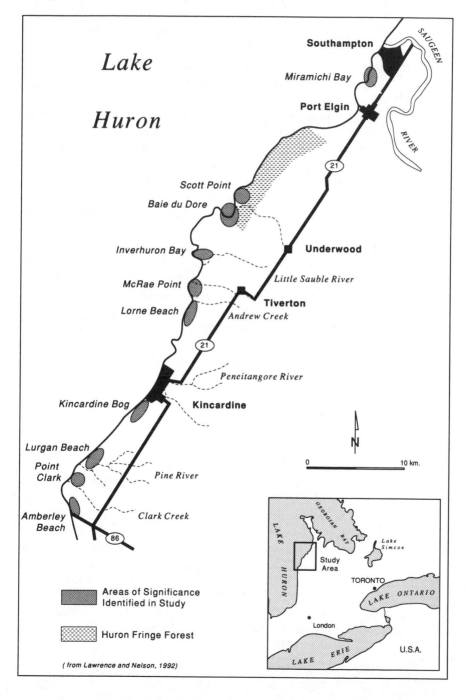

tion; rural residential (cottage) extension; rural industrial development; and, urban growth (Figure 11).

The maps also show some of the more significant features, processes and stresses which require special attention in planning and management. Valuable additional information was made available to the research team by agencies and citizens, along with a strong indication as to the priorities for action. For example, the issue of public access to the shore was often identified as a critical one for local people, but one which was less pressing for many of the agency professionals.

The interactive process led the research team to identify several areas of tension where significant conflicts among conservation and development interests were either already evident or likely to develop in the future (Figure 12). These areas would warrant special attention in any future planning exercise concerned with the coast. Issues were also identified which initially had not been anticipated as major ones by either the research team, the SVCA or local people. A notable example is the degree to which coastal forests and woodlands are being fragmented by various developments.

The final report consisted of maps and a guide to a larger repository of the information gathered during the course of the study (Lawrence and Nelson, 1992). The HRC/SVCA assessment was undertaken on a joint basis from the very start, sharing expertise, information and costs. This has laid the foundation for possible HRC participation in the development of a shoreline management plan for the area. The work provides both a basis, and a point of departure, for further research on shoreline planning and management along the Lake Huron coast.

Long Point, Lake Erie

The third case study is of the Long Point area and this work is ongoing. The project is primarily funded by a 1992 major competitive grant from the Royal Canadian Geographical Society (RCGS), with some additional support from the Social Sciences and Humanities Research Council (SSHRC). The Canada / MAB program approved the nomination of Long Point as a biosphere reserve in June 1985. In 1986 the Long Point Biosphere Reserve was officially designated by the Man and Biosphere Program of UNESCO (Francis, 1985). The Long Point Biosphere Reserve (Figure 13) consists of a core protected area (Long Point National Wildlife Area), buffer area (defined by the 10 metre depth contour offshore and the regulatory 1:100 year flood line onshore) and a undefined "zone of cooperation " (Canada/ MAB, 1990).

Figure 11. Significant Land Use Changes 1953 - 1990 (from Lawrence and Nelson, 1992)

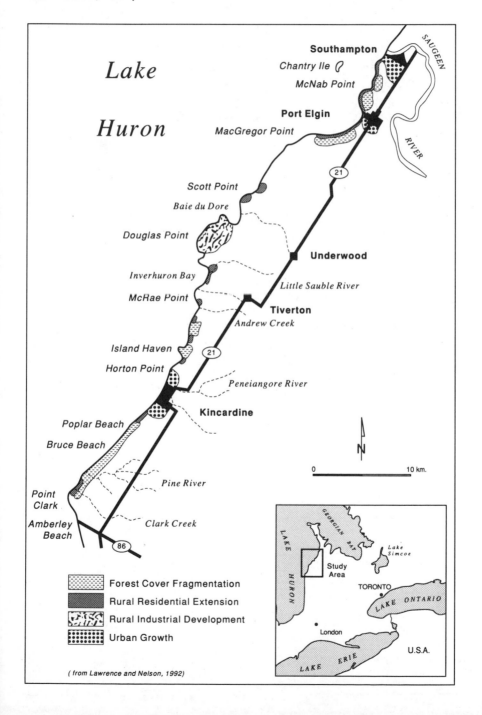

(from Lawrence and Nelson, 1992)

Figure 12. Summary of Management Issues (from Lawrence and Nelson, 1992)

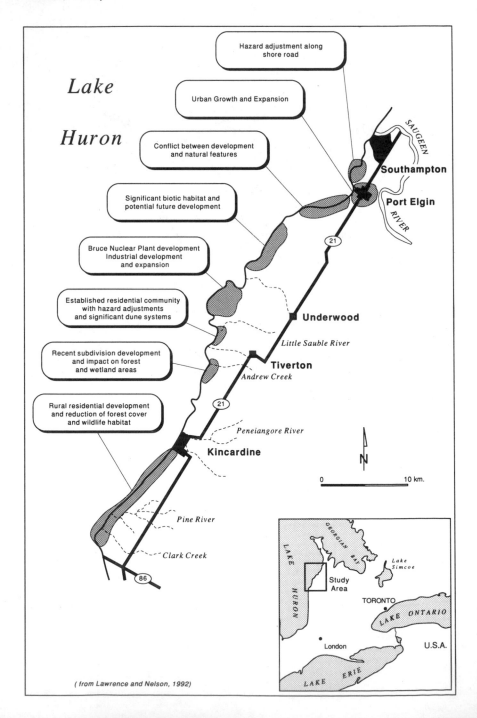

(from Lawrence and Nelson, 1992)

Figure 13. Long Point Region and Study Area

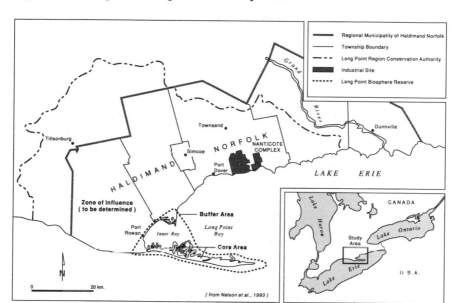

The shoreline is characterized by 30 to 40 metre high eroding clay bluffs to the west, the 40 kilometer long sandy spit environment of Long Point with its associated dune and wetland systems, and low-lying beaches, wetlands and bluffs to the east. The dune and wetland systems have a rich mix of habitats consisting of an open lake, shallow bays, sand bars, beaches, dunes, forests and scrub, ponds, and marshes. The region is host to a variety of land use and resource conflicts and to many significant species and habitats. Some 20 distinct biotic communities have been described on the Long Point sand spit. About 700 species of vascular plants have been recorded. 90 species are considered to be rare in Ontario and at least four occur nowhere else in Canada (Canada / MAB, 1990). The Long Point complex is a major staging area for migrating waterfowl and small migratory birds. Long Point also has a long history of human use, notably for fishing, waterfowl hunting, cottaging and other recreational and tourism purposes (Francis, 1985). The Point is also an area that is well known for flooding and erosion hazards. It is currently also an area in which the decline of tobacco farming as an economic main-stay, has led to the search for other economic opportunities including development of numerous marinas and other recreational facilities and activities (Nelson et al., 1993). These developments are having incomplete-ly understood effects on the wetlands and other resources of the produc-tive Inner Bay and other significant places in the Long Point area.

The aim of the project is to produce an environmental folio which is seen as a means of synthesizing and graphically displaying natural and human information on the Long Point area for use by local governments and citizens in planning and management (Nelson et al., 1993). The preparation of the folio has the approval and support of the local Long Point Biosphere Reserve Committee which consists of government offi-cials and people living in the area. The Committee wants to have available information on the area put in a form where it is more widely intelligible and useful than is currently the case with scientific and scholarly articles and bibliographies. The folio will consist of maps and text built around the major concerns and issues facing the people of the area and Biosphere planning and management. Work in the first year of the project has focused on the collection of existing data from government reports, pub-lished literature, scientific studies and consultations with local people and government agencies. Topics currently under examination include geolo-gy and geomorphology (Figure 14), shoreline flooding and erosion (Figure 15) and significant natural areas and sites (Figure 16).

Discussion

In summary, the human ecological approach is intended to be compre-hensive, dynamic, interactive and adaptive. In the current context the focus is on the interactions among humans and environment in the Great Lakes coastal zone. The approach involves working closely with local people and agencies. It is intended to assist them in preparing to address complex issues on the basis of understanding and assessing a broad infor-mation base consisting of scientific, technical and local knowledge and views. To date the approach seems to have been reasonably successful in that it has led to some significant planning and management decisions and to considerable interest and involvement in our work by local people and responsible agencies. The Frenchman's Bay study helped lead to gov-ernment purchase of a key wetland in the Bay. The Saugeen project appears to have provided a good background for the preparation of a shoreline management plan. Discussion and feedback has been positive on the work to date in the Long Point area.

Figure 14. Physiographic Features

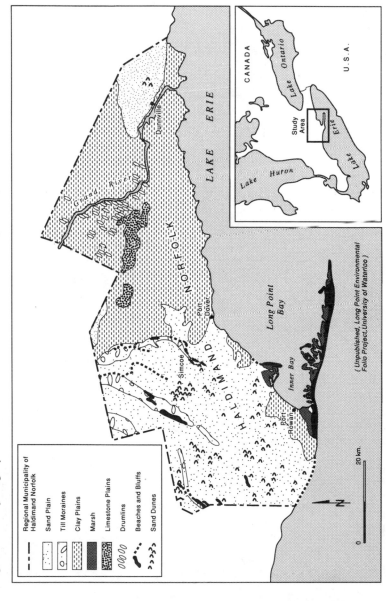

Long Point Environmental Folio Project
Heritage Resources Centre, University of Waterloo

Figure 15. Shoreline Flooding and Erosion

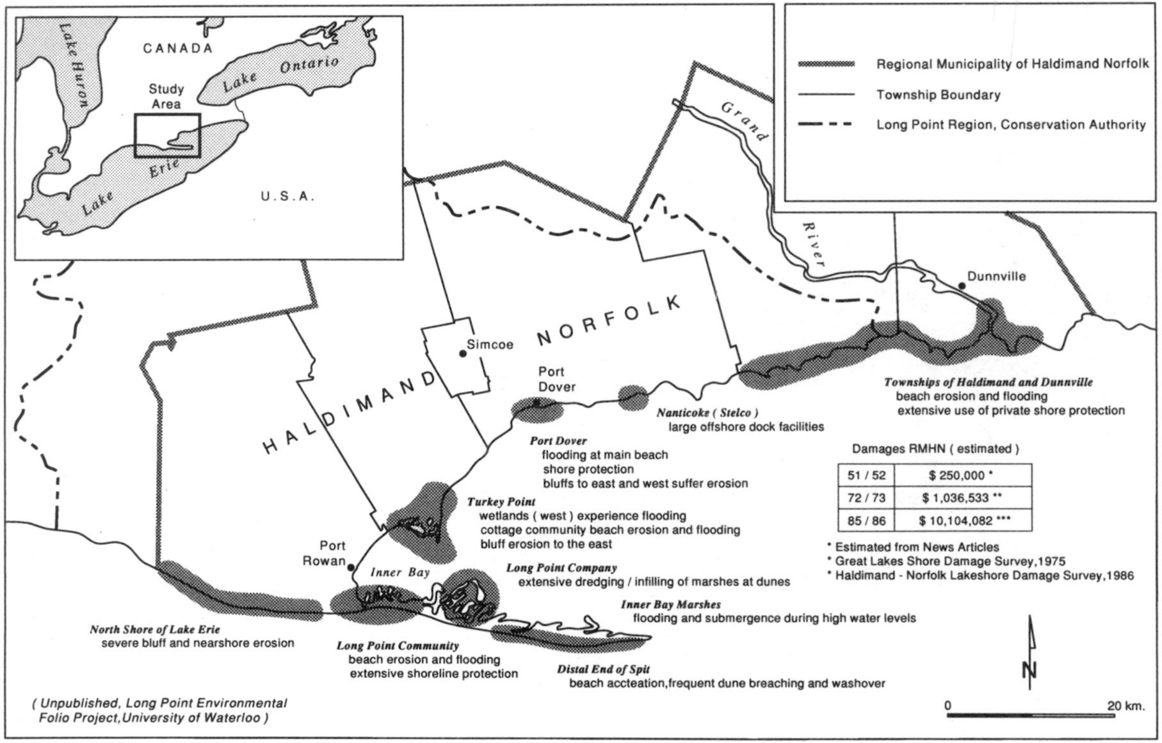

Regional Municipality of Haldimand Norfolk

Township Boundary

Long Point Region, Conservation Authority

Townships of Haldimand and Dunnville
beach erosion and flooding
extensive use of private shore protection

Damages RMHN (estimated)

51 / 52	$ 250,000 *
72 / 73	$ 1,036,533 **
85 / 86	$ 10,104,082 ***

* Estimated from News Articles
** Great Lakes Shore Damage Survey,1975
*** Haldimand - Norfolk Lakeshore Damage Survey,1986

N

0   20 km.

Nanticoke (Stelco)
large offshore dock facilities

Port Dover
flooding at main beach
shore protection
bluffs to east and west suffer erosion

Turkey Point
wetlands (west) experience flooding
cottage community beach erosion and flooding
bluff erosion to the east

Long Point Company
extensive dredging / infilling of marshes at dunes

Inner Bay Marshes
flooding and submergence during high water levels

Distal End of Spit
beach accleation,frequent dune breaching and washover

Long Point Community
beach erosion and flooding
extensive shoreline protection

North Shore of Lake Erie
severe bluff and nearshore erosion

NORFOLK

HALDIMAND

Simcoe

Port
Dover

Inner Bay

Port
Rowan

Grand River

Dunnville

CANADA

Lake Huron

Lake Ontario

Lake Erie

U.S.A.

Study
Area

(*Unpublished, Long Point Environmental
Folio Project, University of Waterloo*)

Long Point Environmental Folio Project
Heritage Resources Centre, University of Waterloo

Figure 16. Significant Natural Areas and Sites

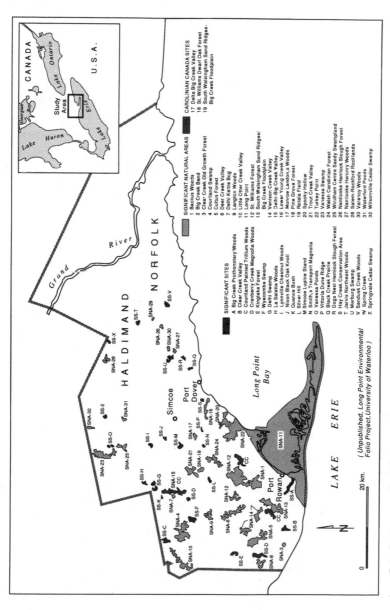

SIGNIFICANT NATURAL AREAS

1 Backus Woods
2 Big Creek Bend
3 Clear Creek Old Growth Forest
4 Courtland Swamp
5 Cultus Forest
6 Deer Creek Valley
7 Delhi Kettle Bog
8 Langton Woods
9 Little Otter Creek Valley
10 Long Point
11 Long Point
12 St. Williams Forest
13 South Walsingham Sand Ridges/
   Big Creek Floodplain
14 Venison Creek Valley
15 Delhi Big Creek Valley
16 Lower Young Creek Valley
17 Monroe Landon,s Woods
18 Pine Grove Forest
19 Rotala Field
20 Spooky Hollow
21 Trout Creek Valley
22 Turkey Point
23 Vanessa Swamp
24 Walsh Carolinian Forest
25 Windham Centre Sandy Swampland
26 Nanticoke Hemlock Slough Forest
27 Nanticoke Hickory Woods
28 Salem-Rockford Rocklands
30 Varency Woods
31 Waterford Ponds
32 Wilsonville Cedar Swamp

CAROLINIAN CANADA SITES

17 Delta Big Creek Valley
18 St. Williams Dwarf Oak Forest
19 South Walsingham Sand Ridges-
   Big Creek Floodplain

SIGNIFICANT SITES

A Big Creek Prothonotary Woods
B Clear Creek Valley
C Courtland Painted Trillium Woods
D Cranberry Creek Magnolia Woods
E Kinglake Forest
F Wyecombe Swamp
G Delhi Swamp
H La Salette Woods
I Lynnville Chestnut Woods
J Nixon Black Oak Knoll
K Quance Bush
L Silver Hill
M Simcoe Lupine Stand
N Smith,s Transport Magnolia
O Vanessa Ponds
P Vittoria Dune Ridge
Q Black Creek Prairie
S Dogs Nest Hemlock Slough Forest
T Hay Creek Conservation Area
U Jarvis Northeast Woods
V Marburg Swamp
W Sandusk Creek Woods
X Spring Creek
X Springvale Cedar Swamp

Long Point Environmental Folio Project
Heritage Resources Centre, University of Waterloo

(Unpublished, Long Point Environmental
Folio Project,University of Waterloo)

The approach allows for better understanding of the issues and areas of interest along the coast as a basis for a more broadly informed and participatory decision making process in land use and development planning. Though information review, public participation and expert opinion, issues such as water quality, forest fragmentation, habitat loss, disruption of natural processes, flood and erosion hazards and land use conflicts are identified and assessed. In light of such factors understanding and knowledge becomes an essential goal in long term, proactive, comprehensive planning of the coast.

Acknowledgements

A number of individuals from the Heritage Resources Centre and Department of Geography contributed to the case studies outlined in this paper; Karen Beazley, Veronica Chisholm, Maria Healey, Kerri Pauls, Monica Quinn, Rafal Serafin, Andy Skibicki, Ron Stenson, Steve Wilcox, and Chi-Ling Yeung. Lisa Weber of the Heritage Resources Centre and Debbie Stenson assisted with text and map preparation. Special recognition is given to the agencies who provided data for the study including the Long Point Region Conservation Authority, Long Point World Biosphere Reserve Committee, Ontario Hydro, Ontario Ministry of Natural Resources, Ontario Ministry of Environment, Royal Commission on the Future of the Toronto Waterfront, and Saugeen Valley Conservation Authority. This research has been supported by financial assistance from the Royal Canadian Geographical Society, the Social Sciences and Humanities Council of Canada, Toronto Waterfront Development Office, Ontario Environmental Youth Corps, and the Saugeen Valley Conservation Authority.

REFERENCES

Bastedo, J., Nelson, J.G., and Theberge, J. (1984) "Ecological Approach to Resource Survey and Planning for Environmentally Significant Areas: The ABC Method," *Environmental Management*, 8(2), 125-134.

Canadian Council of Resource and Environmental Ministers (CCREM) (1978) *Proceedings of the Shore Management Symposium*, British Columbia Ministry of Environment, Victoria, B.C.

Canadian Man and Biosphere (MAB) Committee (1990) *Biosphere Reserves in Canada*, Canadian/MAB Secretariat, Canadian Commission for UNESCO, Ottawa, Ontario.

Clark, J.E. (1983) *Coastal Ecosystem Management*, John Wiley & Sons Ltd., New York.

Davidson-Arnott, R.G.D. and Kreutzwiser, R.D. (1985) "Coastal Processes and Shoreline Encroachment: Implications for Shoreline Management in Ontario," *Canadian Geographer*, 29(3), 256-262.

Day, J.C., Fraser, J.A. and Kreutzwiser, R.D. (1977) "Assessment of Flood and Erosion Assistance Programs: Rondeau Coastal Experience, Lake Erie," *Journal of Great Lakes Research*, 3(1-2), 38-45.

Day, J.C. and Gamble, D.B. (1990) "Coastal Zone Management in British Columbia: An Institutional Comparison with Washington, Oregon, and California," *Coastal Management* , 18, 115-141.

Dilley, R.S. and Rasid, H. (1990) "Human Response to Coastal Erosion: Thunder Bay, Lake Superior," *Journal of Coastal Research*, 6(4), 779-788.

Dorcey, A.H.J. (1983) "Coastal Management as a Bargaining Process," *Coastal Zone Management Journal*, 11(1-2), 13-40.

Francis, G.F. (1985) *Long Point Biosphere Reserve Nomination*, Submitted to the Man and the Biosphere Programme, Canadian Commission for UNESCO, Ottawa, Ontario.

Harrison, P. and Parkes, J.G.M. (1983) "Coastal Management in Canada", *Coastal Zone Management Journal*, 11(1-2), 1-11.

Hildebrand, L.P. (1989) *Canada's Experience with Coastal Zone Management* , Oceans Institute of Canada, Halifax, Nova Scotia.

Jessen, S., Day, J.C., and Nelson, J.G. (1983) "Assessing Land Use Regulations in Coastal Wetlands: The Case of Long Point Area, Lake Erie, Ontario," *Coastal Zone Management Journal*, 11(1-2), 91-115.

Kreutzwiser, R.D. (1987) "Managing the Great Lakes Shoreline Hazard", *Journal of Soil and Water Conservation*, 42(3), 150-154.

Kreutzwiser, R.D. (1988) "Municipal Land Use Regulation and the Great Lakes Shoreline Hazard in Ontario," *Journal of Great Lakes Research*, 14,(2), 142-147.

Lawrence, P.L. and Nelson, J.G. (1992) *Preparing for a Shoreline Management Plan for the Saugeen Valley Conservation Authority*, A Joint Study of the Heritage Resources Centre, University of Waterloo, Waterloo, Ontario and the Saugeen Valley Conservation Authority, Hanover, Ontario.

Needham, R.D. and Nelson, J.G. (1978) "Adjustment to Change in Coastal Environments: The Case of Fluctuating Lake Erie Water Levels," in *Coping with the Coast* , Proceedings of the Fourth Annual Conference of the Coastal Society, Arlington, Virginia, 196-213.

Nelson, J.G. (1991a) "Research in Human Ecology and Planning: An Interactive, Adaptive Approach," *Canadian Geographer*, 35(2), 114-127.

Nelson, J.G. (1991b) "A Step towards more Comprehensive and Equitable Information Systems: The ABC Resource Survey Method," in *Greenways and Green Space on the Oak Ridges Moraine*, Occasional Paper No. 14, Department of Geography, Trent University, Peterborough, Ontario, 27-34.

Nelson, J.D., Battin, R.A. and Kreutzwiser, R.D. (1975) "The Fall 1972 Lake Erie Floods and their Significance to Resources Management," *Canadian Geographer*, 20(1), 35-58.

Nelson, J.G., Grigoriew, P., Smith, P.G.R. and Theberge, J. (1988) "The ABC Resource Survey Method, The ESA Concept and Comprehensive Land Use Planning and Management," in *Landscape Ecology and Management* (edited by M.R. Moss), Proceedings of the First Symposium of the Canadian Society for Landscape Ecology and Management, University of Guelph, May 1987, Polyscience Publications Inc., Montreal, Canada, 143-175.

Nelson, J.G., Skibicki, A.J, Stenson, R.E., and Yeung, C.L. (1991) *Urbanization, Conservation and Development: The Case of Frenchman's Bay, Toronto, Ontario* , Heritage Resources Centre, Technical Paper 5, University of Waterloo, Waterloo, Ontario.

Nelson, J.G., Lawrence, P.L., Beazley, K., Stenson, R., Skibicki, A., Yeung, C.L., and Pauls, K. (1993) *Preparing an Environmental Folio for the Long Point Biosphere Reserve and Region,* Long Point Environmental Folio Publication Series, Working Note 1, Heritage Resources Centre, University of Waterloo, Waterloo, Ontario.

Royal Commission on the Future of the Toronto Waterfront (1992) *Regeneration - Final Report,* Government Printer of Ontario, Toronto, Ontario.

Sorenson,J.C., McCreary, S.T. and Hershman, M.J. (1984) *Institutional Arrangements for Management of Coastal Resources,* Research Planning Institute, Coastal Publication No. 1, Columbia, South Carolina.

Toward a Great Lakes Biosphere Reserve: Linking the Local to the Global

GEORGE FRANCIS
Department of Environment and Resource Studies,
University of Waterloo, Waterloo, Ontario

Introduction

Coastal zone management is a good example of the challenges inherent in 'environmental management'. If done well, it requires the ability to:

- develop consultation processes needed to reach some consensus among a number of different agencies, non-governmental organizations and local groups (the 'stakeholders') on goals and objectives to be sought;
- integrate knowledge and expertise from a number of different sources (inter disciplinarity combined with the experience of lay persons);
- deal with systems phenomena which exhibit discontinuities and uncertainties in the ways in which they function (systems dynamics);
- orient research and monitoring to issues associated with the above ('action research'); and
- maintain a collective capability to adjust and adapt to unanticipated changes (an aspect of 'social learning').

There are also other environmental challenges being addressed in the Great Lakes. For example, under the terms of the Great Lakes Water Quality Agreement, (IJC 1988), work is underway to develop and implement remedial action plans for 43 'areas of concern', i.e. badly degraded nearshore harbours, river mouths and 'connecting channels' (rivers) (IJC/WQB 1991), and to prepare lake-wide management plans, starting first with Lake Ontario and Lake Superior (e.g. IJC/SAB 1991). The Joint Strategic Plan for Management of Great Lakes Fisheries (GLFC 1980) required the participating agencies to determine the preferred fish communities for each lake, and to prepare periodic state-of-the-lake reports; the preferred communities have been identified over the past 2 to 3 years and the first state-of-the-lakes reports are now being issued (e.g. Hansen 1990).

Several collaborative efforts are under way to promote the conservation of Great Lakes wetlands and areas of high biodiversity. These include the Eastern Habitat Joint Venture, under the North American Waterfowl Management Plan (EHJV n.d.), a Canadian Great Lakes Wetlands Action Plan (forthcoming), and a proposed binational "Great Legacy Program" to strengthen protection for areas of high biodiversity within the Great Lakes Basin, or sites for monitoring the "ecosystem health" of the Lakes (CGL 1992).

All of these initiatives face similar challenges.They are oriented by, or are expressions of, a growing commitment to take 'an ecosystem approach' in binational cooperation on Great Lakes issues and they contribute towards expressed goals of restoring and maintaining 'ecosystem health' or 'ecosystem integrity' in the Great Lakes bioregion (e.g. Edwards and Regier 1990).

Linking the Various Initiatives

There is a need for some communication, if not integration of efforts among these different initiatives, and especially with coastal zone planning, in order to avoid contradictions among policies and programs and to seek the 'synergy' that cooperative arrangements can sometimes bring. As one example, an Ecosystem Objectives Working Group (EOWG) established in 1987 under the Great Lakes Water Quality Agreement is developing a set of ecosystem goals, objectives and indicators for the proposed lake-wide management plan for Lake Ontario. The proposed goals are:

"The Lake Ontario ecosystem should be maintained, and as necessary, restored or enhanced, to support self-reproducing diverse biological communities;

The presence of contaminants shall not limit the use of fish, wildlife and waters of the Lake Ontario basin by humans, and shall not cause adverse heath effects in plants and animals; [and]

We as a society shall recognize our capacity to cause great changes in the ecosystem and we shall conduct our activities with responsible stewardship for the Lake Ontario Basin".

The related objectives are:

'The waters of Lake Ontario shall support diverse healthy, reproducing and self-sustaining communities in dynamic equilibrium, with an emphasis on native species;

The perpetuation of a healthy, diverse and self-sustaining wildlife community that utilizes the lake for habitat and or food shall be ensured by attaining and sustaining the waters, coastal wetlands and upland habitats of the Lake Ontario basin in sufficient   quality and quantity;

The waters, plants and animals of Lake Ontario shall be free from contaminants and organisms resulting from human activities at levels that affect human health or aesthetic factors such as tainting, odor and turbidity;

Lake Ontario offshore and nearshore zones and surrounding tributary, wetland and upland habitats shall be of sufficient quality and quantity to support ecosystem   objectives for health, productivity and distribution of plants and animals in and adjacent to Lake Ontario; [and]

Human activities and decisions shall embrace environmental ethics and a commitment to responsible stewardship" (EOWG 1992).

The working group has sub-groups working to develop indicators for benthic, pelagic and wildlife communities, for human health, and for stewardship. There has been some informal discussions about extending these general goals, objectives and indicators to all of the Lakes. The connections with the coastal zone in these statements are clear, but their organizational relations to coastal zone planning apparently have not been worked out.

UNESCO/MAB and the Concept of a Cluster Biosphere Reserve

The UNESCO/MAB programme has, for some twenty years, been trying to foster the development of environmental management capabilities that incorporate conservation objectives with sustainable resource use on a landscape scale that relates management activities at different sites. The MAB perspective and ideals could help reenforce the idea of taking an ecosystem approach to Great Lakes issues, while at the same time, the Great Lakes programs and evolving cooperative arrangements are consistent with MAB and offer good examples of what the MAB programme is trying to promote in practice. This has lead to some exploration of how the two might be brought together, to mutual advantage, mainly by applying the concept of a 'cluster biosphere reserve' within the Great Lakes (Francis 1992 a).

The concept of a "biosphere reserve" and its application in Canada have been described by Francis (1992b). Basically, a biosphere reserve is an international designation of recognition through the UNESCO/MAB programme for particular geographic areas which maintain a good balance between conservation and sustainable resource use. Such areas must exhibit a spatial configuration reflecting three kinds of zonation which collectively serve three main functions. The spatial configuration must include some 'core' area(s) of minimally disturbed and protected ecosystems characteristic of the region, buffer zones around the core within which permitted human uses do not intrude into the core, and a 'transition area' or 'zone of cooperation' extending outwards into some larger area away from core and buffer areas within which the full range of human uses of resources occurs.

The main functions of biosphere reserves are conservation of ecosystems, usually, but not always associated with core areas; the demonstration of sustainable resource use practices including restoration of degraded areas; and 'logistic support' for research, monitoring, and education directed towards issues of conservation and sustainability. With the appropriate organizational arrangements involving owners, managers, and residents, this facilitates comparisons between utilized and relatively undisturbed areas which can provide insights into accumulative impacts on ecosystems from various human uses of them.

Under some conditions, such as applying the concept of a biosphere reserve to a large bioregion, a multiple site 'cluster' configuration is more appropriate. If sufficient communication and coordination is maintained among the different programs and sites serving the different functions, then the concept of a biosphere reserve can be realized in practice. Cluster biosphere reserves have not yet been established in Canada, but for regions at the scale of the Great Lakes, this would seem to be the most feasible approach. Generally, the design and development of these biosphere reserves for the Great Lakes should consider:

Conservation areas with:

- aboriginal cultural sites
- island archipelagos
- coastal wetlands and sand dune complexes
- high community and/or species biodiversity
- Great Lakes endemic species and endangered, rare, threatened species with strong affinities to Great Lakes nearshore and coastal zone habitats;

Demonstration areas for:

- ecologically sensitive uses of coastal zones
- remedial action plans/programs for badly degraded sites
- coastal dune protection measures
- wetlands rehabilitation/management
- "zero discharge" by industries;

And, *logistic support* from sites having:

- facilities for research & monitoring
- environmental education &/or information facilities
- high quality ecosystems which can serve as reference areas for assessing ecosystem health.

Feasibility of a Lake Superior Biosphere Reserve

The Lake Superior Basin was deemed the most appropriate one for exploring ways in which a cluster biosphere reserve might be developed. Besides being the headwater Lake, it is the only Great Lake for which objectives have been agreed to under the Great Lakes Water Quality Agreement and the Joint Strategic Plan for the Management of Great Lakes Fisheries. In addition, and in response to the IJC recommendation that Lake Superior become a demonstration area for the zero discharge commitment under the GLWQA (IJC 1990), federal, state and provincial jurisdictions in September 1991 launched "A Binational Program to Restore and Protect Lake Superior".

The feasibility assessment of a possible cluster biosphere reserve would have to address the configuration of sites representing the different spatial and functional components of a biosphere reserve through consultations with owners and managers of the different sites and programs. Wherever appropriate, exemplary coastal zone management programs should be included as important demonstrations of some of the ways in which conservation can be balanced and integrated with sustainable resource use.

It must be emphasized that a 'biosphere reserve' is an international designation of recognition, which in the case of the Great Lakes would serve to recognize much of what is already in place. The intent would *not* be to create another layer of management authority. There is an expectation that a designation would help foster the development of appropriate networks of communication and cooperation among vari-

Figure 1. Lake Superior Protected Areas and Management Arrangements

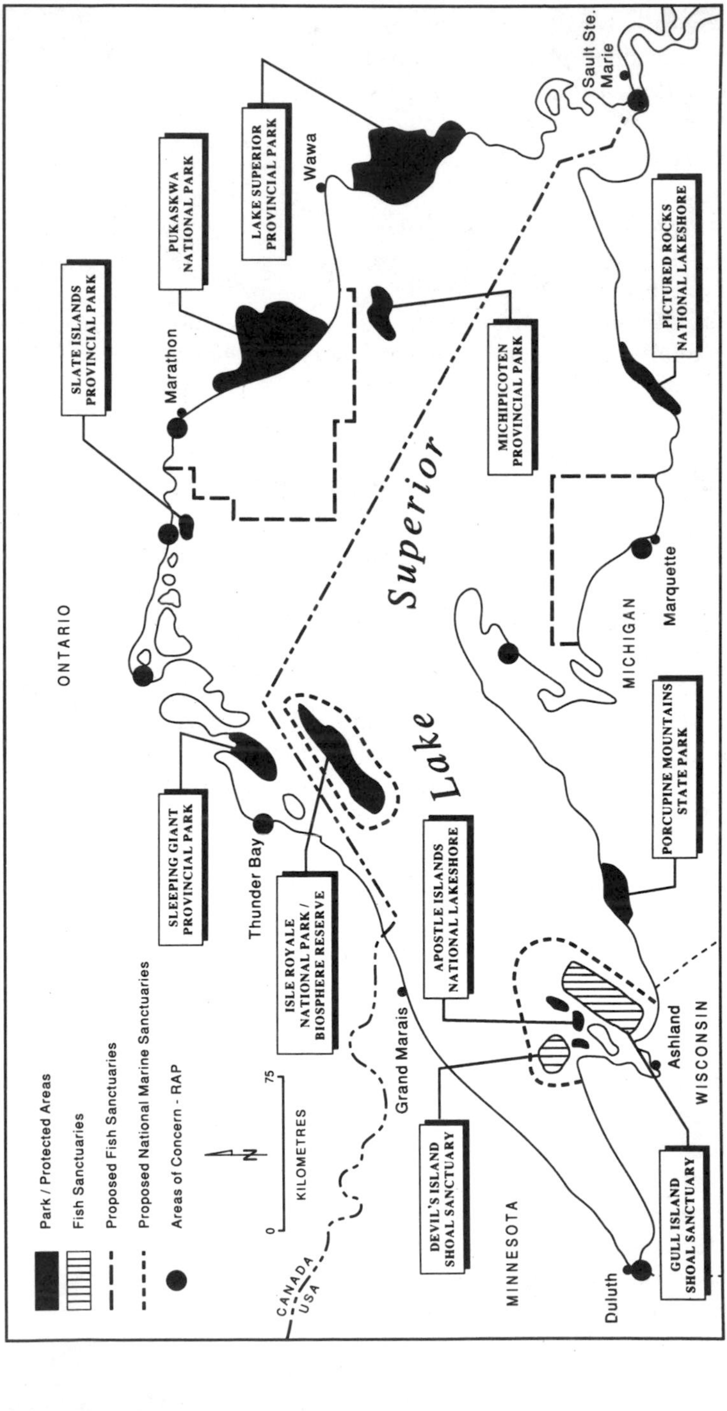

Table1.

Conservation: Larger areas which might be recognized in the "cluster":

Devil's Island Shoal Sanctuary	44,000	ha
Apostle Islands National Lakeshore	17,010	
Gull Island Shoal Sanctuary	70,000	
Porcupine Mountains State Park	26,510	
Isle Royale National Park/Biosphere Reserve	231,403	
Sleeping Giant Provincial Park	4,435	
Slate Islands Provincial Park	6,570	
Pictured Rocks National Lakeshore	28,910	
Pukaskwa National Park	187,800	
Michipicoten Provincial Park	36,740	
Lake Superior Provincial Park	155,659	

(and other smaller sites among 53 designated protected areas)

Demonstration: Some or all of:
The Remedial Action Plan sites
Thunder Bay, Nipigon Bay, Jackfish Bay, Peninsula Harbour,
St. Louis River, Torch Lake, Deer Lake
Watershed and/or forest management demonstration sites
Industrial "zero discharge" operations.

Logistical support: Some or all of the:
University-based research institutes/centres:
Lake Superior Environmental Inventory Data Base, Lakehead University
Lake Superior Research Institute, University of Wisconsin, Superior
Sigurd Olson Environmental Institute, Northland College, Ashland,
Wisconsin
Lake Superior Ecosystem Research Program. Michigan Technological
University,
Vermilion Field Station, Lake Superior State University, Sault Ste. Marie,
Michigan
Interpretive centres in parks
Lake Superior Center, Duluth
Research/monitoring sites in National Forests & National Parks
Reference areas for assessing ecosystem health.

Organizational arrangements: Would strive to draw upon:
Owners/managers of sites and on-going programs at the sites
Lake Superior Task Force
Lake Superior Stakeholders Advisory Group/Forum
Lake Superior Alliance
Western Lake Superior Region Resource Management Cooperative.

ous agencies and non-governmental organizations to help them deal more effectively with issues of conservation and sustainable resource use in the Great Lakes Basin.

The possible components for a Lake Superior Biosphere Reserve (Figure 1) would include the following, although not all would have to become associated with the biosphere reserve in order for it to get under way. The components are identified under the three main functions which biosphere reserves are meant to perform (Table 1).

Comparable specifications for cluster biosphere reserves for the other Great Lakes can be drawn up, with due recognition of coastal zone management demonstration areas as possible components within the areas and programs to be recognized by the biosphere reserve designation. The key to all of this lies in developing the consultation processes among the various stakeholder agencies and non-governmental groups which would have to become involved in order to make the biosphere reserve a functioning reality. The best ways for achieving this on a binational basis have yet to worked out.

REFERENCES

Center for the Great Lakes (1992) *Great Legacy: A Strategic Plan for Protecting Biological Diversity and Enhancing the Regional Economy of the Great Lakes-St. Lawrence River Basin.* Prepared for the Council of Great Lakes Governors, 28 September.

Edwards, C.J. and H.A. Regier, eds. (1990) *An Ecosystem Approach to the Integrity of the Great Lakes in Turbulent Times.* Ann Arbor: Great Lakes Fishery Commission. Special Publication No. 90-4.

Eastern Habitat Joint Venture (1990) *The Eastern Habitat Joint Venture: A Prospectus for Sponsors.* Sackville: Canadian Wildlife Service.

Ecosystem Objectives Working Group (1992) *Interim Report of the Ecosystem Objectives Work Group on Ecosystem Objectives and Their Indicators for Lake Ontario,* New York and Toronto: US/EPA, Region II and Environment Canada, Great Lakes Office.

Francis, G. (1992a) *MAB and the Great Lakes: A Context for the Conservation of Great Lakes Biodiversity,* Waterloo: Heritage Resources Centre Planning Workshop on the Conservation of Great Lakes Biodiversity, March.

Francis, G. (1992b) Applying landscape ecology to biosphere reserves, pp. 241-247 in Ingram, G. B. and M. R. Moss (eds.) *Landscape Approaches to Wildlife and Ecosystem Management*, Morin Heights: Poliscience Publications, Inc.

Great Lakes Fishery Commission (1980) *A Joint Strategic Plan for the Management of Great Lakes Fisheries*, Ann Arbor: Great Lakes Fishery Commission.

Hansen, M.J. ed. (1990) *Lake Superior: The State of the Lake in 1989*, Ann Arbor: Great Lakes Fishery Commission, Special Publication, 90-3.

International Joint Commission (1988) *Revised Great Lakes Water Quality Agreement of 1978 as amended by Protocol signed November 18, 1987*, Washington and Ottawa: International Joint Commission.

International Joint Commission (1990) *Fifth Biennial Report on Great Lakes Water Quality, Part II*, Washington and Ottawa: International Joint Commission.

International Joint Commission/Scientific Advisory Board (1991) *1991 Report of the Great Lakes Science Advisory Board to the International Joint Commission*, Windsor: Great Lakes Office, International Joint Commission.

International Joint Commission/Water Quality Board (1991) *Review and Evaluation of the Great Lakes RAP (Remedial Action Plan) Program, 1991*, Great Lakes Water Quality Board. Windsor; Great Lakes Office, International Joint Commission.

Biodiversity: An Opportunity for Great Lakes Coastal Management

RAFAL SERAFIN
Heritage Resources Centre, University of Waterloo
Waterloo, Ontario

Introduction

By ratifying the Biodiversity Convention at the United Nations' "Earth Summit" held in Rio de Janeiro, many nations - including Canada - have declared their commitment to ensuring that development projects, programs and policies in the public and private sectors benefit and do not degrade biodiversity. Each contracting party is obliged "to develop national strategics, plans or programs for the conservation and sustainable use of biological diversity or adapt for this purpose existing strategies, plans or programs" and "to integrate... the conservation and sustainable use of biodiversity into relevant sectoral or cross-sectional plans, programs and policies" (UNEP, 1992).

Thanks to the impetus provided by the Convention and last summer's Earth Summit, biodiversity has become a major issue in international diplomacy and a focal point for the United Nations' Agenda 21, the principal financing mechanism for securing global environmental security for the 21st century (UNCED, 1992). Indeed, in the run up to the Rio conference, a variety of international commitments and bold declarations were made concerning biodiversity conservation. In the months following the Conference, public expectations have been growing and governments, public interest groups and other organizations have been trying to respond in different ways. Some milestones in the emergence of biodiversity as a public policy issue and responses to it are included on Table 1.

With the emergence of biodiversity as an important public policy issue, the aim of this paper is to draw attention to biodiversity as an opportunity for improving coastal management and planning. Before proceeding any further, however, it is important to consider why those involved in coastal management and planning should care about biodiversity and why might they try to deal with it more effectively.

Table 1.

- 1979. Norman Myers draws attention to an emerging global crisis of species extinction in the Sinking Ark. This is followed by Paul and Anne Ehrlich Extinction (1982) and a National Academy of Sciences symposium (1984) at which the term biodiversity is first coined (Wilson, 1988).
- 1984. Thomas Lovejoy proposes the idea of debt-for-environment swap as a means of securing biodiversity.
- 1987. Our Common Future, the report of the World Commission on Environment and Development draws attention to biodiversity, placing the issue on the international agenda (WCED, 1987).
- 1987. The first debt-for-environment swap is concluded in Bolivia. $650,000 of debt bought for $100,000 in the secondary financial market and retired. In return, the Bolivian government agreed to expand protected areas around the Beni Biosphere Reserve by 1.5 million ha (Zylicz, 1992).
- 1989. World Resources Institute releases influential report Keeping Options Alive: the scientific basis for conserving biodiversity.
- 1990/91. IUBS/SCOPE/UNESCO Program is launched to improve knowledge of the functional role of biodiversity at the species, community, ecosystem and landscape levels (Tolba et al., 1992).
- 1991/92. World Bank, European Bank for Reconstruction and Development and other international financial institutions establish environmental assessment procedures that demand biodiversity is taken into account in proposed projects, programs and policies (World Bank, 1991).
- 1991. The Beijer International Institute for Ecological Economics at the Royal Swedish Academy of Sciences launches research program on the Economics of Biodiversity Loss. (Perrings et al., 1992). •
- 1991. International NGO Task Group created in Amsterdam to lobby and influence the Convention on Biodiversity and its subsequent implementation.
- 1991. Conserving biodiversity recognized by Poland and other countries of Central Europe as an opportunity for reducing debt through debt-for-environment swaps (Zylicz, 1992).
- 1992. Second World Conservation Strategy launched, drawing attention to the life-support functions of biodiversity (WWF/UNEP/IUCN, 1992).
- 1992. Global Biodiversity Strategy launched by World Resources Institute, United Nations Environment Program and World Conservation Union to influence national and international policy and planning (WRI/UNEP/IUCN, 1992).
- 1992. Caracas Declaration on Parks and Protected Areas at the IVth World Parks Congress, recognizes parks as important measures for conserving biodiversity.
- 1992. World Conservation Monitoring Centre publishes Biodiversity Status Report (WCMC, 1992).
- 1992. Biodiversity Convention tabled for ratification at the Earth Summit in Rio de Janeiro (UNEP, 1992).
- 1992. Under the auspices of the United Nations Environment Program (UNEP), many countries conclude national studies of biodiversity.

Why Should Coastal Managers Care About Biodiversity?

A pragmatic answer to this question is that it is only a matter of time before implementation of national and international commitments filters down to the day-to-day matters of coastal management and planning. Local and other government agencies will likely be asked by higher levels of government to include biodiversity considerations in relevant planning, management and assessment procedures. Moreover, citizens and environmental groups will demand that biodiversity be addressed more effectively in land use planning and development policy. Those involved in coastal management would be prudent to learn about biodiversity, since they will sooner or later have to deal with biodiversity issues.

A more substantive answer, however, might refer to the following issues which could provoke wide-ranging reforms in coastal management and planning:

* The **alarming trends of biodiversity loss** are estimated to be occurring in coastal and other areas - despite financial, technical, administrative and other commitments to conserving biological features and processes. According to Wilson (1988), as much as a quarter of the species that now exist will go extinct in the next several decades. Ehrlich and Ehrlich (1982) suggest that 99% of species that have ever existed on Earth are now gone. This state of affairs could lead to suggestions that *coastal management and planning has been ineffective and must be substantially reformed.*
* Many **biodiversity "hot spots"** or areas of particular biological importance or significance have been identified in coastal areas. Myers (1988; 1990), for example, has identified 18 such "hot spots" making up only 0.5% of the planet's surface but which support about 50,000 endemic plant species or about 20% of the total. The hot spots in coastal areas could require *special management and planning provisions that recognize their special biological significance.* (Beatley, 1991).
* The growing concern over **wetland loss** in coastal areas is also coming to focus attention on their significance in terms of biological or life-support values. This leads to the observation that wetlands have not been recognized as critical components of the local, regional and global life-support systems. In this context, according to Francis (1992), there will likely be growing pressure for *more bio*

logically oriented coastal planning and management with regard to wetlands.

- There is a need to **reconcile growing conflicts** between development and conservation interests in coastal areas. In the United States, for example, nearly 50% of the population lives in coastal areas. At the same time, 20 species and sub-species listed on the federal endangered register live within 10 ft. of the shore. Another 33 species are candidates for listing (Reid and Trexler, 1992). To protect biodiversity, *more species are likely to be listed as endangered in coastal areas* and more comprehensive protection procedures are likely to be demanded.

- Concern over **climate change** and potential impacts of sea-level rise on coastal areas has also come to include a concern for disruption in the biological functioning of coastal areas. *Preparing for sea level rise will likely require consideration of biodiversity implication* - whether the response is through engineering coastal defences or adaptive strategies linked to insurance or tax incentives and disincentives.

What is Biodiversity?

Quite literally, biodiversity is used typically to refer to the "variety of life" in a place (Wilson, 1988; Edelstam et al., 1992). There is broad agreement at this rather abstract level. But confusion arises because biodiversity is used to refer to the "variety of life" at different levels of organization:

Genetic - sum total of genetic information contained in genes of individual organisms;

Individual - 'within population diversity' refers to differences between members of a population or species. It provides the hereditary material for selection and so the evolution of life;

Species Diversity - number of species occurring globally or within a particular region. Measures of species diversity may also take into account the relatedness of the species present (taxonomic diversity) or their relative abundance. Diversity differs considerably between different latitudes, between higher taxa (systemic groups) and between habitats;

Ecosystem - describes the species diversity of a system of interacting populations of plant and animal species, usually characteristic of a particular habitat;

Landscape - refers to patterns of biodiversity occurring across specified areas that result from the interaction of human activities, management arrangements and biophysical processes.

Despite various attempts to classify or define biodiversity, the concept remains subject to misunderstanding, not only in terms of what it means to the scientist, planner, manager, citizen, but also in terms of how it relates to human activities and interests (Nelson and Serafin, 1992). As a result, integrating biodiversity considerations into coastal management and planning represents a potential opportunity to understand how human activities influence land use and landscape change and how that influence can be modified so as to ensure more desirable outcomes from both development and conservation perspectives.

Biodiversity and Development Planning

Researchers at the Heritage Resources Centre have been interested in understanding how biodiversity conservation can be integrated more effectively into public policy and development planning. In a recent study conducted with colleagues from the University of Gdansk, Poland, an initial attempt was made to examine the role of biodiversity in coastal management and planning. Such understanding is essential for assessing in what ways existing coastal management arrangements can "deliver" on national and international commitments to protect biodiversity and on how their effectiveness can be improved. Supported by the Beijer International Institute for Ecological Economics at the Royal Swedish Academy of Sciences and its *Economics of Biodiversity Loss* Program, the study sought to find answers to three questions pertaining to coastal management and planning:

- how has biodiversity been defined?
- how and what management and planning activities have been implemented to conserve biodiversity?
- what has been the effectiveness of these efforts from a biodiversity conservation point of view?

In an effort to answer these questions - albeit in a tentative and pre-liminary way - relevant literature and selected coastal management plans from Canada, USA and Poland were analyzed. The three countries were chosen because in each one efforts are under way to reform coastal management and planning. The idea was to compare and contrast different experiences with planning for biodiversity (Serafin et al., 1993).

An analytical framework was used that is based upon a contextual view of decision-making. This is the view that decision-making is not a sequential series of steps as often portrayed in the planning and decision-making literature, but rather involves constant and somewhat messy iteration between adapting, understanding, communicating, assessing, visioning or planning, implementing and monitoring among a wide range of interests involved and affected (Nelson and Serafin, 1992; Serafin et al., 1993). For most of those involved in day-to-day management and planning such a view of decision-making reflects the practical reality of dealing with biodiversity as one of many goals. The framework was used to formulate a series of questions that guided the literature and plan analysis:

Understanding: What kind of knowledge, concepts or information have been used to define and generally understand biodiversity in coastal management and planning?
Communicating: How and among whom has biodiversity been communicated as a concern of coastal management and planning?
Assessing: How has the validity or legitimacy of information on biodiversity been assessed in coastal management and planning?
Visioning/Planning: In what ways has biodiversity constituted a goal or objective in coastal management and planning?
Implementing: How have biodiversity considerations been included in the implementation of coastal management plans?
Monitoring: How have changes in biodiversity been monitored in coastal management plans?
Adapting: In what ways have human activities adapted to biodiversity changes and concerns in coastal management and planning?

The main findings of the analysis are outlined in what follows.

Understanding: Efforts to understand how biodiversity fits into decision-making generally, and in coastal areas in particular, are few. In part, this is because the idea of biodiversity as a crisis and public policy issue is relatively new. To date, understanding of biological productivity has focused primarily on special features on the water side of coasts, such as coral and other reefs, atolls, micro-organisms and inter-tidal areas, or special features on the land side, such as sand dunes, plants, beaches, wetlands and mangroves. Research has focused on understanding the relationship between biological productivity and diversity through experimental research, field observations, numerical methods, simulation, modeling, restoration efforts and elaboration of theoretical concepts, such as viable populations, speciation, scale, habitat, trophic interactions, perturbations, communities and ecosystem. The focus has been most often on individual species or assemblages of species, especially fish and plankton. More recently, a growing interest in climate change and sea level rise has provided another context or setting for understanding changing patterns of biological productivity and diversity, particularly with respect to fisheries and coastal defences.

Communicating: The ecological importance of biodiversity and a biodiversity crisis has proven a difficult one to communicate because it is difficult for many people to envisage just what is being referred to, in contrast to other global crises, such as the ozone hole over the Antarctic or climate warming. In coastal areas, finding an appropriate focus for communication that goes beyond exotic or beautiful animals and plants has so far proven elusive. The result is that the literature concerned with communicating coastal biodiversity beyond the scientific community is sparse. What there is has been focused on promoting a wider understanding of ecological ideas, greater appreciation for features and processes recognized as valuable or important, such as coastal barriers or special areas, such as parks and protected areas. Education and learning are clearly an integral part of communication. With this in mind, efforts have been made to include biologically-oriented public education as an integrative part of planning and management in some coastal areas, such as the Broads in the UK, California, USA and Lake Huron, Canada.

Assessing: Coastal biodiversity has been assessed in a variety of ways. Frequently, biological productivity and diversity have been assessed in relation to the actual or potential impact of particular human activities, such as dredging and reclamation, trampling, population pressure, hydrotechnical construction, hydro generation, fishing, contaminant effects, recreation, fishing pressure, exploitation of particular species, oil development and mineral exploration, coastal marinas, salmonid stocking, wetland impoundment and discharges of concern.

Assessments of biological productivity and diversity have focused on special or valued areas, such as enclosed or semi-enclosed seas; the status of key ecological processes, such as nutrient cycling and oxygen fluxes; important features, such as wetlands, mangroves and inter-tidal communities; estimates of economic costs and benefits; the status of species - both desirable, such as shore birds and Lake Sturgeon, and undesirable ones, such as the sea lamprey in the Great Lakes; rare and endangered species; fisheries habitat and fish productivity and community health.

Only recently has there been growing concern to assess: threats to productivity and diversity in specific areas, such as Florida, the Great Lakes and the Chesapeake Bay; sensitive features, such as coral reefs; and emerging stresses, such as climate change. A number of handbooks and guidelines have also been produced, such as a manual on assessing environmental impacts in the South Pacific Regional Environmental Program, and the series of guidelines and policies prepared by the World Bank.

Planning/Visioning: Biological productivity and diversity is only now coming to figure prominently as a major goal or objective in coastal planning, especially in relation to wetlands and restoration of habitats and parks and protected areas in the United States where such goals are spelled out most clearly. More frequently, the special feature of coastal areas as a biological interface between land and sea has been ignored or underestimated in planning and management activities. The land side has been emphasized over the water side. In part, this is because marine and coastal resources have tended to be seen as always in a state of flux and essentially unlimited, in contrast to limited land resources. Another reason is that federal and international jurisdictions have tended to extend over the water-side, whereas the land side has been the responsibility of more local government and private ownership. As a result, progress has been mixed on designing an integrated approach to planning for land and sea. Some successes have been reported in the parks and protected areas field, notably in regard to biosphere reserves.

Attempts to overcome jurisdictional fragmentation and insufficient cooperation among land-oriented and water-oriented planners, scientists and others have long been a concern of human ecologists. More area specific initiatives to build a common basis for visioning or planning for biological productivity and diversity have included establishing guidelines and principles for coral reef reserves, classification of coastal and marine environments, and thinking of coastal uses and landscapes in terms of a history of human-nature interaction. Some have also suggested that the threat of climate warming and the threat of sea level rise could provide an integrating or visioning basis for thinking about the future of coastal areas.

Implementing: Considerable research has been devoted to understanding better the significance of coastal areas for biological productivity and diversity. Yet little attention has been paid to assessing the effectiveness of management and planning for biological productivity and diversity, even though increasing efforts are devoted to managing for biodiversity. In particular, little effort has been devoted to learning systematically from the experiences of those who have been intimately involved in developing and implementing management and other plans in coastal areas. Important exceptions have been the round of conferences on Environmental Management of Enclosed and Coastal Seas (EMECS) and the Marine Forum for Environmental Issues, a UK based stakeholder group concerned with the North Sea. Such initiatives are becoming important fora for the exchange and sharing of experience on the development and implementation of plans and management arrangements.

Existing guidelines and handbooks for managers and planners and citizens more generally in coastal matters have tended to underplay the importance of biological processes and features in favour of physical or hydrological processes and water quality issues. Salm and Clark's (1982) *Marine and Coastal Areas* is a notable exception, but only deals with conservation through parks and protected areas. Other approaches of practical significance that are gaining in popularity include land trusts, stewardship and co-management arrangements.

Monitoring: Biological production and diversity have been monitored in many coastal areas as part of a suite of indicators or parameters of environmental change. In many cases, this has involved measuring the occurrence of specific species or functional assemblages over time. In other cases, biological characteristics or processes have been measured or estimated in conjunction with the collection of water quality information or changes in habitat conditions or phytoplankton dynamics. Coastal features, such as sand dunes, wetlands, inter-tidal flats and fish communities have also been used to indicate broader scale changes in biological productivity and diversity.

Another prominent theme with regard to monitoring in coastal and marine environments has related to technical difficulties and the development of approaches for overcoming them. This has led to an interest in developing specialized techniques and strategies for sampling and data collection, such as rapid visual and strip transect techniques for censusing reef fish assemblages and coral growth, mussel watch programs, statistical techniques.

Adapting: In the past, the interest in biological production and diversity has centred on expanding and maintaining sources of sustenance, notably fishery resources and wetlands. In more recent times, human activities have come to include a variety of other uses for coastal areas, such as tourism and recreation, settlement, mineral exploration and extraction, coastal engineering and others which come into conflict with one another. Biodiversity has thus been considered as one of many important features of coastal areas that have prompted human adjustment or else which have been modified or transformed by human action and which may now also be affected by climate change.

In recent years, there has been growing interest in describing and analyzing the process of adjustment to change in coastal management and planning or governance particularly in relation to informal, traditional or non-regulatory approaches. Human responses to change in biodiversity in coastal areas has not been much studied, although there is a growing interest in the context of co-management and the trend of democratizing decision-making in the conservation and development fields.

Conclusions

By way of conclusions, it is appropriate to return to the three questions posed at the outset:

How has biodiversity been defined in coastal management and planning? Biodiversity has only recently come to be addressed in the literature and in coastal planning in Canada, USA and Poland in the sense of a concern for the depletion of genetic, species and ecosystem resources in coastal areas. In recent years, there have been a growing number of efforts to assess biodiversity status, monitor rates of depletion and estimate associated economic costs and benefits. But the main focus has been on understanding change in biological diversity and productivity in terms of changes in ecological or biophysical processes at genetic, species and population levels. Much less attention has been devoted to understanding and assessing how human activities or land uses and management arrangements have served to deplete, sustain and even create biodiversity in specific places of interest and value through activities such as wetland restoration and species management. Assessment has focused on particular features of biological importance, such as wetlands, or processes, such as fish production.

How and what management and planning activities have been implemented to conserve biodiversity? It is one thing to describe, document or to understand biodiversity, but quite another to know what to do differently in a management situation. To date, there have been two basic approaches to managing biodiversity:

- separate people and key sites or habitats by "setting them aside".
- try to integrate human activities and habitats in a sustainable development approach.

The first of these has dominated not only coastal management and planning, but land use planning more generally. Despite long standing acknowledgment that coastal areas are biologically important, the emphasis of planning and management has been on contending with physical processes, such as erosion, flooding and water quality, and reducing their impacts on human activities. For example, Canadian, US and Polish coastal planning has been directed primarily at facilitating more orderly development. In each case, biological concerns were considered as one of many competing uses of the coast which must be taken into account in development decision-making. Biodiversity and biological functioning have not been treated in terms of their life support capacity that is indispensable for both conservation and development.

In coastal situations, management of biological concerns has been focused on designating and 'setting aside' areas deemed to be biologically important, such as wetlands, as parks or protected areas. This treatment of biodiversity as largely a biological phenomenon has not proven wholly effective, especially in situations in which an array of coastal values, interests and uses detrimental to biodiversity come into conflict with one another. Indeed, in many cases, development activities have been allowed in and around the parks and protected areas on the grounds that appropriate impact assessment and mitigation procedures had been followed. The area specific approach appears to have been based on a rather static view of nature as a collection of distinct features and processes which can be protected through insulation and containment from human activities. More integrated and dynamic human ecological or landscape-oriented approaches have not appeared prominent in existing coastal management arrangements. The idea that biodiversity is an outcome of an interacting dynamic between human activities, management arrangements and ecological processes has not been prominent in the planning field. Indeed, comparatively little attention has been devoted to understanding how different approaches to coastal planning have contributed to changing patterns of biodiversity and human activities in coastal areas.

What has been the effectiveness of coastal management for biodiversity conservation? Comparing coastal management approaches used in the USA, Canada and Poland suggests that from an institutional or management point of view, there is no single best way for assuring protection of biodiversity in coastal areas. In part, this is because none of the three approaches have proven adept at treating biological diversity and productivity more generally in terms of conflicts over coastal land use and patterns of landscape change linked to the capability of management arrangements to contend effectively with a wide array of conflicts for the benefit for conservation and development. If human activities are to be made less destructive of coastal biodiversity, then the biodiversity must be understood, assessed and managed in relation to the human or institutional context. This means finding ways of integrating a variety of disciplines, information and ways of knowing that relate to thinking about biodiversity in terms of the institutional or management dimension of a place or area of interest.

The opportunity offered by the growing interest in biodiversity lies in developing ways to assess biodiversity as an outcome or product of an historical and ongoing interaction in a particular management situation. Typically, such situations are characterized by multiple and often conflicting planning goals and policies. Thus, to be effective assessment must strive to include the plurality of disciplines, ways of knowing, interests and issues deemed to be relevant by managers, scientists and citizens. This approach contrasts the more common practice of excluding what is deemed to be irrelevant on the basis of criteria that are typically set by one or more disciplines or interests that dominate the particular situation.

In sum, biodiversity assessment could prove an opportunity for synthesizing or bringing together different kinds of information in ways that have meaning and utility to managers and planners engaged in coastal planning generally, as well as to those affected most directly by changes in coastal biodiversity specifically. If the opportunity is to be seized to the benefit of biodiversity conservation and coastal management more generally, however, then those most closely involved must take a more active interest in controversies over defining and managing for biodiversity at the national and international level.

ACKNOWLEDGEMENTS

The author would like to acknowledge the assistance of the Beijer International Institute, Heritage Resources Centre, and the Social Sciences and Humanities Research Council of Canada (SSHRC) in the preparation of this paper.

REFERENCES

Beatley, T. (1991) "Protecting Biodiversity in Coastal Environments: Introduction and Overview," *Coastal Management*, 19, 1-19.

Edelstam, C., G. Skoog, H. Lundberg and C. Ramel (1992) *Perspectives on the Maintenance of Biodiversity*, Stockholm: The Royal Swedish Academy of Sciences.

Ehrlich, P. and A. Ehrlich (1982) *Extinction: The Causes and Consequences of the Disappearing of Species*, New York: Ballantine.

Francis, G. R. ed. (1992) *Conserving Biodiversity in the Context of Great Lakes Biosphere Reserves*. Proceedings of a Planning Workshop held at the University of Waterloo, Waterloo: Heritage Resources Centre and Environment Canada/Parks Service.

Myers, N. (1979) *The Sinking Ark*, Oxford: Pergamon.

Myers, N. (1990) "The biodiversity challenge: Expanded hotspots Analysis". *Environmentalist*, 10(4), 243-256.

Nelson, J.G. and R. Serafin (1992) "Assessing Biodiversity: A Human Ecological Approach," *Ambio*, 31(3), 212-218.

Nelson, J. G. and R. Serafin. eds. (1992) *Assessing Environmental Management and Planning*, Montreal, QU: McGill-Queens University Press (submitted).

Perrings, C., Folke, C. and K-G. Maler (1992) "The Ecology and Economics of Biodiversity Loss: The Research Agenda," *Ambio*, 31(3), 201-211.

Reid, W. V. and M. C. Trexler (1992) "Responding to Potential Impacts of Climate Change on U.S. Coastal Biodiversity," *Coastal Management*, 20, 117-142.

Salm, R. V. and J. R. Clark (1984) *Marine and Coastal Protected Areas: a guide for Planners and Managers*, Gland, Switzerland: IUCN.

Tolba, M. K., O. A. El-Kholy, E. El-Hinnawi, M. W. Holdgate, D. F. McMichael and R. E. Munn. eds. (1992) *The World Environment 1972-1992: Two decades of challenge*, London: UNEP and Chapman & Hall.

United Nations Conference on Environment and Development (1992) *Agenda 21, Chapter 15: Conservation of Biodiversity*, Nairobi: United Nations.

United Nations Environment Program (1992) *Convention on Biological Diversity*, Rio de Janeiro: UNCED, 5 June 1992.

Wilson, E. O. ed. 1988. *Biodiversity*. Washington, D. C.: National Academy Press.

World Bank. 1991. *Environmental Assessment Scourcebook*. 3 Volumes. Washington, D. C.: Environment Department.

World Commission on Environment and Development. 1987. *Our Common Future*. Oxford: Oxford University Press.

World Conservation Monitoring Centre. 1992. *Biodiversity Status Report*. Cambridge: World Conservation Monitoring Centre.

World Wide Fund for Nature, United Nations Environment Program and World Conservation Union. 1992. *Caring for the Earth: the Second World Conservation Strategy*. Gland, Switzerland: WWF/ UNEP/IUCN.

Zylicz, T. 1991. *Debt-for-Environment Swaps: the institutional dimension*. Beijer Discussion Paper Series No. 18. Stockholm: Beijer International Institute of Ecological Economics, The Royal Swedish Academy of Sciences.

A Sustainable Development Approach to Great Lakes Coastal Management

I. MCKENZIE
Department of Geography, University of Waterloo

G. BOYD
Fisheries and Oceans, Ottawa, Ontario

P. BEARD AND G. PEACH
Maitland Valley Conservation Authority, Wroxeter, Ontario

Introduction

Recently, there has been a renewed interest in promoting future-oriented planning policies based on the ecosystem approach. These include the Conservation Foundation's "Coastal Ecosystem Management" (Clark 1983), the International Joint Commissions' Phase I Report" (1989), the Rawson Academy's "Great Lakes Ecosystem Charter" (1989) the Institute for Research on Public Policy's "Great Lakes, Great Legacy?" (1989) and "Save Beaches not Buildings" (Pilkey and Neal 1992). Branches of Ontario's Ministry of Natural Resources, notably fish and wildlife, are advocating an ecosystem approach to the management of these resources. At the same time the public is demanding action on environmental issues.

In concert with this demand, there is a need for a more comprehensive approach to shoreline planning and management in Ontario, one that is based upon the ecosystem and places more emphasis on maintaining the ecological integrity of the shoreline rather than just public safety and property damage issues. A Provincial Policy Statement needs to be created that includes in its goal and objectives a commitment to the ecological integrity of the shore and promote sustainable development. Why? Because, with respect to land use planning and development in Ontario, it is only the Policy Statement that has legal status under the Ontario Planning Act (shore management plans and implementation guidelines have no legal weight). Hence the Policy Statement must encompass strong, clear, and comprehensive policies related to shoreline land use and development.

The premise of a shoreland policy statement should be:

1) to maintain the ecological integrity of coastal systems (i.e. maintenance of essential coastal ecological and physical processes, genetic diversity, sustainable utilization of species and ecosystems);
2) to reduce the potential for future property damage, social disruption, and loss of life;
3) to promote development that is sustainable (ecologically sound and maintains or improves the resource for future generations).

This paper proposes an Ontario shore management policy that incorporates recent advances in our understanding of Great Lakes coastal zone processes, and conforms to an ecosystems approach to planning, in an attempt to rejuvenate an open discussion on some principal considerations. The objectives of this discussion paper include (1) developing an appropriate policy based on scientific principles that is in harmony with coastal zone processes and the physical and biological integrity of the coastal zone, and (2) encouraging implementations of a practical and future-oriented shoreline policy for our Great Lakes shoreline.

The premises of the policy paper are fourfold:

1) that, with regard to shoreline erosion and deposition, littoral drift is a key abiotic process;
2) that the physical and biological processes operating in the complex coastal environment should be understood and accommodated during both planning and management;
3) that other examples such as flood plain management, also based on impacts of physical processes, can serve as models for developing shoreline management strategies;
4) that ultimately all coastal zone management policies should aim towards an ecosystems planning approach and sustainable development.

The Existing Approach

Throughout the world, a great variety of shoreline management techniques are being used, for a variety of reasons. In Puerto Rico, the Commonwealth of Northern Marianas Islands, and the Virgin Islands no shoreline construction is allowed in recognition of the great importance of their shoreline resource. While in other parts of the world such as India and the Persian Gulf States, shorelines are "protected" for the strategic military value. In the Netherlands, to protect the fragile ecosystem, laws prohibit individuals from even walking on sand dunes without a permit. But the most common approaches to shoreline management, are fixed and floating setback lines based on long-term shoreline recession rates. However, this simplistic approach has not been successful since it considers only the results of shore processes (recession) rather than the fundamental elements of the shore zone (littoral). Setbacks do not consider other biological and physical functions and processes such as shoreline ecology. The failure of existing methods has led the US National Academy of Sciences to study alternative shore management strategies and the International Joint Commission to recommend that innovative shore management strategies be developed.

In some regions of Ontario, little shoreline management is occurring so that homes and shore protection are built in areas that are subject to flooding and erosion. Notwithstanding these exceptions, the current Provincial policy is to define a minimum erosion setback based on 100 times the average annual recession rate.[1] This existing Ontario policy is not based on any analysis of shore processes. It has not been supported by any technical or economic analyses but seems to have been simply adopted for the 1:100 year flood concept: the concept that there is a 1:100 chance that a flood will occur in any given year. This is considered a small but acceptable annual risk. However, it is fallacious to transfer this 1:100 year concept to the shoreline. Followed to its logical conclusion, in 100 years a line of homes, granted building permits between updates to the setback line, will fall into the lake. Given that the existing Ontario policy will lead to massive shore property damage in 100 years or less, it is reasonable to state that this planning policy is not planning at all. It is a policy that only defers the problem to future generations.

A second part of Ontario's existing policy allows development if shore protection is installed. This tacitly suggests that economically practicable protection is feasible for private landowners. Experience, and newspaper headlines, tell a different story. As documented in the US side of the Great Lakes, shore protection structures only increase the investment at the shoreline. Hence, each successive high water level period results in increased shore damage on the Great Lakes, shown to be on the scale of billions of dollars. Compounding the problem, shore protection can have adverse affects on neighbouring properties (as well as disrupt the natural physical and biological systems) and therefore has led to numerous legal challenges.

---

[1] The concept also ignores the propensity for home owners to improve and restore structures and even redevelop their property.

In fact, it is quite difficult to derive a useful average annual recession rate, the result being that the recommended setbacks are somewhat unreliable. In spite of scientific uncertainty, extensive shore development and shore protection has been built based on existing water levels. A rise or drop in lake level will make most shore protection obsolete. Under the existing policy, it will cost billions of dollars to rebuild shore protection to combat the new water levels. If development has been discouraged in these areas, this problem on this scale would not exist.

There is one problem that shore protection advocates have never been able to resolve. If shore protection can be designed to work, then, by definition, it is stopping erosion of the shore. However, erosion supplies sand to the littoral drift system. Interrupting the supply of sand denies material needed to maintain downdrift beaches. In Ontario, there is legislation restricting removal of sand from the beach but there is not policy to ensure the maintenance of the source of this sand. Any reduction of shore erosion can negatively affect downdrift owners. In order to manage sediment of the littoral drift, it is necessary to preserve eroding areas, in an eroding state, for the benefit of all users (human and biological), both now and in the future. Despite ownership of the shore being limited to a few, it is the majority of Ontario's taxpayers and tourists who enjoy the beaches. These beaches have been formed and maintained by sand eroded from elsewhere. Without continuing the source of sand, these beaches, over time, will disappear.

A Primer on Great Lakes Shoreline Ecology

In southern Ontario, much of the lakeshore is composed of glacial materials (mainly till) left by the glaciers thousands of years ago. Wind over the lake causes waves. The energy from these waves at the shore erodes the till, causing shore erosion and cliffs (bluffs). These types of areas are the eroding 'source' of littoral sand and continue to provide sand as long as there are waves eroding the shore. The debris from this erosion, the sand and gravel, is moved along the shore until it accumulates. These accumulations are known as beaches (for instance at Grand Bend, Long Point, Toronto Island) and can be defined as the sediment 'sink'. These depositional sites often contain both modern and historical deposits. In the short term, the beaches are constantly being reworked by waves and currents, with a loss of sand to the onshore by wind action. If there is negative sediment balance the beaches can be eroding in the long term: if there is a positive sediment balance, these beaches can become larger through time. Without a regular new supply of sand they will disappear. Fortunately, waves continue to erode updrift areas and provide sand debris, which is transported by waves onto the beaches. The sand comes from not only bluff erosion but from rivers, streams, gullies, and from erosion of the lakebed.

Water levels of the Great Lakes are always rising and falling. Fluctuations in lake levels may affect the short term rate of erosion, but in some areas erosion will continue to occur, even in the long term. The shoreline material being eroded can vary from slowly eroding rock to rapidly eroding glacial tills and sand and gravels. However, the general principle is straightforward. Variably, over time, an eroding 'source' area provides the sand which is transported along the shore and then collects at the depositional 'sink' to form beaches.

In areas of the shoreline where resistant bedrock is exposed, erosion also occurs but at an extremely slow rate. Cobble beaches are common, while pockets of sand beaches form in embayments. The littoral sand within the embayment cells is often relict sand from earlier times or new sources of sand originating inland and brought to the shore by rivers and streams.

Littoral drift is also a cornerstone of the biological diversity of the coastal zone. Fish spawn on the beach or nearshore gravel beds, marshes are bounded by baymouth bars and spits, and these provide a habitat for rare and endangered species of flora and fauna, migratory birds, and overall genetic diversity. In total, the coastal processes establish and maintain the habitat for fish and wildlife, forest and dune vegetation, which create and add to the value, associated with the lakeshore.

Scientists have long been aware of the processes of a shore system. Only recently, for the Great Lakes, have researches begun to estimate the amount of the total sediment budget, the sand coming from the bluffs, rivers, and lakebed, and where it goes (Reinders Ltd. 1989). It is proposed that these studies of sediment budget can be used to develop a new shoreline management policy. A policy that would recognize littoral drift as the critical component of the shore system. It is the littoral drift, the sand itself, that is a primary resource element to be managed to sustain human and biological use of the shore.

PART 1: CONSIDERATION OF THE GUIDING PRINCIPLES

Background

Existing riverine flood plain management practices have evolved to delimit two flood plain zones. One is the 'flood way'. In a flood way, development is not allowed because (1) it is too dangerous, and (2) the structure can, by depriving floodwater of overflow space, increase the magnitude of the flood for others upstream or downstream. The other zone is the 'flood fringe'. This is the zone where flooding will occur infrequently, and where the presence of development will not affect others. Building is permitted in the flood fringe if appropriate safeguards are implemented such as building the habitable portion of the structure above the regulatory flood elevation. A third zone, the river valley wall, is also addressed. Along the sides of the valley, the flood has no frequent effect, but construction must still consider the difficulties of building and servicing development located on a steep slope. Ontario's flood plain management policy has evolved successfully. Flood plain dynamics are different than the processes in the shore zone, requiring a different policy for special interest groups, but many lessons about planning and management have been learned which could be used in developing a management policy for the Great Lakes shoreline.

The Shoreline Policy

Following the precedent of riverine flood plain management, the authors believe that an analogous, two zone management approach could also be used for managing development along the shoreline of the Great Lakes. The first zone would be the eroding source zones which could be compared to the flood way of rivers. Just as in the flood way, construction within eroding zones of the shoreline should not be permitted because (1) it is too dangerous and (2) the construction, interfering or halting the supply of sediment, would affect those beside it or downdrift. The second zone is the depositional zone where the sand accumulates and can be managed like the flood fringe. In the depositional zone of the shoreline, development would be allowed but based on whether it is currently eroding or building up. The proposed policy is intended to **discourage** new development in eroding or hazard zones and permit development in suitable sites in depositional zones following an assessment of the long term (>100 years) stability of the proposed development section of the shoreline.

Development is discouraged in eroding zones because erosion must continue to occur here in order to supply sand to the littoral drift system to maintain downstream beaches. If new development is permitted in source areas, property owners will after repeated failures at shoreline protection, in the future, demand assistance from local and provincial governments to protect their land from erosion - the very erosion that supplies sand to maintain the downdrift beaches. If a policy was developed based on an understanding of how the physical and biological shore systems work, fewer lives and property will be at risk, less confrontation will develop, and less financial problems for homeowners and government agencies will arise. A sustainable shoreline policy will, most importantly, identify alternate shore areas that can be maximized, safely, for development within the context of conserving coastal ecosystems.

Given that shore protection of updrift eroding shorelines denies the downdrift shore property owners of valuable littoral sand, a philosophical dilemma arises as to whose property rights should be defended. The updrift owners perceives a right to retain littoral drift. The downdrift owner perceives the right to receive littoral drift. This paper calls for downdrift rights on a riparian basis, in the face of updrift owners who would interrupt the natural system to the disadvantage of others. Also, the majority of citizens who use the Great Lakes shoreline do so at the biologically rich, depositional areas: they, and future generations, are stakeholders not represented in this dispute and must therefore be represented through government policy. Finally, there is precedent in riparian law that downdrift riparian owners have a right to the natural uninterrupted flow (of water): this is assumed to be representative of sand rights as well.

This proposed policy offers three solutions to the above predicament. First, that future use of the shore be conducted fully cognizant of the policy that eroding shorelines are hazard lands and as duly recognized, are not developable without risk of loss of property or life. Second, the protection of new development in eroding source zones will not be allowed unless shown to be harmless to downdrift owners and the shoreline ecosystems. The third, that new, permanent development will not be allowed in eroding zones, or in temporary depositional zones based on lake levels, so that erosion related damage does not become a problem in the future.

PART II: OUTLINE FOR A SHORELINE DEVELOPMENT POLICY

A Provincial Shoreline Development Policy should allow development to locate in areas that are compatible with physical and biological shoreline processes, while minimizing disruption to littoral drift resources. Such a policy would discourage development within eroding areas. The basic premise of this policy is that the shorebluffs and beaches of the Great lakes should be kept free of inappropriate development and be maintained as natural buffers between the lake and inland development. Development should be restricted to inland of the future shoreline position for the current water level regime, or, in depositional areas with a positive sediment balance, behind the foredunes. Only then can we confidently live and work in the shore zone without fear of disaster and lessen associated conflicts related to our wise use of the Great Lakes.

Decision Matrix for Determination of Zones

This paper proposes a two zone management approach: a source zone and a depositional zone. The decision process in determination of zones is as follows.

Step 1   Is the site a depositional feature? Is it a place where sand and gravel have accumulated to form a distinctive depositional feature at the shoreline?
If no, it is a "source zone" then use standards for source zones.
If yes, it is a "depositional zone". Go to Step 2.
Step 2   Is it now eroding in the long term? If no, then use standards for depositional zones. If yes, use standards for depositional zones plus the long term erosion rate.

Standards for Depositional Zones
(eroding and non-eroding)

Depositional zones are areas where sand and gravel has, or is, accumulating to form beaches. They are the spits, baymouth bars, and fillet, compartment, or embayment beaches found throughout the Great Lakes. They may have either a negative sediment balance and therefore are eroding, as at parts of Long Point and Point Pelee on Lake Erie or a positive sediment balance and therefore may be becoming larger, as at Clark Point on Lake Huron.

If the depositional zone is not eroding in the long term, development can be allowed and sustained but set back an appropriate distance from the shoreline. This appropriate distance should be at least the limit of a 1:100 year flood and the long term high water level wave uprush. If sand dunes exist, development must be behind the foredune. The density of development should be based on research on the carrying capacity' of the area. Determining development suitability of the shore zone will include traditional planning criteria such as habitat, vegetative communities, ecological sensitivity; the stability of the site for access; the availability of services; and the regional need for natural environmental areas. Existing development would remain, and be allowed to expand unless located lakeward of the above limits. No further shore protection should be permitted if it would cause further damage to the shoreline ecology.

Depositional shoreline zones often have features, such as marshes, wildlife habitat, and public access to large recreational beaches and harbour facilities, that go beyond simple consideration of shoreline erosion and deposition. Often they are partially sustained by alluvial deposits brought to the shore by rivers. These factors need to be considered and incorporated into a comprehensive coastal zone management plan to further limit uncontrolled development in flood prone and biologically rich depositional areas as well as to preserve its supply of sand. This relates directly to the concept of the carrying capacity of the site. Nonetheless, the above standard represents a minimum in terms of the hazard presented by lake wave processes.

If the depositional zone is eroding in the long term, in addition to the above standard, a further setback is required based on this long term erosion rate. This is determined by historical information or records of beach position and bluffs and data on the present local sediment balance.

Standards for Source Zones

Source zones are those sections of shoreline where erosion historically has, and will continue, to provide sand to the littoral transport system along the shore. They may be continually eroding areas (such as many glacial till shores of the lower Great Lakes), slowly eroding (such as the rock shores of Lake Superior), or sites that only infrequently erode during times of high Great Lakes water levels. Given the current and future potential for damage to shore property and structures, and the value of the eroded sand to the natural littoral system, new development and shore protection can not be permitted in these areas.The inland extent of the no development zone in source areas can be derived. The mature shoreline position for the current water level regime is reasonably obvious for the rock shores of Lake Superior, Georgian Bay, upper Lake Huron, the western basin of Lake Erie, and eastern Lake Ontario. For lower Lake Huron, Lake St. Clair, the western basin of Lake Erie and much of central Lake Ontario, research can determine a more mature shoreline position. Permanent development would be permitted only landward of this position while less permanent uses could continue subject to reasonable controls (no basement, slab on grade, carrying capacity of the beach zone) but the primary use should be agriculture, open space, and other non-permanent development.

Existing development lakeward of the mature shoreline position should not be allowed to expand, or, if damaged, not be permitted to rebuild, and incentives could be used to encourage relocation of the structures that are at risk. Existing lots of record should be zoned to restrict any new development and no severances or new lots should be created.[2] For the small percentage of Great Lakes shoreline where the mature shoreline position cannot yet be determined, an alternative approach is needed. As an interim measure, setbacks can be calculated based on the nature of the proposed development. That is, for instance, a toxic waste disposal site would need to be set back further than a trailer park.

Shore protection or "hardening" should not be permitted in eroding source zones. Protection has proven to be ineffective for individual shore property owners, costly, and has a negative impact on the littoral drift resource of downstream owners.[2] Artificial nourishment as a solution to erosion also presents problems since the material must be continually brought from inland areas. This would be a costly and unwise use of a finite aggregate resource and may create local problems at the borrow sites. However, some offshore sources of sand are available, in certain areas, or when historically trapped artificially by large jetties. Any expenditures planned for shore protection structures should be used, and perhaps supplemented by loans from government, to move development that is at risk back from the shore rather than allow additional shoreline investment. Government policy and land use controls should be amended to incorporate appropriate and moveable setback limits; encourage deep lots to give room for home relocation; encourage architectural designs that anticipate relocation of the structure ("I" beam supports for ease of relocation, no basements or brick chimneys); encourage road allowances that are perpendicular to the shore (not parallel); and encourage existing township roads to be closed and relocated (not protected) when erosion threatens them.

Urban Shorelines and Shore Protection

The above policy is applicable for all of the shoreline in Ontario. Had this policy been available 150 years ago we would not now be faced with severe Great lakes shore damage and, if implemented, the problems 150 years hence will be lessened. Unfortunately, it was not in place so extensive shoreline development has proceeded in inappropriate and unsafe locations. What can be done with locations where extensive urban-type shoreline development now exists?

---

2 See end notes.

Firstly, these exceptional situations are not the norm and therefore should not be cause for delay in acceptance of this policy approach. To delay would only allow further development along the shore, limiting any future management options and creating more atypical locations. Secondly, one can again fruitfully refer to the solutions developed for a similar predicament during development of Ontario's riverine flood plain management experiences where existing structures (indeed, whole communities) existed in flood prone areas. This experience suggests that the basic philosophy should be to avoid allowing the problem to worsen (in terms of both increased development at risk or increased negative impacts to shoreline ecosystem).

To promote discussion to resolve this difficult issue of shore management planning in extensively developed and protected areas, the authors suggest:

- that, in areas of extensive shore development and protection, investigations be executed to determine the existing shore processes and the impacts of the development and shore protection;
- that unless there is evidence to the contrary, one should assume that privately installed shore protection will fail, therefore "source area" standards should be used, but with consideration of the above investigations;
- that there should be no further shoreline development until environmentally sound, sustainable, shore protection is in place.

This approach will encourage municipalities and developers to upgrade the quality, and lessen the negative impacts, of shore protection measures. This is the same approach that has been used successfully in developed riverine situations. In the riverine situation, it has resulted in a direct improvement in the quality of remedial works.

Implementation

It is not the objective of this paper to define the implementation details for the above proposed policy but rather provide the philosophy for it. However detailed implementation guidelines do need to be developed and in such a way as to allow those who must implement it to buy into it. A bottom-up approach to policy development therefore recommends itself whereby the vast intellectual resources and expertise available in Ontario are brought together and become directly involved in policy development and implementation details.

Conclusion

Knowledge of shore processes has increased dramatically over the past ten years. The opportunity has been presented to use this knowledge to develop a shoreline management policy that will ensure that future shoreline use will be compatible with physical and biological shore systems. If this policy approach is adopted it will result in the sustainable use of shorelines and reduce the potential for future damage, loss of life, and social and economic disruption, and protect the integrity of the coastal ecosystems. The most reckless approach to shoreline management is to try and superimpose our impression of what shorelines should be on to what nature wants them to be. A policy based on the natural shore system is the logical alternative for living with the Great Lakes.

Recommendations

That Great Lakes shore managers within agencies such as the Ontario Ministry of Natural Resources must further develop and implement this sustainable development policy, for the Great Lakes shoreline, based upon managing the littoral drift resource, understanding and accommodating the physical and biological processes operating at the shore, and maintaining the shore ecosystem's integrity.

That all individuals, organizations, and agencies involved in shoreline planning and management be encouraged to participate in the development of a comprehensive shoreline planning policy statement.

That the Province of Ontario incorporate the goal of shoreline physical and ecosystem integrity and sustainable development into the Shoreline Planning Policy Statement.

***

Definitions

Ecosystem: the interacting complex of living organisms and their non-living environment.

Carrying Capacity: the limit of the amount of life that can be supported by any given habitat, specifically the number of particular species that can be supported by a habitat (in another sense, the reasonable limits of human occupancy or use of a resource).

Ecosystem Integrity: the state of health of an ecosystem. This encompasses integrated, balanced, and self-organizing interactions among its components, with no single component breaking the bounds of interdependency to singularly dominate the whole.

End Notes

1) The concept of a floating setback of 100 times the average annual recession rate, although seemingly logical at first, is really quite an indefensible concept. Why use a multiplier of 100 rather than 50, or even 300? Some suggest the 100 multiplier will provide 100 years of safety for the structure, at which time it will be worthless and pointing to the absence of 100 year old homes in Canada. Our ever increasing investment in shoreline property and buildings will only lengthen our tenure on the shoreline. Historic cities such as London, England and the cost of the Thames River barrier or the sinking of Venice, Italy point out that once occupied the shoreline, will not be abandoned. More logical would be a setback based on the size and value of the structure (a cottage versus a multi-storey condominium) and the risk associated with the development should it erode (a trailer park versus a toxic waste dump).

2) A more laissez-faire view would suggest that landowners be allowed to locate a structure wherever they wished on their lot if clearly informed that they could not protect their shore property from erosion. This would meet the criteria for maintaining a source of supply for the littoral drift system and may well have valid economic arguments since it would permit maximum use of the lot. In practice, however, it appears unworkable unless the lot extends landward of the ultimate shoreline position. It is further complicated by the removal of necessary services (roadways, hydro, septic tanks) and the political difficulties of refusing shore protection once the structure becomes endangered. The solution presented in this paper is not to allow the structure to be placed in a hazardous zone in the first place until this option could be further investigated.

   Indeed, the intent of the 1988 South Carolina Beachfront Management Act was to prohibit development seaward of a baseline that corresponds to the crest of an actual or hypothetical dune line. After Hurricane Hugo in 1989, the opportunity was presented that would see damaged structures not rebuilt. However under special permit, some shore protection structures and buildings were rebuilt. To complicate further the shoreline manager's mission of a sustainable shoreline is the U.S. Supreme Court Case (June 29, 1992) in favour of Lucas v South Carolina Coastal Council.

   Shoreline managers are now aware of the costs of shoreline regulations. D.H. Lucas was denied permission to develop two shoreline lots seaward of the established baseline (Platt, 1992). Compensation was awarded Lucas, recognizing that not only had property values been reduced by regulation, but totally destroyed.

3) In fact, many property owners use attempts at shore hardening to challenge erosion rates and therefore reduce their set back limits. Yet, over time (years, decades) buildings along the shoreline, where they do not belong , will be overtaken by erosion.

REFERENCES

Boyd, G.L. (1981) *Final Report: Great Lakes Erosion Monitoring Program*, Report No.13, Fisheries and Oceans, Burlington, Ontario.

Clark J.R. (1983) *Coastal Ecosystem Management*. The Conservation Foundation, R.E. Krieger: Florida.

Houlahan, J.M. (1989) "Comparison of State Construction Setbacks to Manage Development in Coastal hazard Areas," *Coastal Management Journal*, 17.

Institute for Research on Public Policy (1989) *Great lakes, Great Legacy?* Toronto, Ontario.

International Joint commission (1989) *Phase One Report for the References on the Adverse Affects of Fluctuating Great lakes Water Levels*, Ottawa, Ontario.

McKenzie, D.I. (1990) "Shoreline Erosion on Ontario's Great Lakes," in *Ontario: Geographic Perspectives on Economy and Environment*, B. Mitchell (ed), Department of Geography Publication Series, University of Waterloo, 253-268.

Pilkey, O.H., and W.J. Neal (1992) "Save Beaches Not Buildings," *Issues in Science and Technology*, 8(3), 36-41.

Platt, R. (1992) "Life after Lucas, the Supreme Court and the Downtrodden Coastal Developer," *Natural Hazards Observer*, 17(1), 8-9.

Rawson Academy for Aquatic Sciences (1989) *Great Lakes Ecosystem Charter*, Ottawa, Ontario.

Reinders Ltd. (1989) *Lake Huron Shore Processes Study*, Report to the Saugeen, Maitland, Ausable-Bayfield, and St. Clair Conservation Authorities, Toronto, Ontario.

Session III

CONCEPTS, ROLES AND INSTITUTIONS

Main public beach, Port Elgin, Lake Huron with intensive recreational use
by bathers and boaters
(photo provided by Patrick Lawrence, University of Waterloo)

Great Lakes Management and the Role of the International Joint Commission

CHRISTIAN J. STEWART
Environment Canada, Inland Waters Directorate - Ontario Region
Burlington, Ontario

Introduction

Management of the Great Lakes - St. Lawrence River basin's physical and human resources falls under the responsibility of a number of diverse institutions including the federal governments of both Canada and the United States, the Provincial Governments of Ontario and Quebec and the State Governments of Minnesota, Wisconsin, Michigan, Illinois, Indiana, Ohio, Pennsylvania and New York. In addition, responsibilities are also often shared by many different levels of local government, as well as other government related agencies and authorities. Perhaps the one agency considered by many to be the lead agency for Great Lakes - St. Lawrence River management is the International Joint Commission (IJC), a bi-national agency with key responsibilities commonly addressing issues related to water quality and water quantity. This paper will examine the role of the IJC in management of the Great Lakes, with specific reference to water level and shoreline management activities that are currently being undertaken as part of an IJC directed study of fluctuating water levels on the Great Lakes and their connecting channels.

What is the IJC?

The Boundary Waters Treaty of 1909 between the United States and Great Britain on behalf of Canada, established the International Joint Commission to serve as a bi-national body with three members appointed by each country. The Commission acts as a single body seeking common solutions rather than as separate national delegations representing the positions of their Governments. Though the treaty was entered into primarily to prevent disputes regarding the use of boundary waters and to provide for the adjustment and settlement of questions arising between the two countries along their common frontier, it has provided the framework for cooperation on questions relating to air and water pollution and the regulation of water levels and flows (International Joint Commission, 1992).

The IJC issues *Orders of Approval* in response to **Applications** for the use, obstruction or diversion of waters that flow along, and in certain cases across, the boundary if such uses would affect the natural water levels or flows on the other side. The IJC also undertakes investigations of specific issues, or monitors situations, when requested to do so by Governments. Implementation of IJC recommendations made under such **References** is at the discretion of the two federal governments. Experts from both countries serve on technical boards for the IJC to carry out the required studies and field work. *Boards of Control* are appointed to report on compliance with Orders of Approval, while study or advisory boards assist in References. Public hearings and other opportunities for input by interested citizens are organized when Applications and References are considered (International Joint Commission, 1992).

IJC Activities in the Great Lakes - St. Lawrence River Basin

The Commission has been involved in a number of activities in the Great Lakes - St. Lawrence River basin since it's beginning in 1909. These are summarized below (from International Joint Commission, 1990).

Lake Superior

Since 1914, when the IJC approved applications for the diversion of water from the St. Marys River for the purpose of hydro-power development and for a control structure, the International Lake Superior Board of Control has supervised the operation of regulatory structures in the river pursuant to conditions established by the Commission. The Board monitors levels and supply conditions of Lakes Superior and Michigan-Huron and determines monthly outflows of Lake Superior at Sault Ste. Marie.

Lake Ontario / St. Lawrence River

In 1952, the Commission approved construction of hydro-power development works in the international rapids section of the St. Lawrence River. It established the International St. Lawrence River Board of Control to monitor the discharge of water from Lake Ontario and the flow of water through the River.

Niagara River

The International Niagara Board of Control was established in 1953 to review and approve construction of works controlling flows over Niagara Falls. The Board monitors the operation of the Chippewa Grass Island Pool control structure to meet the requirements of the 1950 Niagara Treaty. Under a 1964 Order of Approval, the Board also supervises the annual installation and removal of an ice boom at the outlet of Lake Erie.

Great Lakes - St. Lawrence River Water Quality

Under the 1978 Great Lakes Water Quality Agreement between Canada and the United States, amended in 1983 and 1987, the IJC assists Governments by monitoring progress and providing advice on matters related to the Agreement. The Great Lakes Water Quality Board and the Great Lakes Science Advisory Board assist the Commission in this regard. Since 1978 the Commission has held major biennial meetings to hear reports from Boards and comments from the public. Biennial Reports are issued by the Commission to assess progress dealing with water quality problems in the Great Lakes.

Great Lakes - St. Lawrence River Water Levels

The issue of fluctuating water levels and their associated impacts has been a concern of the IJC for much of the last 30 years, beginning in the mid-1960's with an examination of methods to combat extreme low water levels, through to the present "Levels Reference Study" which is examining ways to alleviate adverse consequences of fluctuating water levels. A brief summary of each of these water level studies follows.

Regulation of Great Lakes Water Levels

As a result of severe *low* water levels on the Great Lakes in the early to mid-1960's, the Governments of Canada and the United States submitted a Reference to the IJC requesting them to determine whether measures could be taken to further regulate the levels of the lakes and connecting channels so as to reduce the extremes which had been experienced. To accomplish this task, the IJC established the International Great Lakes Levels Board, which completed the various technical investigations and submitted a final report, which examined a number of possible water level regulation plans, to the IJC in December of 1973 (International Great Lakes Levels Board, 1973).

Lake Erie Water Level Study

In February of 1977, the Canadian and U.S. governments requested the IJC to determine whether limited regulation of Lake Erie water levels would be in the public interest of both countries. The request came about as a result of record *high* water levels on Lake Erie and Lakes Michigan-Huron in the early 1970's, and as a result of IJC recommendations to Governments based on the results of the Great Lakes Levels Board (1973). The IJC established the International Lake Erie Regulation Study Board to perform the investigations. Specific committees were established by the Board to deal with studies on regulation, hydro power, regulatory works, coastal zone, environment, recreation and navigation. This Board completed its work and submitted a report to the IJC in July of 1981 (International Lake Erie Regulation Study Board, 1981), indicating that further regulation of the Lake would not be economically justified.

Great Lakes Diversions and Consumptive Uses

Also in response to recommendations made by the International Great Lakes Levels Board (1973), the Governments of Canada and the United States requested the IJC to examine and report upon the effects of existing and proposed diversions within, into or out of the Great Lakes Basin. As a result, the IJC established the Great Lakes Diversions and Consumptive Uses Study Board to conduct the technical investigations. Their work led to the development of a number of recommendations regarding the future management of diversions and consumptive uses, which were submitted to Governments in January of 1985 (International Joint Commission, 1985).

The 1986 Levels Reference Study

On August 1, 1986 the Governments of Canada and the United States, in response to record high water levels on four of the five Great Lakes issued a Reference to the International Joint Commission to examine and report upon methods of alleviating the adverse consequences of fluctuating water levels in the Great Lakes-St. Lawrence River Basin. To accomplish this task, the IJC carried out a number of different tasks. First, the Commission submitted an initial report to Governments describing actions the Commission had taken during the crisis, actions recommended to be taken by Governments, and measures that utilized existing facilities, which might be implemented immediately.

Second, the Commission formed a Task Force in the fall of 1986 to undertake a technical evaluation of measures that could be implemented within approximately one year to reduce high water levels. The Task Force submitted a summary report of its analyses to the Commission in October 1987. The Commission subsequently transmitted an Interim Report to Governments that contained the Task Force summary and included additional recommendations for actions Governments could take.

As a third step, the Commission continued to seek broad expert advice for addressing the longer term objectives of the Reference and engaged the services of water resource agencies of Federal Governments of both the United States and Canada (primarily Environment Canada and the U.S. Army Corps of Engineers) to help conduct the study and answer the many questions asked in the Reference.

A Project Management Team was organized with affiliated functional groups to respond to issues identified in the Reference concerning hydrology, hydraulics, and climate; coastal zone resources and management; socio-economic and environmental impact assessments; public participation and communications; and systems analysis and synthesis. The Phase I Study culminated in a Progress Report with seven annexes, dated July 1989 (Project Management Team, 1989). This Phase I Progress Report identified problems related to the management of water level issues and explored potential avenues for problem-solving. It recommended that a broad planning approach be developed that would include:

- the development of a guiding set of principles designed to provide broad guidelines for future decisions regarding water level issues;
- the development of an overall strategy for deploying measures, encompassing the needs of the entire Basin as well as the circumstances of specific locales; and
- the development of a framework for an effective governance system, including considerations for the role of interests and the public.

In February 1990, as a fourth and final stage to the 1986 Reference, the Commission established the Levels Reference Study Board and issued a Directive to the Board for carrying out Phase II of the Study. The Directive was amended in April of 1990 by further establishing a set of objectives to guide the development of the Study plan and the Study conduct (Levels Reference Study Board, 1990).

In accordance with the Directive, the Board appointed a Citizens Advisory Committee consisting of eighteen members with an equal number of members from the U.S. and Canada. The Citizens Advisory Committee is an advisory committee to the Board and in that capacity provides representative advice on the general and specific aspects of the Study.

The Board appointed four Working Committees to address the issues identified in the Phase II Plan of Study (see Levels Reference Study Board, 1991). The four Working Committees and their responsibilities are:

Working Committee 1 - Public Participation and Information
This Committee is promoting discussion between the various levels of the Study and public interests and ensuring that there is ample opportunity for the public to have influence over the direction of the Study.

Working Committee 2 - Land Use and Management
This Committee is examining the physical shoreline and the effects of water levels on shoreline processes including potential damage to property and long term erosion. This Committee is also looking at the natural resource impacts of fluctuating water levels for wetlands, fisheries and wildlife. Social impacts are also being examined through various surveys. Land use and management practices along the shoreline are being evaluated for their effectiveness and impacts.

Working Committee 3 - Existing Regulation, System-Wide Regulation and Crises Conditions
This Committee is investigating the causes of water level fluctuations and the ranges that occur as a result of both natural and anthropogenic effects. They are also examining possible future changes that may occur as a result of climate change, or as a result of the implementation of system-wide regulation, or the alteration of existing regulation plans. They are also examining crisis conditions and what situations create a crisis condition; forecasting of lake levels; and the impact of fluctuating water levels on hydro-power, navigation and recreation interests.

Working Committee 4 - Principles, Measures Evaluation, Integration and Implementation

Data gathered by Working Committees 2 and 3 on fluctuations and their impacts will contribute to an overall evaluation of measures. The application and administration of the evaluation methodology is the responsibility of Working Committee 4. This Committee is responsible for developing the principles for Study evaluation, for applying these principles in the chosen evaluation methodology and for undertaking the evaluation. Specific emphasis has been given to system regulation schemes and land use and shoreline management practices. In addition, considerable effort has been devoted to the examination of institutional issues and to developing a set of guiding principles that the Commission could propose to Governments to assist them in dealing with fluctuating water levels in the Great Lakes-St. Lawrence River Basin.

As of this writing, the work of all four of these Committees is continuing. The Working Committees and The Levels Reference Study Board anticipate having the bulk of their technical investigations completed in early 1993 and will be submitting a report to the IJC on March 31, 1993.

Great Lakes Shoreline Management and the IJC: Activities within the Present (1986-1993) Levels Reference Study

Previous water level reference studies on the Great Lakes have focused primarily on the examination of methods to control, regulate or somehow manipulate water levels and flows. Detailed regulation plans have been developed, with associated detailed evaluations of their economic, environmental, hydrologic and social impacts. The same type of detailed analysis however, was not completed for those actions commonly viewed as "shoreline management" alternatives. In many cases, results of the previous water level studies indicated that further water level regulation was not economically feasible and that shoreline management practices should be considered. Yet, there was no real indication of what some of these practices might be, or what their economic, environmental and social impacts were. As a result, such recommendations tended to go unheeded by governments.

In their 1986 Reference to the IJC (see Levels Reference Study Board, 1990), the Governments of Canada and the United States recognized this lack of detailed analysis of shoreline management measures and in "acknowledging previous Commission reports which have encouraged appropriate jurisdictions to institute improved shoreline management practices" directed the IJC (in addition to examining once again, lake regulation practices) to:

> "examine past, present and potential future changes in land use and management practices along the shorelines of the Great Lakes, their connecting channels and the St. Lawrence River"; and to

> "determine, to the maximum extent practicable, the socio-economic costs and benefits of alternative land use and shoreline management practices and compare these with the costs and benefits of lake regulation schemes."

To address these directives, Working Committee 2 established the Land Use and Shoreline Management Task Group to carry out tasks falling into three main categories:

1) catalogue land uses, land use trends and shoreline management practices in order to provide information necessary for correlation of damages to shoreline use, targeting of high risk areas, projection of potential high risk areas and evaluation of the effectiveness of response measures to lake level fluctuations;
2) develop a working definition of shoreline management, including a comprehensive listing of all relevant terminology for use throughout Phase II of the Reference Study; and
3) provide a detailed evaluation and assessment of the effectiveness of selected shoreline management practices, including the provision of comprehensive information on the merits and disbenefits of the various practices, estimates of the costs of implementation and the benefits (i.e. their success at alleviating adverse consequences of fluctuating water levels) that they have provided to the implementing agencies and municipalities (counties, cities, etc.).

A brief review of each of these tasks is found below, with particular focus on items 2 and 3.

Current Land Use and Land Use Trends

Current land use information for the Great Lakes - St. Lawrence River shoreline was obtained from a number of sources, including data gathered and stored in U.S. and Canadian Geographic Information Systems during Phase I of the Study (see Functional Group 2, 1989). For the Canadian shoreline (see Triton Engineering and Ecologistics Limited, 1992) land use data was presented in both hectares (ha) for area calculations and also as a kilometre length of land use along the shoreline. Percentages of total land use length were also provided on a lake-by-lake and basin-wide basis. Similar statistics are being prepared for the U.S. shoreline (Roger Gauthier, U.S. Army Corps of Engineers, personal communication).

Land use and land use patterns are constantly changing in form and intensity. In order to make sound and reliable evaluations of management options and their potential impacts on the shoreline, planners and decision makers need to have an understanding of what past and future land use patterns were and are likely to be in the basin. As such, historical changes were examined using previously published land use information, with their comparison to data contained in the existing data bases of both countries. Future trends were examined through the use of a questionnaire that was sent to appropriate agencies and municipalities along both the Canadian and U.S. shoreline. The questionnaire asked the respondents to provide an estimate of the expected changes in a number of land use categories (e.g. residential, undeveloped, recreational) that would occur within the next ten years. Data was then presented as a percentage change expected in each of the land use categories. For Canada (see Triton Engineering and Ecologistics Limited, 1992) this information is available on a Conservation Authority, or Ministry of Natural Resources District basis. For the United States, data will be presented on a county-by-county basis (Roger Gauthier, U.S. Army Corps of Engineers, personal communication).

Shoreline Management Practice Assessment and Evaluation

While information on current land uses and land use trends is important, of greater concern in this study was a detailed assessment and evaluation of specific shoreline management practices that have been utilized throughout the basin. A key first step in this process however, was to clearly define those shoreline management practices that were to be considered.

Measures For Evaluation

A number of shoreline management measures have been put forth by the Study Board for detailed analysis. They can be grouped loosely into three main categories: 1) land use regulatory practices; 2) land use incentive based practices; and 3) shoreline protection alternatives. An introduction to these categories is provided below, along with a brief definition of the specific measures within each category.

Regulatory Based Practices

Regulatory based practices are those in which certain regulations, restrictions, by-laws, etc. would be applied or enforced to control or modify existing shoreline uses in a manner that will minimize the potential "conflict" with shoreline processes and water level fluctuations. Regulatory based practices include:

- Setback requirements
  Regulations requiring new buildings to be set back to a predetermined erosion or flood control line. These could also require existing dwellings lakeward of this line to relocate landward. Construction lakeward of the control line could be permitted if structures are portable or moveable. This measure is supported by hazard mapping.

- Elevation requirements
  Regulations requiring new buildings to be elevated above a predetermined 1:100 year flood level. These could also require retrofit flood proofing or raising of buildings above the flood elevation. This measure is supported by hazard mapping.

- Habitat protection
  Public acquisition of barrier beaches, wetlands, dunes and other shore habitat, and regulations to protect habitats located on private land from the impact of land development.

- Shoreline alteration requirements
  Regulation of privately or publicly constructed shore protection and navigation structures; extraction of beach and nearshore deposits; and land filling to protect adjacent land uses and the environment from any adverse effects of shoreline alteration.

- Deed restrictions/regulations
  Notice of shoreline hazards in property deeds or the requirement for disclosure of hazards in real estate transactions, to alert prospective purchasers of shore property. This could include deed restrictions on the type and location of development permitted on hazard susceptible property.

- Development controls for public infrastructure
  Design or location of roads, public buildings, water supply and sewage lines, and other infrastructure outside of recognized hazard areas or range of water level fluctuations.

- Non-structural land use practices
  Public acquisition of hazard land and buildings, or publicly financed relocation of structures outside of hazard areas. Public agencies could convert acquired land to recreation uses or resell for private development with conditions to minimize hazard susceptibility.

Land Use Incentive - Based Practices

Incentive-based practices are those designed to provide incentives (or disincentives) to the various shoreline user groups to encourage changes in the way they use the shoreline. Examples of measures in this category that have been considered for further evaluation are:

- Tax incentives/disincentives

  A variety of incentives to encourage maintenance of shoreline habitat or relocation of structures landward of a hazard setback line, and tax penalties to discourage development of hazard land or to fund coordinated shore protection in designated shore reaches.

- Loans
  Loans to property owners to encourage various nonstructural and structural measures, including flood proofing or relocation of buildings, or shore protection. This could include the elimination of loans that encourage new development in hazard susceptible shore areas.

- Grants
  Grants to property owners to encourage various nonstructural and structural measures, including floodproofing or relocation of buildings, or shore protection. This could include the elimination of grants that encourage new development in hazard susceptible shore areas.

- Insurance

  Subsidized or actuarial rate insurance for properties located in recognized hazard areas. Insurance could be conditional on municipal or property owner actions to reduce hazard susceptibility.

Shore Protection Alternatives

Shore protection alternatives are engineered methods by which sections of the shoreline are protected from flooding, wave action, erosion, etc. From a shoreline management perspective, measures in this category which have been considered for further evaluation include the following:

- Structural shore protection to prevent erosion

  Public agency design and construction of various large-scale shore protection works, including seawalls, breakwaters, groynes, revetments, artificial headlands or artificial barrier islands.

- Structural shore protection to prevent flooding

  Public agency design and construction of large-scale shore protection work, including temporary or permanent dykes.

- Non-structural shore protection

  Public agency implementation of various non-structural shore protection measures, including beach nourishment, landfilling, bluff grading, bluff drainage, or vegetation planting.

Inventory and Assessment of Shore Management Practices

Once the types of shoreline management practices under consideration within the study were defined, an inventory of their use and extent throughout the basin was completed (see Triton Engineering and Ecologistics Limited, 1992 and Ecologistics Limited 1992a and b). In addition to this, a detailed evaluation of each practice was undertaken, utilizing three broad sets of evaluation criteria: effectiveness, compatibility and implementability.

The effectiveness criterion was designed to assess the broad effectiveness of individual measures and mechanisms in meeting the shoreline management objective of damage reductions. It includes subcomponents addressing the cost of the measure (capital / maintenance / administrative), damages avoided (where determinable) and the net benefit of the measure. Net benefits are measured as the cost of the measure minus the damage avoided due to its installation. To the degree possible, numerical information was used to compute these values.

The compatibility criterion sought to identify and evaluate the potential impacts (positive and negative) of the various shoreline management practices on both the natural environment, and on various land and water related uses and users (interest groups) within the basin. The application of the compatibility criterion is qualitative in nature, but attempted to the maximum extent possible to provide a relative assessment of the direction (positive or negative) and magnitude (weak, moderate or strong) of the impact.

Finally, the implementability criterion sought to identify and evaluate the constraints and facilitators to shoreline management practices. This criterion was broken down into four subcomponents: technical feasibility, social acceptability, institutional compatibility and jurisdictional issues. Technical feasibility addresses the degree of difficulty involved in the physical implementation of a measure. Social acceptability considers the degree to which individual measures are likely to be perceived by the public. Institutional compatibility is the degree to which certain shoreline management measures may conflict with mandates of shoreline institutions. Lastly, jurisdictional issues address compatibility and conflicts between government ministries and agencies in administering shoreline management measures.

For full details on the evaluation results of each of the individual measures the reader is referred to Ecologistics Limited (1992a and b).

Shoreline Management Versus Water Level Regulation - An Initial Evaluation

The Evaluation Process

Recall that Working Committee 4 is responsible for developing an evaluation methodology to assist in determining the preferred measures or combinations of measures for reducing the adverse consequences of fluctuating water levels. To do this, they have relied on a technique known as Multi-Criteria Measures Evaluation (MCME), which allowed a number of measures to be evaluated by comparing them with a set of evaluation criteria, which functioned as standards to evaluate and rank potential measures (Working Committee 4, 1992a). The core criteria, which were very similar to those used in evaluating shore management practices included: 1) economic impacts, which included benefit-cost relationships and other economic and social impacts; 2) environmental impacts, which included subcriteria of environmental purity and ecological productivity; 3) distribution of impacts, both among interest groups and among regions in the Basin; and 4) feasibility, which covered technical, operational and legal and public policy feasibility.

The evaluation process incorporated both qualitative and quantitative data pertaining to each measure, using information made available from the evaluation of shore management practices described above, as well as from the evaluation of "water level regulation measures which were evaluated elsewhere in the study. All impact information was presented to Working Committee 4 and was summarized in a "workbook" titled, "Impacts of Measures For Evaluation Summary" (Working Committee 4, 1992a) which was distributed to all study participants in advance of a "Measures Evaluation Workshop," (held on September 28-30, 1992) one of the first steps in establishing preferred measures or sets of measures for consideration.

In preparation for the workshop, study participants were asked to review the impact evaluation data for each measure and to provide a ranking (or score) for each measure (on a scale of +3 to -3), for each of the evaluation criteria and subcriteria listed. Score sheets were submitted to Working Committee 4 prior to the meeting and tabulated summaries were distributed to workshop participants as they arrived. The purpose of the workshop was to review these initial rankings of measures and to determine if there were any patterns in the various responses that would allow the group to establish any preliminary findings on the measures, including clear statements regarding the strengths and weaknesses of them. If there were clear preferences for particular measures, or groups of measures, they were to be put forth to the Study Board for further consideration, and would form the initial draft of an "Options" document for governments (i.e. the options governments could take to alleviate adverse consequences of fluctuating water levels).

Initial Evaluation Results

In general, it was very clear from the workshop discussions (see Working Committee 4, 1992b), that study participants, which include representatives from the various interest groups being considered, viewed water level regulation scenarios as predominantly negative, particularly with regard to economic and environmental criteria, and viewed shoreline management and shoreline protection measures as predominantly positive, particularly in areas of benefit-costs and technical feasibility. Five-lake regulation plans, which would see construction of new control structures on Lakes Michigan-Huron and Lake Erie, were viewed by all to be highly negative from both an economic and an environmental stand-point, and as such would receive no further consideration as potential "options." Similarly, other 3-Lake Plans (construction of control works on Lake Erie only, combined with existing regulation), and those plans devised to satisfy the needs of one interest only, were also dropped from consideration for many of the same reasons. In summary, of the 17 water level regulation measures that were put forth for initial evaluation, 8 have been put forth for further evaluation and consideration, 6 of which simply involve modification of the existing regulation plans that exist on Lakes Superior and Ontario. Two 3-Lake plans however will be considered further and will be subject to additional impact evaluation.

Perhaps a key result of the initial evaluation of measures was that all of the 14 shoreline management practices described were put forth for further consideration and evaluation and inclusion in the initial "Options" document. It was recognized that many of these practices can not be used in isolation and that they lend themselves readily to combinations. It was also recognized that the way in which these measures are applied will vary considerably from one jurisdiction to another, and that the measures should be viewed as "tools" available to decision makers rather than as one measure which needs to be applied uniformly over the entire shore. Finally, it was clear that consensus among workshop participants was that even with water level regulation measures in place, shore management practices such as setbacks and development controls, would be equally as important in alleviating flood and erosion hazards.

There was some modification of the description of some of the shore management practices. For example, Loans and Grants were not viewed as practices per se, but rather as implementation mechanisms for use in combination with other shore management practices such as shore protection construction, or dwelling relocation. Other changes simply included refinements to the definitions of the various practices.

The Options Document

A draft Options Document has been prepared (Levels Reference Study Board, 1992) and includes summary descriptions of all of the measures put forth for further consideration, as well as all available information on their potential costs, benefits, impacts, etc. At the time of writing of this report, this document was awaiting Study Board approval. It will eventually be distributed to study participants, the public and various levels of government, in advance of a series of public and policy forums scheduled for late 1992. Comments and discussions at these forums will help to identify a final list of recommended measures, and hence form the final conclusions of the Reference Study.

Implications for Future Great Lakes Management

As the final list of recommended measures has not yet been formalized, it is difficult to make any final conclusions regarding what the outcome of the Reference Study will mean for future Great Lakes management. Some preliminary comments, however, can be offered.

First, the detailed evaluation, assessment and inclusion of comprehensive information on shoreline management practices, side by side with information on possible water level regulation measures represents the first time in an IJC sponsored study that "land side" measures have been evaluated and examined to the same level of detail as water level regulation measures.

It is clear from this "equal" assessment and from the initial measures evaluation exercise that shoreline management practices are heavily favoured over such options as 5-Lake and 3-Lake water level regulation plans and that they should likely be considered as options for governments to take whether or not water level regulation practices are modified, or extended to other lakes.

A recommendation for shore management measures by the IJC may serve to send notice to governments of the need for programs to address the longer term implications of flooding and erosion, or low water hazards. Government responses are often crisis related with programs and associated funding being predominant during or immediately after a crisis, and an elimination of programs and funding when a crisis is over. Commitment to long term shoreline management planning programs may help overcome this "issue-attention" cycle and allow for consistency in dealing with future water level and shoreline planning related issues.

Whether or not the governments choose to follow recommendations of the IJC is another issue. The IJC, in its present form, has a lack of authority for program initiation, implementation or regulation, so while they can synthesize technical information into policy recommendations, the advice is not binding on the government agencies with the implementation powers and may go unheeded. On the positive side however, many of the mechanisms and facilitators for the implementation of shoreline management practices are already in place, and new programs for implementation would likely not have to be developed. For example, the development of the Ontario Shoreline Management Program (see McKeen, 1992 this volume) and the development of individual shoreline management plans by Ontario Conservation Authorities incorporate many of the regulatory and protective measures described. Recommendations handed to federal levels of government by the Levels Reference Study Board and the IJC, describing the merits and benefits of such practices, can only serve to strengthen support and coordination of programs of this nature.

Similarly, the United States Coastal Zone Management Program also provides federal guidance to individual States for the development of coastal management programs. Not all of the eight U.S. Great Lakes States however, participate in this program. Again, recommendations from the IJC as to the strength of such programs and associated practices, may provide the impetus for the non-participatory states to become involved, so that all Great Lakes States have uniform shoreline management policies in place.

In summary, the IJC, although it is not the ultimate implementing institution, can play a key role in influencing the future management of the Great Lakes, particularly in areas relating to water levels and shoreline management, by recommending to governments a set of measures that will alleviate the adverse consequences of fluctuating water levels experienced by many interest groups. While this list of preferred measures might include recommendations for further water level regulation of the lakes, it will almost certainly contain recommendations for the implementation of specific shoreline management practices. Recommendations for these types of measures will hopefully awaken governments to the need for long-term commitment to shoreline hazard issues and will allow for the better coordination and implementation of those shoreline management practices and programs that are already in place.

REFERENCES

Ecologistics Limited (1992a) Evaluation of Shoreline Management Practices - Canadian Shoreline. Final Report Submitted to The Land Use and Management Task Group, Working Committee 2, IJC Levels Reference Study, 249pp. plus Appendices and Maps.

Ecologistics Limited (1992b) Evaluation of Shoreline Management Practices - United States Shoreline. Final Report Submitted to The Land Use and Management Task Group, Working Committee 2, IJC Levels Reference Study.

Functional Group 2 (1989) Living With The Lakes: Challenges and Opportunities, Annex B - Environmental Features, Processes and Impacts: An Ecosystem Perspective on The Great Lakes - St. Lawrence River System. Report Submitted to the Project Management Team, IJC Water Levels Reference Study, 169pp.

International Great Lakes Levels Board (1973) Regulation of Great Lakes Water Levels. Final Report Submitted to the International Joint Commission, 294pp. plus Appendices.

International Lake Erie Regulation Study Board (1981) Lake Erie Water Level Study, Main Report. International Joint Commission, 232pp. plus Appendices.

Levels Reference Study Board (1990) Phase II Plan of Study. International Joint Commission Levels Reference Study, 24pp. plus Attachments.

Levels Reference Study Board (1991) Phase II Workplans, Working Committees 1-4 and Citizens Advisory Committee. International Joint Commission Levels Reference Study, 80pp.

Levels Reference Study Board (1992) Options Document - Including Key Results of Technical Studies, Guiding Principles For Governments, measures To Reduce Impacts of Fluctuating Water Levels, Emergency Actions in Response to Crisis Conditions, Institutional Arrangements, and Communications Practices. IJC Levels Reference Study, October 1992.

McKeen, P. (1992) "A Review of the Ontario Shoreline Management Program ". in Proceedings of a Workshop on Managing the Great Lakes Shoreline: Experiences and Opportunities, Heritage Resources Centre, University of Waterloo, October, 1992 (this volume).

Project Management Team (1989) Living With The Lakes: Challenges and Opportunities. A Progress Report To The International Joint Commission, 108pp. plus seven Annexes.

Triton Engineering and Ecologistics Limited (1992) Inventory and Assessment of Land Uses and Shoreline Management Practices. Final Report Submitted to The Land Use and Management Task Group, Working Committee 2, IJC Levels Reference Study, 48pp. plus Appendices and Maps.

Working Committee 4 (1992a) Impacts of Measures For Evaluation Summary. A Workbook Prepared For the Measures Evaluation Workshop, Toronto, September 1992, IJC Levels Reference Study, 286pp.

Working Committee 4, (1992b) Summary of Key Decisions, Study Meeting on Measures Evaluation. IJC Levels Reference Study, 15pp.

Canada's Great Lakes Cleanup Fund

I. GRIFF SHERBIN
Great Lakes Environment Office, Environment Canada
Toronto, Ontario

Introduction

The message to our governments is clear: The citizens of the Great Lakes Basin will no longer tolerate the use of these magnificent bodies of fresh water as waste receptors. They want action now. They want pollution sources stopped, cleanup actions undertaken and pollution prevention programs put in place.   The 1972 Canada-United States Great Lakes Water Quality Agreement (GLWQA) was the first major step by governments towards cleaning up the Great Lakes. The focus of this historical binational agreement was eutrophication. Within six years, toxic chemical contamination of the Great Lakes led to the "Revised Great Lakes Water Quality Agreement of 1978". The purpose of this Agreement was to restore and maintain the chemical, physical and biological integrity of the waters of the Great Lakes Basin Ecosystem. The 1978 Agreement focused mainly on controlling toxic chemicals which went into the Great Lakes. The agreement's second priority centred on the use of an "ecosystem approach to toxic chemicals management".

By the late 1980's, there was a growing recognition that even further measures had to be taken as areas of the Great Lakes were still seriously polluted. After intensive consultations with governments, environmental groups and citizens around the basin, Canada and the United States amended the 1978 Agreement. The 1987 Protocol clearly recognizes the need for extending and increasing existing programs as well as for the establishment of new programs.

Canada-United States Great Lakes Water Quality Agreement (GLWQA)

The GLWQA was signed by the federal governments of Canada and United States (the Parties). It is implemented in cooperation with the

Great Lakes States and the Province of Ontario. Federal programs are developed through the Great Lakes Action Plan, under the direction of a federal Great Lakes Working Group (GLWG). The GLWG is made up of representatives from Environment Canada, Fisheries & Oceans, Agriculture, Transport and Health and Welfare. The Federal/Provincial commitments are delivered under the Canada-Ontario Agreement, under the direction of the COA Board of Review.

Under the GLWQA, Canada and United States are required to meet twice a year to review progress and agree on binational efforts and programs. The Parties are also required to submit biennial reports to the International Joint Commission (IJC). The IJC in turn, evaluates the progress of the Parties in meeting the requirements of the 1987 Protocol. Then, the IJC, with advice from experts on its Water Quality and Science Advisory Boards, reports back to the federal governments. These reports are filed every two years.

The 1987 Protocol to the GLWQA, as mentioned earlier, clearly recognizes the need for existing programs to be extended and for new programs to be added. The Protocol is a renewed commitment to virtual elimination of persistent toxic substances in the Great Lakes. The new provisions cover issues such as:

- Remediation of severely polluted areas - these are called Areas of Concern (AOC) - through Remedial Action Plans (RAPs) and for lakewide problems, through Lakewide Management Plans (LAMPs).
- Development and demonstration of technology for the assessment, removal, treatment and disposal of contaminated sediments.
- Airborne toxic depositions and the development of a binational monitoring network.
- Addressing human health impacts.
- Development of new objectives and environmental and human health indicators for the Great Lakes Basin ecosystem.

Great Lakes Action Plan (GLAP)

In response to the signing of the 1987 Protocol, Canada introduced $125 million to the ongoing and new commitments.

There are three programs under the Great Lakes Action Plan. These are:

1. Preservation Program	- $50 million
2. Health Effects Program	- $20 million
3. Cleanup Fund	- $55 million

The Preservation Program is under lead of the Great Lakes Working Group. The program is designed to address, in a comprehensive manner, the wide-spread contamination of the Great Lakes Ecosystem by toxic chemicals. The program has six components which address the major pollution aspects of the Great Lakes as well as the requirements of the 1987 Protocol. Those components are:

- Cleanup Plan - RAPs and LAMPs.
- Ecosystem health.
- Pollution from land-based sources.
- Shipping.
- Contaminated Sediments.
- Airborne Contaminants.

The second program under the Great Lakes Action Plan is the Health Effects Program and is managed by Health and Welfare Canada. This program is designed to meet the new human health requirements of the 1987 Protocol. The program has four main features:

- Evaluation of environmental data as they relate to human populations
- Assessment of health risks within the Basin.
- Protection from exposures to mixtures of chemicals.
- Providing environmental health information to the public.

Cleanup Fund (CuF)

The third Great Lakes Action Plan program is the Cleanup Fund (CuF). CuF is used to support the development, demonstration, and implementation of cleanup programs in Canada's 17 Areas of Concern. There are a total of forty-three Areas of Concern on the Great Lakes designated by the IJC. Seventeen AOCs are solely Canadian with five (St. Lawrence, Niagara, Detroit, St. Clair and St. Marys Rivers) shared by both countries. The Cleanup Fund was established to ensure that remedial measures for the AOCs, which fall within federal jurisdictions and for which there are no existing programs, are adequately funded. The program operates under the following principles:

- Polluter pays
- Pollution prevention
- Zero discharge
- Ecosystem approach

CuF projects focus on the following priority areas:

- Contaminated Sediments (assessment, removal, treatment)
- Wastewater Technology (controlling urban runoff)
- Habitat rehabilitation (fish and wildlife)
- Non-point sources (rural runoff)
- Communication (technology transfer).

Since its creation in 1990, the CuF has provided approximately $12 million to 34 projects. Another $16 million has been provided by various contributors including other federal agencies, the Ontario Ministry of Environment and Natural Resources, municipal governments, Regional Conservation Authorities, private industry and public interest groups. To initiate the sediments program, a notice was published, seeking proposals or expressions of interest to demonstrate technology suitable for "safely" removing and treating contaminated sediments. Approximately 300 companies responded to the notice. Details on specific technologies for treating contaminated sediments were submitted under the following categories:

• Chemical treatment	16
• Biological treatment	20
• Solidification/Stabilization	18
• Extraction	26
• Incineration	11
• Alternate Heat	12
• Pre or Post Treatment	<u>12</u>
	115

Approximately 70 proposals were received on sediment removal. All submitted proposals and technologies have been reviewed for potential application. Over the next several years CuF will be supporting bench-scale testing, pilot and full-scale field demonstrations of various technologies. To date, two successful contaminated sediment removal demonstrations have been completed using two different innovative technologies. In the Welland River (Niagara River AOC) approximately 230 cubic metres of sediment were removed using a modified Mud Cat dredge. Modifications involved changes to the auger head, the boom, hull and hydraulic system. An instruments package was added to allow for dredge performance verification.

The second demonstration took place in Toronto's inner harbour. A cable-arm bucket was demonstrated by L.B. Tanker Inc. Approximately

250 cubic metres of sediments were removed with minimal disturbances to the water column. The sediments were treated at the Toronto Harbour Commissioners Soil Recycling pilot plant. The sediments went through a three-stage treatment process: washing, metals extaction and bioremediation.

Sediments from Hamilton Harbour were treated in a pilot scale thermal destructor. The Ecologic Thermal Destructor destroyed up to 99.9 percent of the organics in the contaminated sediments. Other treatment technologies (sequential leaching, fixation, bioremediation, etc.) are being tested at bench-scale. If successful, some could be recommended for pilot or full-scale demonstration.

In-place treatment of contaminated sediments has the potential to be considerably less expensive than the remove and treatment alternative. In-place treatment techniques are still a research topic but recent demonstrations in the St. Marys River and Hamilton Harbour are showing promise. Scientists from Environment Canada's National Water Research Institute have developed a system to treat sediments in place. A boat is used to drag a spray boom through the sediments. The system then injects an oxidant (ferric chloride, calcium nitrate) into the sediments. The St. Marys River demonstration showed that approximately 50 percent of the oil in the sediment biodegraded within seven months of treatment. A high proportion of the contaminates in the sediment however, appears to be resistant to biodegradation.

The CuF also addresses other areas that are having an impact on sediments in the aquatic environment. In cooperation with the Ontario Ministry of Environment, Ontario Municipal Engineers Association and Areas of Concern Municipal Governments, a major program is addressing combined sewer overflow control, stormwater management and optimizing sewage treatment plant operations. Urban pollution must be controlled before sediment removal and treatment can begin.

While technology demonstration projects are underway, one of the final products of cleaning up an AOC is the implementation of habitat rehabilitation projects. A good example is the planning, design and environmental assessment actions underway on a project for Hamilton Harbour and Cootes Paradise. The long term goals of the project are to:

- improve water quality
- alter the fish community
- provide spawning, nursery and adult habitats for fish
- recover lost wetlands
- create habitats for shorebirds, waterfowl
- provide better access to the waterfront

The cost of the project is estimated at approximately $14 million and will take up to 5 years to complete. The CuF has committed $4 million with other funding coming from private and public organizations. The prevention of future pollution is critical to the delisting of Areas of Concern. Canada's Green Plan has committed $25 million to a Great Lakes/St. Lawrence Pollution Prevention Initiative. The initiative will seek to develop strategies and pollution reduction plans, demonstrate and support the development of pollution prevention technologies and provide support to education and awareness programs.

Conclusion

To meet the GLWQA objectives of "restoring and maintaining the chemical, physical and biological integrity of the waters of the Great Lakes Basin Ecosystem" is an enormous task for everyone involved. It is obvious that the total cost of cleaning up the Great Lakes will be in the hundreds of millions of dollars. Just as important however, is the need to develop, demonstrate and put in use the proper cleaning technologies and equipment. Both countries must continue to share ideas and solutions for the many Great Lakes cleanup challenges.

Climate Change and the Great Lakes

MARIE SANDERSON
The Water Network, University of Waterloo
Waterloo, Ontario

Introduction

Containing 20% of the world's fresh water, the Great Lakes are a unique and priceless resource shared by Canada and the United States. The Great Lakes basin is home to some forty million people, including one third the population of Canada. These lakes are a gift of the great ice ages that once covered this land and excavated the large depressions that the lakes now occupy. Table 1 shows the physical characteristics of the five major lakes: Superior, Michigan, Huron, Erie and Ontario. Hydrologically, lakes Michigan and Huron are considered one lake since they are connected by the broad Strait of Mackinac and have the same level. Superior has the largest surface area of any freshwater lake in the world and a volume of water 25 times the volume of Lake Erie. The total area of the basin is over 500,000 sq. km^2 and that the lakes themselves occupy a large percentage (one third) of the total drainage basin.

Table 1. Physical Characteristics of the Great Lakes
(from Great Lakes Basin Commission, 1976)

	SUPERIOR	MICHIGAN-HURON	ERIE	ONTARIO	TOTAL
Total Basin Area (km2)	127,000	252,000	58,800	70,000	507,800
Lake Surface Area (km2)	82,100	117,200	25,660	19,000	243,960
Lake Volume (km3)	12,230	8,460	480	1,640	22,810
Ave. Depth (m)	149	72	19	86	
Average annual Outflow (m3/sec)	2,250	5,200	5,570	6,690	

It can also be seen from Table 1 that the largest proportion of the Great Lakes' outflow (the average annual runoff or renewable resource) is contributed by the upper lakes, Superior and Michigan-Huron because of their very large basin areas. This average outflow of 5,200 m^3/sec (cubic meters per second) is increased to almost 6,700 m^3/sec by the time the water reaches the St. Lawrence river. It can also be seen in Table 1 that very little of the volume of water in the lakes is a renewable resource, since in an average year only 1% of the water flows through the system.

Great Lakes Water Levels

The levels of the lakes have been measured by agencies of the federal governments of the United States and Canada for more than one hundred years. The monthly and yearly mean water levels for the period 1948-1977 are seen in Figure 1. This graph shows that there is an annual cycle of levels on the lakes - low in winter and high in summer. Also evident are long term changes in lake levels: not identical for all lakes but with similarities, high levels in the 1920's, lows in the 1930's, highs in the 1950's, lows in the 1960's and high levels in the 1970's and 1980's. The difference between record highs and lows increases from 1.1 m for Lake Superior to 2 m for Lake Ontario. This range in levels may not seem extreme when compared with ocean tidal ranges, but in the inland waterway of the Great Lakes, changing levels are of great concern because of the multiple and often conflicting uses of the lakes. Shore owners prefer low levels with less risk to their properties, while shipping and hydroelectric power companies prefer high levels permitting them to carry more cargo and generate more electricity.

During periods of high levels, concern is expressed by shore residents that man-made diversions into the lakes cause the high water levels. There are presently two diversions which bring water into the Great Lakes basin. The Ogoki and Long Lac diversions redirect water that ordinarily would flow into James Bay, south into Lake Superior. These diversions were constructed in the 1940's for hydroelectric power generation and together average about 200 m^3/sec. The increases in lake levels caused by these diversions are very small: 6 cm on Lake Superior, 10 cm in Michigan-Huron, 7 cm in Erie and 6 cm in Ontario.

Similarly, during periods of low levels, there is concern over diversions of water out of the Great Lakes basin. Such a diversion has been in existence at Chicago for more than 100 years, providing water for domestic and industrial use and sewage disposal into the Mississippi River through the Illinois River. A maximum flow of 120 m^3/sec out of

Figure 1. Annual Average of Great Lakes Water Levels 1950 - 1986
(from US Army Corps of Engineers, 1986)

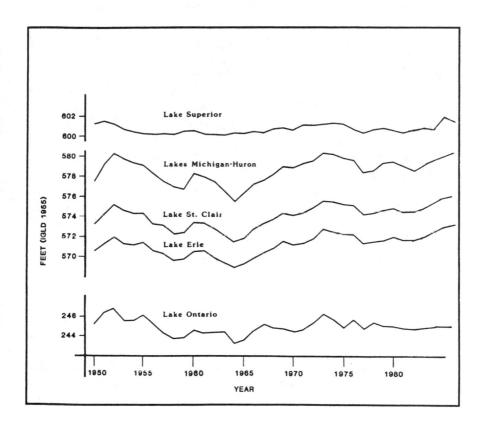

Lake Michigan is allowed by the United States Supreme Court. The effect is to lower the lakes, 2 cm for Superior, 6 cm for Michigan-Huron, 4 cm for Erie and 3 cm for Ontario. The net effect of the two diversions on the lakes is thus a small rise in level.

At the present time the lakes are approximately at their average levels, having declined from record highs to average levels (a difference of one m) in just two years. This is in contrast to predictions in 1986 that it would take at least five years for the lakes to return to average levels. A similar situation existed in the early 1960's when lake levels fell from average to extreme low levels in just two years.

The question asked by shore owners during the periods of high as well as periods of low levels, is "what causes these changes in level"? The causes lie in the great variability in climatic factors. The level of a lake is a result of the inflow from the upper lake minus the outflow to the lower lake, but this is a relatively conservative parameter. More important are changes in the net basin supply, defined as precipitation on the surface of the lake minus evaporation from the lake plus runoff from the land area of the basin (as below).

$$NBS = P-E+RO$$

The manner in which these factors vary throughout an average year for Lake Erie for example, is seen in Figure 2. Precipitation is relatively constant throughout the year, averaging about 7 cm per month. Runoff from the land areas is greatest in spring (10 cm on the surface of the lake in April) when the snow melts and rivers carry this spring flood to the lake. The third factor, over lake evaporation, cannot be directly measured, but is estimated using complex mass transfer models which require the use of parameters like air temperature, water temperature, wind and humidity. It is seen in Figure 2 that over-lake evaporation can amount to more than 15 cm in late fall, when the water is warm in relation to the overlying air and the saturation vapour deficit is large. The combination of these three factors is called the net basin supply, and this controls the levels of the lakes. When it is positive, levels rise; when negative, levels fall.

Future Water Levels and Climate Change

What will the future hold? It is usually assumed that future Great Lakes levels will resemble those of the past and that the next 100 years will see the range in levels of 1.5 to 2 m that we have seen in the past one hun-

Figure 2. Lake Erie Average Annual Water Level Variations (Monthly Mean Water Levels) (from Great Lakes Basin Commission, 1976)

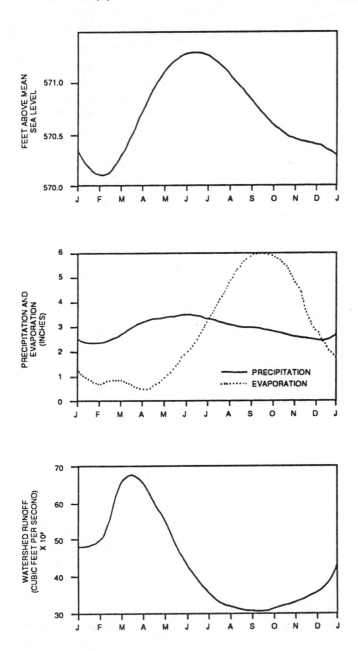

dred years. In view of the present consensus among world scientists concerning climatic change, this may not be the case. The so-called "greenhouse" gases such as water vapour and carbon dioxide (CO_2) in the earth's atmosphere have the capability of altering the earth's radiation balance. They do not affect the short wave radiation from the sun as it passes through the earth's atmosphere, but they absorb the long wave radiation given off by the earth's surface, and re-radiate it back to earth, thus acting somewhat like the glass in a greenhouse, increasing surface temperatures. This is a natural phenomenon which makes the earth habitable. What is of present concern to climatologists is that additions of man-induced CO_2 into the atmosphere may cause changes in climate not hitherto experienced in human history.

Carbon dioxide concentrations in the clean atmosphere at approximately 4,000 m at Mauna Loa observatory in Hawaii began to be monitored in 1957 (Figure 3). Other stations show similar trends, from concentrations of approximately 312 ppm (parts per million) in 1957 to about 350 ppm in 1990. It is predicted that by the year 2050, concentrations will be double that of a pre-industrial atmosphere (called a $2xCO_2$ climate).

Whether the increase in CO_2 in the atmosphere is reflected in world temperature records is difficult to determine because of the great natural variability in temperature. Figure 4 indicates that since world records began to be kept, approximately 100 years ago, world temperatures appear to have risen by about 0.5 C. Canadian temperatures during that time increased by about 1 C.

During the past twenty years, atmospheric scientists have attempted to model the world's present atmospheric circulation and have added the projected increased concentrations of greenhouse gases to the models to predict the $2xCO_2$ climate. Some general circulation models commonly used are those of the Geophysical Fluid Dynamics Laboratory (GFDL), and the Goddard Institute of Space Studies (GISS), both U.S. models, and the Canadian Climate Centre (CCC) model of Environment Canada.

Since these are world models, the output is for a very coarse grid. For example, for the GISS model, there are only 10 data points in the Great Lakes basin as seen in Figure 5. The output from the model for points (1) and (10) is shown in Table 2, indicating that under this scenario, temperature changes may average approximately + 4.5 C, more in winter and less in summer, and that precipitation may increase in the north western part of the basin (point 1), and decrease in the south east (point 10). Present and projected January temperatures in the basin are shown in Figure 6 for the GISS scenario. While average January temper-

Table 2. Present and Projected Future Mean Monthly Temperature and Precipitation in the Great Lakes Region (from Marchand et al., 1988)

	(1) Temperature °C			(1) Temperature (cm)			(10) Temperature °C			(10) Precipitation (cm)		
	NORM	CH	2xCO2	NORM	EFFECT	2xCO2	NORM	CH	2xCO2	NORM	EFFECT	2xCO2
Jan.	-20.2	5.6	-14.6	1.2	117.6	1.4	-4.5	5.6	1.1	2.4	104.2	2.5
Feb.	-17.5	5.6	-11.9	1.1	116.7	1.2	-5.5	5.1	-0.4	2.7	104.2	2.8
Mar.	-9.5	5.3	-4.2	1.2	109.7	1.3	-2.5	4.8	2.3	3.2	100.0	3.2
Apr.	0.2	4.5	4.7	1.4	107.7	1.5	4.5	4.5	9.0	3.5	100.0	3.5
May	7.8	3.6	11.4	2.1	103.2	2.2	13.0	4.0	17.0	3.4	100.0	3.4
Jun.	14.5	3.0	17.5	3.0	110.0	3.3	18.0	3.8	21.8	3.3	103.3	3.4
Jly.	17.0	2.9	19.9	3.0	111.1	3.3	21.0	4.0	25.0	4.0	103.8	4.2
Aug.	14.8	3.1	17.9	2.9	113.0	3.3	18.5	4.3	22.8	3.7	95.2	3.5
Sep.	9.5	3.7	13.2	2.9	110.0	3.2	15.0	4.4	19.4	3.3	77.8	2.6
Oct.	4.0	4.6	8.6	2.1	116.7	2.5	10.0	4.5	14.5	3.2	70.0	2.3
Nov.	-6.0	5.2	-0.8	1.8	123.5	2.3	1.5	5.0	6.5	3.3	78.3	2.5
Dec.	-15.5	5.5	-10.0	1.3	123.5	1.6	-4.0	5.6	1.6	2.4	88.0	2.1
MEAN		4.4			113.5			4.6			93.7	

NORM = 1951-80 normals
CH = magnitude of change between 1951-80 normals and 2xCO2 normal)GISS Scenario)
2xCO2 = projected normals under 2xCO2 conditions

Figure 3. Monthly Average Carbon Dioxide Concentration (from Hansen and Lebedeff, 1987)

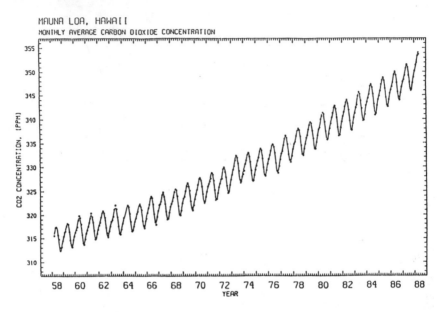

Figure 4. Changes in World Temperatures 1880 to 1980 (from Hansen and Lebedeff, 1987)

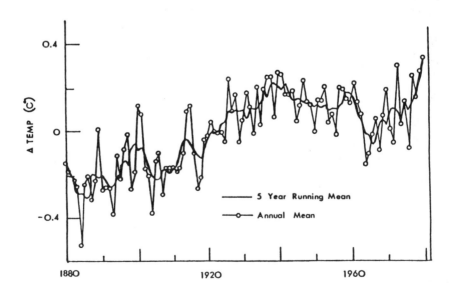

Figure 5. GISS Grid Points in the Great Lakes Basin (from Marchand et al., 1988)

Figure 6. Present and Projected January Temperatures, GISS Scenario (from Marchand et al., 1988)

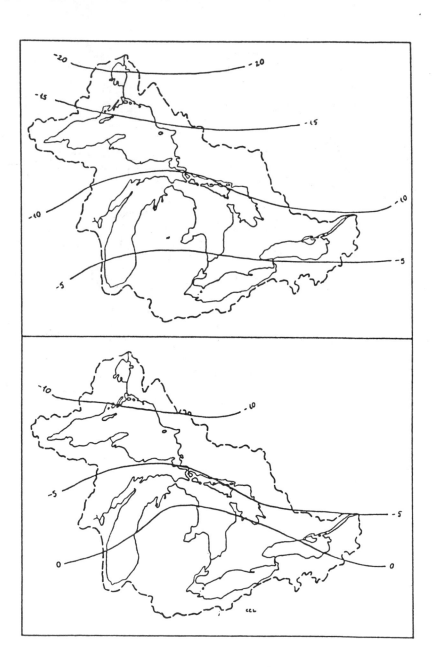

atures presently are approximately -5 C for most of Southern Ontario, the GISS scenario projects above freezing temperatures for this area under climate change. This would mean very little snow cover, a lengthened growing season and also little ice cover on the Great Lakes. Under climatic change, Southern Ontario will have a climate much like that of present day Kentucky.

In a study of the impact of climate change on future lake levels, the outputs of the GFDL and GISS scenarios were used with various sub models to determine the runoff and lake evaporation and the subsequent net basin supply for all the lakes for the period 1956-83. This period was called the basis of comparison (BOC). Under the GISS climatic change scenario, runoff from the land areas of the basin would be reduced since evapotranspiration would be greater with higher air temperatures. Overlake evaporation would be increased because of increased water temperatures and decreased ice cover. Actually, the models showed that under the GISS scenario, none of the lakes except Erie would have any ice cover in an average year. Under this scenario of climate change, the net basin supply for Lake Erie would be decreased by about 40%.

Applying this decrease in net basin supply to a long period of lake level record (1900-1978) gives the situation seen in Figure 7 for Lake Erie. The solid line shows BOC conditions or the actual record of lake levels. The dashed line shows the lake levels that would have occurred if the GISS scenario had been in effect during the period 1900-1978. This methodology was used to illustrate the range in lake levels that could be expected under a $2xCO_2$ climate since we are assuming that climatic variability will not change. The dashed-dotted line adds the scenario of increased consumptive use of Great Lakes water, water that is withdrawn from the lakes but not returned, as for example for irrigation or manufacturing, (International Joint Commission 1985). Under the scenario of climatic change plus increased consumptive use, the frequency of low lake levels as in the early 1960's would be increased to 77% of the years. This situation would cause great concern and the loss of millions of dollars to the shipping and hydro electric power companies.

Conclusions

If the GISS climatic change scenario were to occur, the average levels of the Great Lakes will be lowered by about 1/2 m, and that the frequency of extreme low levels will be much greater than in the past, especially if

Figure 7. Lake Erie Yearly Mean Water Levels: 1900-1978, Three Scenarios (from Marchand et al., 1988)

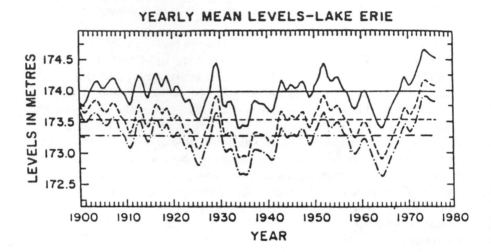

climatic change is accompanied by increases in consumptive use. In a recent study of climate change and Great Lakes levels, Croley and Hartmann of the Great Lakes Environmental Research Laboratory in Michigan (1988) found larger declines of 2 to 2.5 m in average lake levels of the lower lakes.

If decreases in lake levels as suggested by the climate change scenarios do occur, there will doubtless be demands from the users of the lakes for governments to "do something" to restore the lakes to their historic levels. This will be especially true for shipping and hydro electric power companies as well as marina and harbour operators. We have heard today of the results of lobbying on the part of another group, shore owners, which led to the International Joint Commission reference on fluctuating lake levels. There will doubtless be a whole new set of problems for shoreline managers in the 21st century!

REFERENCES

Great Lakes Basin Commission (1976) *Limnology of Lakes and Embayments,* Appendix #4, Great Lakes Basin Framework Study, U.S. Government, National Ocean and Atmospheric Administration.

Hansen J. and S. Lebedeff (1987) "Global trends in measured surface air temperature," *Journal of Geophysical Research*, 92(13) 345-72.

Marchand, D. M. Sanderson, D. Howe and C. Alpaugh (1988) "Climate Change and Great Lakes Levels: the impact on shipping", *Climate Change*, 12, 107-133.

NOAA Summary Report (1986) *Geophysical Monitoring for Climate Change #15*, (editor R.C. Schnell), Washington, D.C.

Sanderson, M. (1987) "Implications of climate change for navigation and power generation in the Great Lakes," *Climate Change Digest*, 87-03, Environment Canada.

U.S. Army Corps of Engineers (1976) *Great Lakes Water Level Facts*, Detroit, Michigan.

A Green Plan Initiative: The GLSLB Project and its Relationship to Shoreline Management Issues in the Great Lakes Region

GRACE KOSHIDA and LINDA D. MORTSCH
Canadian Climate Centre, Environment Canada
Downsview, Ontario

The Great Lakes-St. Lawrence Basin (GLSLB) is a region rich in natural resources, with diverse industries and complex infrastructures. Key to the successes and failures in the Region is how well its society and its industries have adapted to the climate. Any future change in the climate resulting from global warming will introduce new risks and opportunities and these must be considered in the social, economic and political decision-making in the Region. The task of managing the multiple activities within the Basin under the exacerbating conditions of climate change resulting from global warming must be addressed; first through research, and then by applying the research to the bilateral, Canadian-U.S. management of the Basin.

As part of the growing concern about climate change, a number of research and monitoring programs have been carried out in Canada and the United States. Although there is still much uncertainty about the timing, the rate and the magnitude of climate change, initial assessments provide a significant "first look" at the possible impacts of climate change by identifying the potential biophysical, social, economic and political consequences of global warming on specific sectors within the Basin. They have demonstrated the complexity of the situation.

A Canada-U.S. symposium, "The Impacts of Climate Change on the Great Lakes Basin", held in Chicago in 1988, recommended that a binational, integrated study of the Great Lakes Basin be developed as a regional pilot project. As part of the Canadian Federal Green Plan initiative "Reducing the Uncertainties", the Canadian Climate Centre, Environment Canada will develop projects to conduct second generation climate impact assessments which will incorporate regional adaptation strategies. A proposal for a Canadian project in the Great Lakes region has been developed recognizing these needs (Canadian Climate Centre, 1992).

The study area for the GLSLB Project is the Great Lakes Basin and the St. Lawrence River Basin down to Trois Riviéres, Québec. This corresponds to the study area defined by the International Joint Commission (IJC) for its Water Levels Reference Study. Complementary boundaries were chosen to take advantage of ongoing data assembly, model development, research and impact assessments.

The focus of the GLSLB Project is to assist in the development of adaptation responses which will minimize the negative impacts of climate change and take advantage of the opportunities afforded by climate change in the Basin. The GLSLB Project will focus on a limited number of key climate-sensitive issues since it is not possible to identify all the climate-biophysical-societal linkages and to address all the potential impacts and benefits. Four key issues have been identified by the GLSLB Project Advisory Board: water quantity, water quality, ecosystem and human health, and land use.

The shorelines of the Great Lakes-St. Lawrence Basin are geologically diverse, ranging from rock cliffs and cobble beaches to glacial bluffs and sand beaches. Various wildlife species and plant life flourish in adjacent coastal wetlands and other natural shoreline areas. However, the Great Lakes coastal zone is an area of dynamic change. Sediments are eroded, transported and deposited, thereby constantly changing the extent, content and character of the Great Lakes shorelines.

Climate change may significantly alter the water levels of the Great Lakes. Shoreline property owners, land developers, marina operators, park managers and recreationalists may face new challenges and opportunities with a changing water level regime. Mean Great Lakes water levels, as well as the timing, range and extremes in water level fluctuations may change under a new climate. However, even with new mean water levels, the Great Lakes will continue to fluctuate both over the long-term (inter-annually) and short-term (storm surges, wind set-up), thus affecting the magnitude and rate of erosional and depositional processes and flooding along its shorelines.

A regional consultation workshop will be held in Québec in February 1993 to identify expertise, data, models and integration methods, as well as develop a collaborative team drawn from Canadian government agencies, academia, interest groups and industry, and to enhance the understanding of the climate change issue. Green Plan funds allocated to the GLSLB Project will be used as "seed money" to support relevant studies.

REFERENCE

Canadian Climate Centre (1992) *A Canadian Proposal For the Great Lakes - St. Lawrence Basin Project on Responses to the Impacts of Climate Change and Variability.* (Canadian Climate Centre, Environment Canada, Downsview, Ont.).

Session IV

ONTARIO GREAT LAKES SHORELINE MANAGEMENT PROGRAM

Scarborough Bluffs, Lake Ontario located at the eastern end of Toronto, these
glacial clay and sand deposits are up to 100 metres in height representing some of
the highest shore bluffs on a freshwater lake in the world
(photo provided by Patrick Lawrence, University of Waterloo)

A Review of the Ontario Great Lakes Shoreline Management Program[1]

PEARL L. MCKEEN
Lands and Water Policy Branch
Ontario Ministry of Natural Resources, Toronto, Ontario

Introduction

More than half of Ontario's population lives within the shoreline communities of the Great Lakes - St. Lawrence River Basin. Competition for use of the shoreline, by a diverse range of shoreline owners has exerted considerable strain on this limited resource. Uses have often included shore protection works which have been incompatible with neighbouring installations as well as works which have been installed in an ad hoc fashion or which have largely ignored coastal processes and environmental impacts.

High lake levels, during the mid-fifties, early seventies and mid-eighties, in combination with storm surge, resulted in millions of dollars in flood and erosion damages along Ontario's Great Lakes shorelines. Most damages having been sustained in areas which had experienced losses in the past. Government response to each high water period consistently proposed the pursuance of three key actions. First, that shoreline flooding and erosion concerns be examined, second, that damages be investigated and third, that appropriate criteria to define flood and erosion hazards be considered. Unfortunately, with the ebbing of high water levels and the corresponding decline in public demands for action, the resolve of governments to lead short-term emergency actions into the establishment of coordinated long-term shoreline management programs also declined.

With the most recent water period of the mid-eighties, however, the provincial government acknowledged that high water periods are not just a once-in-a-lifetime phenomena. Rather, that they are a function of a naturally continuing process that will occur again. Recognizing that shore damages are borne not only by affected shoreline property owners but also by taxpayers, generally through short-term and long-term assistance programs provided by various levels of government, all have acknowledged that the tragedy of loss of life, the destruction of property, and social disruption are often immeasurable.

In December 1986, the Honourable Vincent G. Kerrio, Minister of Natural Resources announced the establishment of a provincial shoreline management program. The program, encompassing a wide variety of short-term and of more importantly, long-term solutions to shoreline management problems, is viewed as a major step forward in addressing the recurring concerns associated with flooding and erosion along the shorelines of the Great Lakes - St. Lawrence River system.

Challenges

Development and implementation of a coordinated, multi-faceted shoreline management program does not instantaneously occur with its announcement. There are, and will continue to be, a number of challenges which face the provincial government in finalizing program directions, in addressing public concerns and in balancing the interests of a diverse range of shoreline owners. The ultimate objective, however, remains the same—to ensure the sustainability of shoreline resources for the social, economic and environmental well-being of present and future Ontario residents.

Four key challenges face the provincial government in determining the overall direction the provincial shoreline management program will ultimately take. These include: developing a more comprehensive understanding of natural influences; responding to public misconceptions; resolving questions relating to hazard vs. ecosystem management; and determining the extent of political commitment to shoreline management concerns.

Natural Influences

The shorelines of the Great Lakes - St. Lawrence River system have undergone considerable change with the passage of time. Changes have resulted from fluctuations in water levels during and following their glacial and post-glacial history, from natural processes of erosion and sedimentation, and from long-term and seasonal variations and influences of storm surge, and wave, ice and wind action. These, along with the significant influence the hydrological cycle has on fluctuating water levels, have shaped and contoured our shorelines.

Recognition, first and foremost, that we are dealing with a "process not a problem" is of significant importance in determining the ultimate direction provincial shoreline management programs will take. Acknowledging that human intervention and development on flood and erosion susceptible shorelines have resulted in conflicts between natural influences and human interests is also fundamental to determining long-term solutions.

Development of a provincial shoreline management program needs, therefore, to study and acknowledge the influences of fluctuating water levels, storm surge, and wind, wave and ice action in the establishment of criteria to define and delineate shoreline hazards and in determining and selecting management strategies to minimize the potential for loss of life and property damage.

Misconceptions

Several misconceptions and misunderstandings have historically influenced public demands for actions and the responding directions taken by governments. The three major ones being water level regulation, ownership of the "problem" and the balancing of shoreline interests.

Water level regulation by construction of dams and other structures has been viewed for years as the ultimate "quick fix" solution to reducing the destructive influences of shoreline flooding and erosion. Studies have repeatedly shown, however, that the influence of such structures on fluctuating water levels can be measured merely in terms of centimetres of change: An influence which is virtually inconsequential when compared to the meters of change in still water levels which storm surges have caused.

The primary influence on water level fluctuations within the Great Lakes Basin is the hydrological cycle, an influence which was clearly and dramatically demonstrated during the mid-1980's. Record levels of precipitation in late 1985-86 resulted in high water levels throughout the Basin. Then contrary to all predictions, several months of record low levels of precipitation and high evapotranspiration rates resulted in just as dramatic a drop in water levels during 1987/88.

Ownership of the problem has for years influenced the level of government involvement in addressing recurring shoreline management concerns. The question of who should bear the costs of shoreline destruction whether the owner, the community or governments, and to what degree, has and will continue to influence the direction and level of responsibility to be borne by the shoreline owner, taxpayers in general, and the various levels of government.

Balancing of public and private interests, with the ultimate objective of sustaining shoreline resources and ensuring continued acces and enjoyment of these resources, provides a continuing and ever changing dilemma for government agencies: A dilema which is compounded by the extensive diversity of interests along Ontario's shorelines.

Hazard vs Ecosystem Management

One fundamental question faced by governments when developing a comprehensive shoreline management program is whether or not such programs should be based solely on principles of hazard management or on a more holistic or ecosystem management basis. Some have argued that focusing on hazard management and the issues of flooding and erosion, ignores the influence and protective benefits provided by natural physical and biological features within shoreline environments.

Alternatively, some have suggested that requiring all components of shoreline management program to be based on an ecosystem approach (i.e.. necessitating an environmental assessment and analysis of a wide range of possible impacts) reduces ability to address short-term needs or to focus on shoreline management issues requiring immediate response.

Political Commitment

Commitment of governments to shoreline management issues is essential to establishment and implementation of effective, coordinated, long-term solutions to recurring management problems. This commitment, however, should not be misconstrued as being only financial in nature, To ensure flexibility and responsiveness to shoreline management issues, government programs must incorporate a variety of legislative, administrative, financial and planning initiatives to address effectively the issue of public safety as well as ensuing continued social, economic and environmental viability of shoreline areas.

Beyond the financial aspects of program establishment, the political "will" to take a stand, recognizing that full public support may not be an immediate or even an eventual reality, is often jeopardized by the desire to ensure political longevity. As history has demonstrated, the establishment of short-term structural solutions to emergency situations (i.e.. appeasing public demands for actions during crisis situations) has often been viewed as an appropriate government action: Despite the fact that long-term preventative approaches to shoreline management have consistently been shown to offer a more cost-effective means of addressing naturally recurring problems.

Provincial Shoreline Management Program

In December 1986, the Honourable Vincent G. Kerrio Minister of Natural Resources, announced the establishment of a long-term provincial shoreline management program. The main goal of the provincial program is to minimize danger to life and property damage from flooding, erosion and associated hazards along shorelines. The main emphasis of the program is to focus on preventive approaches to shoreline management.

The Ministry of Natural Resources was identified as the lead ministry having responsibility for overall program administration. Conservation Authorities were designated as the local agency having responsibility for implementing and administering the shoreline policies of the Ministry. Where Conservation Authorities do not exist, the Ministry of Natural Resources is to assume responsibility for program delivery.

The provincial shoreline management program incorporates three main components:

- Prevention - implementation of development controls, regulations and approaches to prevent threats of flooding/erosion to new development
- Protection - implementation of capital works, provided there is no adverse impact to updrift/downdrift properties
- Emergency Response - provision of emergency action by local municipalities and governments and the coordination of municipal, other governmental and private resources

Implementation of the provincial shoreline management program, and its ultimate success, is seen to depend on the adaptability and responsiveness of the program to local, regional and basin-wide management issues. To do so requires the development of a multi-facetted program encompassing both short-term, but more importantly, long-term management strategies.

Within each of the three main components, the Province has established and is in the midst of developing several key initiatives. An examination of each initiative, the rationale for its existence and an evaluation of its current status follows.

Prevention Component

As stated earlier, the prevention component of the provincial shoreline management program deals with the establishment and implementation of development controls and regulations aimed at preventing flooding and/or erosion threats to new development. In other words, the intent is to direct new development towards less hazardous portions of the shoreline and in doing so, preclude or minimize the risk of loss of life and property damage. Several initiatives combine to address the prevention aspects of the provincial shoreline management program including:

1. establishment of a provincial policy statement
2. development/refinement of provincial databases
3. mapping/delineation of shoreline hazards
4. development/implementation of shoreline management plans
5. active participation in plan input and review
6. training and technical development of staff
7. liaising with other agencies
8. informing/educating the public

The rational and status of each of these initiatives are as follows:

1. Provincial Policy Statement

Prepared jointly by the Ministries of Natural Resources and Municipal Affairs, the Great Lakes - St. Lawrence River Flood and Erosion Policy Statement will recognize shoreline flood and erosion concerns as being matters of provincial interest. Under section 3 of the Planning Act, the policy statement will formalize the provincial position on Great Lakes flood and erosion hazards as they relate to new development within flood and/or erosion susceptible portions of the Great Lakes - St. Lawrence River shoreline.

Initial drafts of the policy statement have been prepared and circulated internally to implementing agencies for review and comment. Revisions, based on comments provided by field and main office staffs, are now nearing completion. The next step, seeking Cabinet approval to release the draft policy statement for public review and comment, first requires the formal review and approval of several internal, inter-ministerial, and Cabinet committees. It is anticipated that this process will require 6 to 8 months to complete.

Accompanying the policy statement will be two documents: Implementation Guidelines and Technical Guidelines. The Implementation Guidelines will provide further explanation and interpretation of the policy statement and will offer direction on alternative approaches within the planning process which can be used to implement the various components of the policy statement. The Technical Guidelines will provide information on: a range of shoreline management issues warranting evaluation; technical criteria leading to the calculation and delineation of flood/erosion hazards; and on criteria for evaluating prevention, protection and/or emergency response alternatives.

2. Provincial Databases

With the announcement of the provincial shoreline management program, it was determined that an evaluation was required of existing criteria used to define and delineate shoreline flood and erosion hazards. As a result, the Hazard Land Technical Committee, having representation from both the provincial and federal government, was established. Added responsibilities of the Committee included assessing the effects of recent high water levels relative to existing 100 year criteria, evaluating existing databases and making recommendations on studies or databases which were required, on a provincial basis, to assist implementing agencies in fulfilling their responsibilities as shoreline management agencies.

The Committee determined that:

- recent high lake levels were only slightly greater than existing 100 year levels, and that as such, the existing 100 year criteria should be maintained;
- floodproofing standards were needed;
- new wave uprush standards were needed; and
- updated recession rates were required.

Resulting from the recommendations of the Committee, the Province commissioned three key provincial studies:

- Wave Climate Database
  - intended to develop a comprehensive long-term set of offshore wave statistics
  - report completed in 1988
- Littoral Cell and Sediment Budget Analysis

- intended to define littoral cells and subcells, to develop pre-
liminary sediment budgets, and to identify sites warranting
further study
- report completed in 1988
• Erosion Analysis
- intended to update monitoring information, to determine
revised recession rates, and to assess the value/utility of photogrammetric cross-sections in determining recession rates

3. Mapping/Delineation of Shoreline Hazards

During 1972-73, Fisheries and Oceans Canada, Environment Canada and
the Ministry of natural Resources initiated the Canada/Ontario Great
Lakes Shore Damage Survey. The result was the printing and circulation of the Great Lakes Coastal Zone Atlas in 1976. The Atlas, based on
a 1973 airphoto mosaic base with 3 metre contours, provides information on historical changes in the position of the edge of the shore bluff.
The Atlas also contains maps and information on shore damage, shoreline ownership, land value, land use, physical characteristics and existing protective works that sustained damage during the 1972-73 floods.
Included also are the histograms of shore recession and accretion rates.
Although the Atlas is a valuable source of historical information, the
scale of the mapping limited the ability of implementing agencies to provide detailed information on a site-by-site basis.

In the interests of providing a more comprehensive database at a
more appropriate mapping scale, the Province and the federal government, through the Canada/Ontario Flood Damage Reduction Program,
jointly initiated a 1:2000 scale mapping program of the Great Lakes
shoreline. Commencing in the fall of 1987, the program, at an approxi-
mate cost of $800,000 per year, began to map developed shoreline areas
threatened by flooding and/or erosion and to map flood and/or erosion
susceptible shoreline areas which are experiencing increasing development pressure.

4. Shoreline Management Plans

An integral component in the implementation of the provincial shoreline
management program is the development and implementation of shoreline management plans. Based on a comprehensive stretch of shoreline,
the plans are intended to provide the necessary information to assist
management agencies in future decision-making processes. Developed
using a multi-agency approach, the plans promote liaison between key
shoreline management agencies having an interest in shoreline areas.

To assist local implementing agencies in preparing shoreline management plans and to ensure a more coordinated and consistent approach to shoreline management across the Province, a set of generic "Guidelines for Developing Great Lakes Shoreline Management Plans" was published and circulated in August 1987.

The major goals of a Shoreline Management Plan are:

- to minimize danger to and property damage from flooding, erosion and associated shoreline hazards, and
- to ensure that shoreline development adequately addresses flooding and erosion hazards through a combination of public and private management and development alternatives.

The key components of the shoreline management plan include:

- Prevention
  - implementation of development controls and regulations governing newdevelopment through the Conservation Authorities Act, Lakes and Rivers
    Improvement Act, Public Lands Act and the Planning Act

- Protection
  - the implementation of capital works, provided there are no adverse updrift/downdrift impacts

- Emergency Response
  - the initial responsibility for reacting to emergencies is at the local municipal level. The local implementing agency is responsible for recommending to each of their member municipalities that an emergency plan including the provision of emergency action and the coordination of municipal and other governmental and private resources be prepared

- Public Information
  - outlines the extent, timing and resource requirements for a public information program to aid in developing and implementing a Shoreline Management Plan. The main emphasis of this component is to be on the dissemination of information and the education of the general public regarding shoreline management

- Environment
  - involves a review of environmental inventories, an assessment

of both short-term and long-term potential effects of preventa-
tive/protective measures to both terrestrial and aquatic ecosystems, and an outline of feasible mitigation measures

- Monitoring
  - outlines changes to local conditions and physical, biological,
    social and economic factors affecting shoreline management as
    well as how modifications to the Shoreline Management Plan
    will be incorporated at appropriate intervals

At present, Shoreline Management Plans throughout the Great
Lakes Basin are in varying stages of development. Key to the finalization
of these plans, is the completion and adoption of the draft Provincial
policy statement, the ongoing mapping initiatives under the
Canada/Ontario Flood Damage Reduction Program and the completion
of numerous complementary provincial database studies and literature
reviews addressing a wide range of shoreline management issues.

5. Plan Input and Review

Reviewing and providing comments on development proposals provides an opportunity for implementing agencies to promote and ensure
compliance with provincial shoreline management policies and interests.

Recognizing the duplication of jurisdiction of Conservation
Authorities and Ministry of Natural Resources' District Offices in southern Ontario, the Province needed to clarify the roles and responsibilities
of each, relative to the review of development applications in shoreline
areas.

As stated earlier, Conservation Authorities, where they exist, were
identified by the Province as the local agencies responsible for program
implementation, otherwise the Ministry of Natural Resources was to
assume this role. However, with both agencies having jurisdiction and
legislative mandates over much of southern Ontario, and given the
provincial desire to promote a 'one window approach', the Minister of
Natural Resources, in February 1988, conferred full responsibility for
reviewing and commenting on shoreline development applications to
Conservation Authorities where they exist.

Prior to full conferral, however, a number of actions were required
to be taken by the Province, the Conservation Authorities and the field
offices of the Ministry of Natural Resources. These included:

- extension of official jurisdiction into the Great Lakes system,
  through Order-in-Councils, for all Conservation Authorities, ensur-

ing their legal mandate to make comments, approve and/or deny applications foe development which involve extensions and/or intrusions into the water. Extension of Authority jurisdictions through Order-in-Councils were completed in 1988.

* negotiation and documentation of memorandums of understanding between field offices of the Ministry of Natural Resources and Conservation Authorities to promote a "one window" approach to reviewing and commenting on development applications, while at the same time ensuring that other interests of the Ministry of Natural Resources are not neglected (e.g.. fisheries, public lands).

* hiring and naming of Conservation Authority staff responsible for the technical/planning aspects of plan input and review. Additional staffing and training necessary to complete full conferral to all shoreline Conservation Authorities was completed in December 1988.

* reviewing and revising the Lakes and Rivers Improvement Act to incorporate the legislative ability to control filling and construction within hazardous shoreline areas similar to those powers which exist under the Conservation Authorities Act. Revisions to Lakes and Rivers Improvement Act are currently being finalized. Timing of internal review and approval leading to the seeking of Cabinet endorsement of the proposed revisions is currently unknown.

6. Staff Training

With the introduction of approximately thirty new staff into the Conservation Authority system, and two new support positions to assist Ministry staff in shoreline areas outside of Conservation Authorities. considerable interest and time was spent over the initial two years of the provincial program in the area of training and development.

Courses, some in cooperation with academic institutions, were offered by main office or regional staff to introduce and refine staff technical skills in the areas of coastal engineering, coastal processes, planning and public information and education.

7. Liaison with Other Agencies

Communication, where this involves promoting an awareness and understanding of provincial interests in shoreline management and of the rationale for participating in cooperative shoreline management initiatives, is key to the ultimate success of the provincial shoreline management program.

Consequently, local implementing agencies are encouraged to develop and maintain liaisons with local, regional, provincial, federal, and other public and/or private agencies having an interest in the shoreline.

8. Public Information and Education

Communicating provincial shoreline management interests to local shoreline residents is crucial to ensuring awareness, understanding, and support for shoreline management programs.

Protection

The protection component of the provincial shoreline management program deals with the implementation of capital works provided such works, do not pose adverse impacts to updrift/ downdrift properties. In other words, implementing a range of non-structural and structural approaches to existing and new development with the intent of minimizing the risk of loss of life and property damage.

Several initiatives combine to address the protection interests of the provincial shoreline management program including:

1. a capital works program
2. cooperative projects (acquisition)
3. structural and non-structural measures

1. Capital Works Program

The overall intent of the proposed capital works program is to provide funding for large scale protection works in shoreline areas where properties and infrastructure are in imminent risk or where large public capital investments require protection.

The merits of establishing such a program were referred to an interministerial task group in 1987. The recommendations of the group are currently being incorporated into a Cabinet submission with Cabinet review and decision on the proposed propose, direction and funding levels of the program anticipated within the next fiscal year.

2. Cooperative Projects

Dependence on governmental funding, whether federal, provincial or municipal, has in recent years been annually affected by increasing fiscal constraints. As a result, communities, shoreline residents and local implementing agencies have been actively pursuing and encouraging the implementation of cooperative projects. These have involved the joint funding and implementation of both non-structural and structural measures of varying magnitudes, the acquisition of high risk areas, and the pursuance of information and education programs through the joint efforts of local public and private interest groups.

3. Structural, and Non-Structural Measures

For many people the development of the protection component of the provincial shoreline management program meant focusing on the implementation of large scale structural works. Questions over what constitutes structural vs.. non-structural measures has confused and continues to affect the application of such measures; for example is site grading a structural or a non-structural response? Through the preparation of the Technical Guidelines accompanying the draft provincial policy statement, the completion of several provincial studies scheduled over the next few years, and provincial participation in studies being considered under the current International Joint Commission Reference, the Province intends to provide further clarification and direction on the future application of structural and non-structural shoreline measures.

Emergency Response

The emergency response component of the provincial shoreline management program primarily focuses on promote municipal preparation of emergency action plans. Several additional initiatives combine to complement the preparation of emergency action plans including:

1. floodwarning and storm warning
2. training sessions
3. short-term emergency programs
    * sandbagging
    * technical advice
    * emergency funding

The rationale and status of each of there initiatives are as follows:

1. Floodwarning and Storm Warning

The Provincial Streamflow Forecast Centre circulates flood and storm warning information received from Environment Canada and the Atmospheric Environment Service to local Conservation Authorities and

Ministry of Natural Resources offices. If this information indicates risk to life and property, actions identified under the local municipal emergency action plans are initiated.

2. Training Sessions

The Province, in encouraging municipalities to prepare and implement emergency action plans and responses, continue to offer a number of training sessions. These sessions have dealt with the actual development of an emergency plan, the preparing of public, private and local resources and people in emergency situations, and the training of individuals to provide technical direction and supervision during emergency operations.

3. Short-term Emergency Programs

Beyond direct assistance to municipalities, the Province, during times of emergency, has the option of establishing a short-term emergency program to provide additional funding or assistance to shoreline residents. This option was implemented during and following the high lake water level period of the mid-1980's to provide:

- free sandbags to local municipalities during high risk periods of storm surge or flood inundation to protect shoreline properties;
- free technical advice through local implementing agencies to assist shoreline residents in evaluating, selecting and installation of shoreline protection; and
- emergency funding to local implementing agencies where capital investments were in high or imminent risk of failure or loss.

Future Directions

Although considerable progress has been made in the development, refinement and implementation of the provincial shoreline management program, much remains to be done.

Over the foreseeable future, the overall goals and objectives of the provincial shoreline management program will essentially remain the same. Proactive, rather than reactive, "crisis management" program initiatives, emphasized through the implementation of prevention alternatives, will continue as the cornerstones of the provincial shoreline management program.

The short-term emphasis of the provincial management program will focus on securing Cabinet approval of the draft provincial policy statement to assist local agencies in program implementation, and on the initiation, documentation and refinement of our understanding of the technical aspects and inter-relationships among coastal processes, ecosystem management and structural/non-structural shoreline management alternatives. The introduction and utility of geographical information systems (GIS), and the integral role such systems may play in the development of shoreline management plans, plan input and review, and in informing and educating the public, will be actively pursued.

Over the long-term, program emphasis will also be directed to participation in and promotion of basin-wide shoreline management approaches. To provide a more comprehensive indication of how each of the above initiatives will be addressed, the following section examines the intent, direction and proposed implementation of each initiative.

Provincial Great Lakes Flooding and Erosion Policy Statement

Although recognition of other provincial environmental and resource management interests within shoreline areas will be acknowledged (e.g . wetlands, fisheries), the overall intent of the policy statement will continue to focus on flood and erosion hazards and the dynamic nature of beach environments. The major goals of the policy statement will be to minimize risk to life and property, minimize social disruption and encourage a coordinated approach to the use and management of lands susceptible to flooding and/or erosion.

The policy will explicitly recognize the influence and importance of coastal processes, the differentiation among littoral drift, source areas and sink areas, as well as clarifying shoreline hazard management along the Great Lakes - St. Lawrence River system as being a matter of provincial interest.

The one issue yet to be resolved is that of the extent to which development, including the installation of shore protection, will be restricted or prohibited both in source areas identified as significant to maintaining downdrift sediment budgets and littoral drift and in sink areas where the "stability" of the area is uncertain.

Technical Guidance

Developing and supporting technical criteria for the policy statement and the shoreline management program in general will constitute the second key area of focus over the short-term. Three main areas of interest involved in preparing technical support for the program include the determination of flood and erosion criteria, the identification of concerns associated with the dynamic nature of beach environments, and the clarification and documentation of structural and non-structural shoreline management alternatives and their potential benefits and impacts on shore environments.

With respect to clarifying the provincial flood criteria, early in 1989 the Province evaluated, calculated and circulated 100 year flood levels and floodproofing levels for all of the Great Lakes. The calculation, documentation and circulation of similar information for the St. Lawrence River is intended by the end of 1990. Two associated water related hazards requiring further investigation are that of the influence of ice and wave spray on shore environments. The extent of future provincial study efforts in each of these areas is unclear at present.

The development of provincial erosion criteria in the past has been hindered by the absence of continuous, consistent erosion monitoring information over a statistically significant period of record. Alternative methods of calculating the 100 year erosion limit, and the viability and utility of each method will continue to be assessed over the next couple of years. These alternatives include: an analysis of photogrammetric cross-sections (taken 1950s, 1970s, 1980/90s); the digitizing and subsequent evaluation of a series of 1922-36 Ontario Land Survey maps delineating the water's edge and toe and top of bluff; and, an evaluation of the provincial erosion monitoring program. The latter includes a reassessment of merits of an erosion monitoring program, the implementation of recommendations for existing monitoring stations, and an analysis of the frequency and merits of monitoring both offshore and onshore changes.

Beyond the definition and calculation of shoreline hazard criteria, a need exists to conduct studies, to undertake literature reviews and document findings associated with a wide range of key shoreline management issues. These include studies related to dune management, beach nourishment, sediment budgets, the influence of water levels on rates of bluff erosion and the design, and the effects of a wide range of structural and non-structural shoreline management alternatives. This information would then be used by field offices when assessing the merits and potential impacts of various shoreline management strategies and development proposals.

Associated with these initiatives, the Ministry is interested in pursuing the development of a resource library of research associated with shoreline management, particularly that which relates to the Great Lakes Basin.

Hazard Shoreline Mapping

The Canada/Ontario Flood Damage Reduction Program, is intending to prepare hazard mapping of critical Great Lakes - St. Lawrence River shorelines currently at risk and those experiencing high development pressure by the mid-1990s. In an effort to keep pace with technology, the mapping is being undertaken digitally at a scale of 1:2000, providing the Province and local implementing agencies with the ability to develop and utilize the unique display, modelling and educational capabilities associated with emerging geographical information systems (GIS).

Shoreline Management Plans

The preparation of Shoreline Management Plans has been underway for approximately two years. In keeping with the Province's interest in ensuring that guideline documents reflect current provincial policies, the complexities of shoreline environments and coastal processes, the needs of implementing agencies, and current and emerging technologies, an evaluation of the Guidelines for Developing Great Lakes Shoreline Management Plans and the overall direction of the shoreline management planning program has been pursued (McKeen, and Law, 1990). While providing excellent general direction to the preparation of Shoreline Management Plans, the Guidelines were not always reflective of specific shoreline conditions or management concerns. Evaluation of the Guidelines and the general direction of the provincial shoreline management program indicated that there were four individual areas where possible revisions to the Guidelines may be considered. These involve the technical, policy-oriented, administrative and the public information and education aspects of the Guidelines and program.

A perception that the Province was advocating the littoral cell concept as the one single means of delineating the limits of a Shoreline Management Plan created some concern. For certain stretches of shoreline where littoral cells do not exist (i.e . embayment beaches, rocky and/or structurally hardened shorelines), particularly in the northern portions of the Great Lakes, questions arose as to the means of defining the limits of the Shoreline Management Plan. In such areas, the Guidelines suggest the defining of plan limits based on a "comprehensive shoreline" or on stretches of shoreline having similar physical, environmental, social and economic characteristics.

Another area requiring attention is the need to improve the technical understanding and competence of shoreline management staff, public and private agencies and academic institutions. Only through creating an informed multi-disciplinary team of decision-makers can we ensure the preparation of technically sound Shoreline Management Plans.

In addition, compatibility of the Guidelines to the developing Great Lakes Flood and Erosion Policy Statement is essential to the viability of the Shoreline Management Plans. Keeping local implementing agencies informed of policy-oriented directions ensures that the inter-relationship between provincial policy and the Shoreline Management Plans remains consistent.

Administratively, there is a need to ensure the acceptance of the selected shoreline management alternatives by the general public. Public perceptions of government over-regulation and loss of riparian rights continues to require attention by all levels of government and particularly local implementing agencies. For example, do the rights of a single shoreland owner to install structural measures supersede that of an adjacent shoreland owner who may be detrimentally impacted or that of "provincial interests" in minimizing risk to life and property, and in minimizing the adverse environmental, social and economic consequences of such works?

To date, participation in current shoreline management planning projects suggests a limited understanding of the dynamics of coastal processes, a strong reliance on short-term structural or technical "fixes" to shoreline problems, a perceived notion that lake regulation will solve all flood and erosion problems on Lakes Huron and Erie indefinitely, and a "not on my lake" syndrome where residents on the lower Great Lakes are advocating increased storage of water on Lake Superior without detailed consideration of the consequences along that lakeshore.

In resolving these concerns, the promotion of public awareness, understanding and acceptance of selected management strategies is of key importance. Historically, public participation in shoreline management planning has tended to focus more on contributing to the review and selection of management strategies and/or to being the beneficiaries of information and education activities rather than on the development of management alternatives. Although the Guidelines suggest that "it may be desirable to inform/seek input from the public" the manner of and emphasis placed on seeking public involvement is left to the discretion of the local shoreline management agency.

The Guidelines do require, however, that each Shoreline Management Plan outline a public information program involving methods of informing the public and in promoting public involvement in the actual implementation of selected shoreline management strategies. For the Guidelines to provide detailed direction on the manner in which the complexities of local shoreline management issues are to be addressed would not be only impossible but impractical. As an alternative, to ensure flexibility of application to the complexity of shoreline management issues within the study area, to the needs of the general public, and to the fiscal realities of local implementing agencies, the Guidelines provide only general direction on the content of the public information program.

In conclusion, the Guidelines generally have provided sound overall direction to local implementing agencies in the preparation of shoreline management plans. Despite the broad nature of the planning process identified, the Guidelines have been developed in such a manner as to provide sufficient flexibility to recognize unique or specific shoreline characteristics. Strengthening the Guidelines through periodic revisions in response to shifts in policy direction, to advances in technical knowledge and understanding of coastal processes, and to changes in legislative and administrative implementation mechanisms, will ensure the continued viability and utility of all the Shoreline Management Plans.

Shoreline Geographical Information System

Over the past several months the Province has been examining various strategies to improve the capabilities of local implementing agencies in developing and implementing shoreline management plans and the overall policies of the provincial shoreline management program (Law, 1990). Although the benefits of a GIS appear numerous, one must first clarify and confirm what and how a GIS can be utilized. A GIS is basically a computer-based "tool" which captures, displays and manipulates geographically-referenced data and which allows the user to work with spatial data in solving management problems. In addition, a GIS permits the integration of data from many sources in a wide range of formats, enabling the construction of versatile and flexible geographical models in a quick, cost-effective manner.

The interactive capability of a GIS system is one of its strongest "appeals" to local implementing agencies within the Province. Agencies are required to provide never ending amounts of detail to an unquenchable public. The ability of a GIS to analyze or explore relationships among spatial data sets, to identify locations which meet specified criteria, and to assess the impact of proposed projects or actions, are definite assets to those responsible for the development and assessment of shoreline management strategies, particularly, those agencies which are heavily involved in the plan input and review process.

Provincially speaking, the ability to ensure compatible and consistent application of provincial policies across jurisdictional boundaries is another major benefit a GIS has to offer. Through the use of a common GIS the potential also exists for providing a mechanism to establish standards for data collection and assessment through the creation of standard database formats and assessment subroutines. In addition, the GIS provides the ability to formulate standardized reporting and presentation standards to facilitate ease of communication locally, regionally and provincially. As such, implementation of a common GIS will not only improve communication between local agencies but will also assist regional and provincial offices in assessing the success and future needs of the shoreline management program on either a regional or provincial basis (Law, 1990).

Great Lakes Basin Management

One philosophical change in the direction that the provincial shoreline management program has taken in recent months is a shift to increased participation in "basin management" approaches and programs. This is evidenced by increased emphasis on communication between Ontario and the other Great Lakes Basin, federal, provincial and state agencies on matters of mutual interest.

The key provincial interest in this "shift" in program direction is the sharing of technical knowledge and the pursuance of joint or cooperative studies, sessions and programs dealing with a wide range of shoreline management issues. These include: the development and sharing of compatible databases; the development of cooperative GIS applications and models for local, regional and provincial implementation; a sharing of technical knowledge and understanding in the areas of coastal processes; the definition, calculation and delineation of flood and erosion hazards; the identification of shoreline management strategies; and the examination and assessment of the merits and impacts of non-structural and structural shoreline management alternatives.

Each of the above "interests" are intended to be pursued through the implementation of a series of Great Lakes Shoreland Management Workshops, the possible establishment of a Bi-National Great Lakes GIS Information Centre, and through the strengthening of existing and developing communication linkages among each of the Canadian and American state, provincial, and federal agencies bordering the Great Lakes - St. Lawrence River system.

Beyond the creation of new lines of communication, the Province actively participates in a number of boards, commissions, task groups and advisory committees dealing with a wide range of Great Lakes Basin water quantity and hazard management issues. These include the issue-oriented Task Groups established by the Great Lakes Commission, observer status on the Council of Great Lakes Governors Board, and participating as technical advisors, members or observers on the various Great Lakes Control Boards and associated Water Advisory Committees.

One major study currently underway on which the Province has been and will continue to be an active participant, is the International Joint Commission (IJC) Reference which is examining the Impacts of Fluctuating Water Levels. Participation in the Reference is viewed as providing the Province with an opportunity to examine critically shoreline management alternatives applied throughout the Basin, to influence the direction analysis may take, and to work jointly with other government agencies in the development of shoreline management strategies for possible future implementation of shoreline management programs. The aim is that the Reference put forward recommendations which are consistent with provincial/state interests, which are compatible with administrative and/or legislative mandates of local, regional and provincial/state implementing agencies, and which are compatible with provincial/state shoreline management program directions.

Beyond promoting the relevance of the Reference recommendations to provincial program interests, there is the matter of maintaining consistency in approach and in the information and messages being directed to the general public. The public often does not differentiate between municipal, provincial, federal and bi-national governmental mandates. As such, government agencies are often all viewed as being directly connected. The assumption is often made, therefore, that what is recommended by one level of government must have been agreed to and as such must be implemented by all other levels of government. Through active participation in the current IJC Reference, the Province is endeavoring to ensure that recommendations put forward by the IJC are in fact supported by, implementable through, and consistent with provincial mandates and shoreline management program interests.

Conclusions

Reference has been made throughout this paper to the considerable progress which has been made in the development, refinement and implementation of the provincial shoreline management program. Much, however, remains to be done. The overall goals and objectives of the provincial shoreline management program, although remaining essentially the same, will in the future, involve the examination and utilization of emerging technologies in the areas of technical analysis, modelling, mapping, GIS, and communication. Such an evolution in approach and program implementation is necessary if shoreline management programs are to maintain a proactive, rather than reactive, "crisis management" philosophy. Active participation in the development of shoreline management strategies at all levels of government, including internationally; interest in developing a more informed network of shoreline resource management users, administrators, shoreline owners and the general public; and, the desire to develop and maintain a provincial shoreline management program which is reflective and consistent with local, regional and provincial interests; will all collectively enable the Province to pursue a path toward effective shoreline management now and in the future.

REFERENCES

Ontario Ministry of Natural Resources (1987) *Guidelines for Developing Great Lakes Shoreline Management Plans,* Conservation Authorities and Water Management Branch, Toronto, Ontario.

McKeen, P.L. and Law, M.N. (1990) *Provincial Guidelines to Great Lakes Shoreline Management Plans,* Proceedings of the Symposium on International and Transboundary Water Resources Issues. Joint Canadian Water Resources Association and American Water Resources AssociationConference, Toronto, Ontario, April 1990, pp.205-211.

Law, M.N. (1990) *Application of GIS to Local Shoreline Management Plans,* Proceedings of Flood Plain Management Conference, Toronto, Ontario, March 1990, paper no.56.

Functional Group 2 (1989) A Spatial Perspective on Description, Process and Impact, *Annex B: Living With the Great Lakes: Challenges and Opportunities,* International Joint Commission Water Levels Reference Study, pp. 140-159.

Evaluation of Ontario Conservation Authority Shore Development Regulations

REID D. KREUTZWISER and M. JAN SLAATS

REID D. KREUTZWISER and M. JAN SLAATS
Department of Geography, University of Guelph
Guelph, Ontario

Introduction

The Great Lakes shorelines provide many opportunities for housing, recreation and industrial development and use. Waterfront properties are often sold at premium prices due to their desirability. However, shoreline development is also constrained by flooding during storms and/or high lake levels, and by erosion. As a result of these hazards, property damages have been rising during periods of high lake levels (Table 1). While differences in lake levels and storm activity during the last three high water episodes influenced damages, overall damage increased in large measure as a function of increased development on flood- and erosion-prone shorelines (Kreutzwiser, 1987).

Table 1. Ontario Lake Erie shoreline property damage in constant 1985 dollars. (Kreutzwiser, 1987, p.151).

High Lake Level Episode	Property Damage
May '51 - April '52	$3,300,000
November '72 - October '73	$10,800,000
January - December '85	$26,300,000

Individual property owners may fail to develop or manage their land in a manner that is compatible with natural hazards. Such mismanagement shifts the real cost of their land use to the community or to government. In response, government, charged with the responsibility of providing for safety and general welfare, then takes actions to manage hazard areas to minimize these costs to the community (Baker and McPhee, 1975).

Following the most recent episode of Great Lakes flooding (1985-86), and upon recommendation of the Ontario Shoreline Management Review Committee, the Ontario Government initiated a Shoreline Management Program (1986). As part of this shoreline management program, Ontario Conservation Authorities (CAs) were mandated in 1988 to implement shoreline development regulations. Controlling filling, construction and alterations to shorelines, such development control had previously been a municipal responsibility. The shift in responsibility reflected recommendations from the Ontario Shoreline Management Review Committee to the Ministers of Natural Resources and Municipal Affairs. Evidence showed that riverine flood damages had successfully been reduced by CA regulations, and many municipalities were apparently unwilling to reduce hazard susceptible development aggressively (Kreutzwiser, 1988).

Since 1988, four CAs have implemented shore development regulations, while five others have worked towards their implementation. In light of expanding CA regulation of the Great Lakes shoreline, this study evaluates existing regulation programs to determine if and why they have been successful or unsuccessful in controlling hazard shoreline development. The research focussed on the regulation process (how do the regulations work?) and on the outcome (do the regulations succeed in meeting their objectives?). This evaluation aims to benefit CAs which have yet to implement shoreline development regulations.

Methodology

In April 1991, all CAs bordering the Great Lakes were surveyed to determine the status of regulation implementation (Slaats and Kreutzwiser, 1993). We discovered that only four CAs (Sault Ste. Marie, Essex Region, Metropolitan Toronto and Region and Napanee Region) had regulations in place. Of these four, the Essex Region Conservation Authority (ERCA) and the Metropolitan Toronto and Region Conservation Authority (MTRCA) were selected for case study based on the following selection criteria: a) time since regulation implementation;

b) types of development activities regulated, c) flood and erosion susceptibility of the shorelines; and d) access to CA permit files. Permit files were the principal data source, since the regulations are implemented using a permitting process. In addition, two questionnaires were designed to survey regulation program staff at the selected CAs and to survey shore property owners who had received shoreline development permits under the regulation.

After study area selection, an evaluation framework was designed to evaluate both the process and outcome of the regulations using distinct criteria. This evaluation framework had eight criteria (Table 2). These evaluation criteria were selected on the basis of their relevancy to assessing regulatory success or lack of success. We focussed on potential problems that could impede effective regulatory control of indiscriminate hazard shoreline development.

Table 2. Evaluation criteria selected to assess CA regulations

Process Criteria	Outcome Criteria
Clarity	Regulation Effectiveness
Comprehensiveness	Enforcement Effectiveness
Stringency	Penalty Provision and Sanction Effectiveness
Commitment of Staff	Regulation Equity

A justification for the selection of the above evaluation criteria follows.

Process Evaluation Criteria

Clarity

Effective implementation of regulations depends on clear, precise specification of program goals (Englander et al., 1977; Rutman, 1977; Rosenbaum, 1981; Crichton and Kreutzwiser, 1985). Without clarity in stated goals, regulation administrators may not have a sufficient legal basis to implement effective regulations. Since it focuses on the basis for regulation, clarity of program goals was selected as an evaluation criterion.

Comprehensiveness

Insufficient regulatory authority has been cited as a factor which can impede effective regulation (Englander et al., 1977). Geographic limitations of local jurisdiction or lack of regulatory powers have been identified as reasons why local government agencies may improperly manage coastal hazard areas (Englander et al., 1977; Kreutzwiser, 1988). On the basis of these findings, regulation comprehensiveness was selected as an evaluation criterion. Comprehensiveness assessed the spatial jurisdiction and the development activities that could be controlled by the CA.

Stringency

Stringency was selected as a process evaluation criterion because it influences the effective outcome of the regulations. Other research (Sabatier, 1977; Rosenbaum, 1981; Crichton and Kreutzwiser, 1985) reported that a focus on stringency could reveal permissiveness of the regulations. Permissive regulations demand little change in the regulated group's behaviour, while stringent regulations may require those regulated to adopt significantly modified behaviour (Rosenbaum, 1981). The degree of change demanded of those regulated will influence the need for enforcement, and ultimately the success of the regulation in achieving its goals.

Staff Commitment

Two factors, related to staff commitment, may influence the regulation's effectiveness. First, a lack of funds and, second, a lack of properly trained and educated personnel are both cited as potential impediments to effective regulation (Englander et al., 1977; Crichton and Kreutzwiser, 1985; Parry, 1989). Regulation can be expensive and labor intensive, therefore, inadequate funding and staffing can impede effective implementation. The staff commitment criterion was selected with a focus on staff training and experience, funding, and distribution of responsibility for the administration of regulations.

Outcome Evaluation Criteria

In addition to the above process criteria, four outcome evaluation criteria were selected to assess the regulation's impact on development of hazard shorelines. The following criteria evaluate the regulation's effectiveness:

Regulation Effectiveness

Effectiveness was selected as an evaluation criterion for it assessed the regulation's accomplishments in controlling hazard shoreline development. This criterion has been used in previous research by Jessen et al. (1983) in assessing land-use regulations along coastal wetlands in Lake Erie's Long Point area.

Enforcement Effectiveness

Regulations must be enforced to be effective (Mitchell et al., 1978). Not all owners or users of regulated shoreline property comply voluntarily, or even know about the regulation that affects them (Parry, 1989). Therefore, CA enforcement efforts influence the regulation's potential effectiveness and were evaluated with the enforcement effectiveness criterion.

Penalty Provision and Effectiveness of Sanctions

Closely related to enforcement are penalty provision and sanction effectiveness. Penalties are seen as disincentives to violations of the regulations (Sabatier, 1977; Crichton and Kreutzwiser, 1985; Parry 1989). Therefore, weak penalties may increase violations and reduce the regulation's effectiveness, conversely, strong penalties likely enhance compliance. Therefore, penalty provision and sanction effectiveness were selected as an evaluation criterion.

Regulation Equity

The perception of the regulation's fairness by those regulated can further influence the effectiveness of the regulations. To be accepted by those regulated, the regulation must be consistently and evenly applied. If people who comply with the regulation find that others do not comply, public support for the regulation may deteriorate (Parry, 1989). Therefore, equity could influence the effectiveness of the regulation, and was selected as the final evaluation criterion.

For each evaluation criterion, critical questions and rating systems were developed. For example, to evaluate regulation *stringency*, we asked: How permissive are the regulations? Then, we categorized data from the CA permit files into the following three categories:

a) Stringent: all development excluded.
b) Moderately Stringent: only flood- and erosion-proofed development permitted.
c) Lenient: development proposals are exempted or variances are made.

As both the ERCA and the MTRCA issued permits to allow flood- and erosion-proofed shoreline development, they were rated moderately stringent.

Findings

Evaluative ratings were synthesized for each criterion and for both the ERCA and MTRCA.

The Regulation Process

The clarity evaluation revealed no differences between the ERCA and the MTRCA. Both had clear regulation goals to implement the regulations. The CA Act and CA policy documents contained the regulation goals and outlined program policy.

A synthesis of comprehensiveness resulted in moderately comprehensive ERCA and MTRCA ratings. The ERCA regulations controlled development along only 15% (19 km) of shoreline. In effect, shoreline stretches at the outlets of rivers were only regulated. However, this spatial limitation changed in October 1991, when the ERCA received government approval to regulate the entire shoreline within the ERCA jurisdiction. This expansion occurred after data for this research were obtained. The MTRCA had only moderately comprehensive development controls, since the regulations could only effectively control filling and alterations to shorelines but not construction activity.

In terms of the stringency evaluation, both the ERCA and MTRCA rated moderately stringent as described above.

The staff commitment evaluation showed that qualified and committed staff performed regulation work, however, both CAs suffered from under-staffing and low budget allocations.

The Regulation Outcome

In terms of regulation effectiveness, the Authorities granted permits for all applications. While resulting in a rating of not effective, this indicator was of less importance given that virtually all permits (99%) were issued with conditions. A closer examination of these conditional permits revealed that the Authorities effectively reduced flood- and erosion-prone development. The ERCA was however, not effective in informing shore property owners of the reasons why their properties were regulated. Considering all three questions, these findings indicated that, in terms of reducing flood- and erosion-susceptible shoreline development, the ERCA regulations were moderately effective, and the MTRCA regulations were effective.

The enforcement effectiveness evaluation revealed that MTRCA regulations were well enforced and, therefore, effective. MTRCA enforcement staff detected 79 % of violations while inspecting regulated areas, and 83 % of permit recipients were monitored to check for compliance to permit conditions. The ERCA regulations' enforcement was moderately effective. The ERCA monitored fewer permits (70 %) after they were issued. However, the ERCA reported fewer violations than the MTRCA.

The evaluation of penalty provision and sanction effectiveness revealed several weaknesses. The ERCA had a wide range of sanctions available (orders to remove offending fill and structures, imprisonment, fines, probation orders, and stop work orders). However, due to costly and time consuming legal proceedings, these sanctions were seldom used and were considered insufficient. The MTRCA had few sanctions available, and these were also rated insufficient, although they were very frequently imposed. If non-compliance was detected along the Lake Ontario shoreline, violation notices were issued relatively quickly (within 3 days) by the MTRCA. A synthesis of these findings points to ineffective sanctions at both Authorities.

The equity evaluation revealed that the ERCA regulations were fair. However, relatively lengthy waiting periods (47 days) for permit applicants at the MTRCA were evident, and the majority (63 %) of shore property owners did not find these waiting periods acceptable. Thus, MTRCA regulations were rated moderately equitable to equitable.

Public Opinion

In our shore property owners survey, respondents were asked to describe the purpose of the CA shoreline regulations. We assumed that if the regulation raised awareness of the need to control shoreline development among SPOs, then the regulation's effectiveness should also increase. It should be stressed that all respondents had received permits from the Authorities. In the Essex region, only 43% of respondents correctly identified the regulation's aim: "to ensure new development is protected from flood and erosion". Thirty percent of Essex region respondents "did not know" the regulation's purpose. Of Metro Toronto region respondents, two-thirds of respondents accurately described the regulations' purpose, thus, the MTRCA regulations were better understood.

During the shore property owners surveys it became apparent that if respondents knew the reason for shoreline regulations, then they also had a tendency to believe that regulations were an effective way to reduce flood and erosion damages. A chi-square test was performed to investigate a possible correlation between respondents' knowledge of the regulation purpose and their support for the regulation. The test indicated that, 19 times out of 20 (95% confidence level), 86% of shore property owners who knew about the regulations' purpose were also supportive of the regulations. In contrast, of the shore property owners who did not know the regulation purpose, only 48% were supportive.

Conclusions

The following conclusions summarize the research findings:

- To date, the implementation of development regulations along Ontario's Great Lakes shoreline has been uneven. This will likely remain, unless all CAs work towards shoreline development regulations.
- A lack of clarity and comprehensiveness in the CA Act with regard to shoreline regulations and penalties, combined with limited budgets and staff allocations, have reduced regulation effectiveness. The Conservation Authority mandate to regulate shoreline development was clearly defined in CA internal documents, but was less clear in the Conservation Authorities Act. McKeen and Law (1991) have recently also called attention to this issue. The deficiency had important implications for the regulation program at the MTRCA. Construction activity could not be regulated on flood- and erosion-prone shorelines because the CA Act had not defined the 'regional storm' (producing regional floods) for Lake Ontario. Spatially, shoreline regulations implemented by the Essex Region

Conservation Authority (ERCA) were not comprehensive, as they only applied to shorelines along river outlets. Their spatial extent became comprehensive in 1991 when regulations were expanded to the entire ERCA shoreline.

- Enforcement of the regulations has generally been effective. However, insufficiently strong penalties provided in the CA Act, (maximum imprisonment 3 months or a $1000 fine), have not deterred potential violators. This lack of deterrence likely contributed to a frequent violations (38 per 100 development projects) in the MTRCA jurisdiction.

- Qualified Authority staff are committed to shoreline regulations. Enforcement effectiveness, particularly the follow up inspections of permit recipients, was impaired by understaffed enforcement sections with limited budgets. In addition, ERCA convictions of regulation violators suffered as a result of limited budgets.

- Shoreline development regulations implemented by the ERCA and MTRCA have been moderately effective in reducing flood- and erosion-susceptible shoreline development. Rather than prohibiting shoreline development outright, CA regulations conditionally allow development provided it is flood or erosion proofed.

- The regulations were equitable at the ERCA. However, at the MTRCA, the long permit approval times, which are partly attributable to under staffing, reduced regulation equity for shoreline property owners. Regulation of fill activity and shoreline alteration works, while not controlling construction further reduced MTRCA regulation equity.

- Shore property owners were more likely to support the regulations if they were aware of the purpose of the regulations. This finding indicated that through public information campaigns, the CAs could increase support for regulatory programs.

- In comparison to Ontario municipal shoreline regulations, which were studied by Jessen et al. (1983) and Kreutzwiser (1988), the CA regulations are more comprehensive in scope, that is in the range of activities controlled. The CA regulations also proved more stringent than the municipal regulations. Furthermore, with full responsibility for the regulations and with fewer commenting agencies, the CA permit approval process was more efficient than municipal regulation process.

The above conclusions indicate that Conservation Authorities are well suited to the regulation of Great Lakes shoreline development. In contrast, Ontario municipalities have not effectively controlled shoreline development, and should, therefore, support Conservation Authorities of which they are members, to control development of flood- and erosion-prone shorelines efficiently and effectively.

Recommendations

1) Conservation Authorities which have not planned to implement shoreline development regulations should be encouraged to do so by the Ministry of Natural Resources and by member municipalities, if uneven implementation of a provincial shoreline management policy is to be avoided.

2) The Conservation Authorities Act requires a clarification of terms to improve implementation of the Act by regulators and interpretation by those regulated. The following require clarification: the definition of 'fill' and 'structure', and the definition of flood-prone Great Lakes shorelines. The 'regional storm' and 'regional flood' definitions should be changed to a 1:100 year flood elevation plus wave uprush definition. The latter concept would be more applicable to Great Lakes flooding.

3) CA Act penalties should be strengthened to discourage those who contravene shoreline development regulations. Fines should be increased and should be applicable for each day in which the violation occurs or persists.

4) CAs should increase efforts to inform and educate shoreline property owners about regulations if they are to secure greater support for these development regulations.

REFERENCES

Baker, E.J. and J.G. McPhee (1975) *Land use management and regulation in hazardous areas: a research assessment*, Boulder, Colorado: University of Colorado, Institute of Behavioural Science.

Crichton, L.M. and R.D. Kreutzwiser (1985) *An Evaluation of State Forest Practice Legislation in the United States with Implications for Ontario*, Report for Ontario Ministry of Natural Resources, Guelph, Ontario: Department of Geography, University of Guelph.

Englander, E., J. Feldmann and M. Hershman (1977) "Coastal Zone Problems: A Basis for Evaluation," *Coastal Zone Management Journal*, 3(3), 217-236.

Jessen, S., J.C. Day and J.G. Nelson (1983) "Assessing Land-Use Regulations in Coastal Wetlands: The Case of the Long Point Area, Lake Erie, Ontario," *Coastal Zone Management Journal*, 11(1-2), 91-115.

Kreutzwiser, R.D. (1987) "Managing the Great Lakes Shoreline Hazard," *Journal of Soil and Water Conservation*, 42(3), 150-154.

Kreutzwiser, R.D. (1988) "Municipal Land Use Regulation and the Great Lakes Shoreline Hazard in Ontario," *Journal of Great Lakes Research*, 14(2), 142-47.

McKeen, P.L., and M.N. Law (1991) *Provincial Legislation and Regulatory Controls along the Shorelines of the Great Lakes - St. Lawrence River*, Toronto, Ontario: Lands and Waters Policy Branch, Ontario Ministry of Natural Resources.

Mitchell, B., J. Gardner, R. Cook and B. Veale (1978) *Physical Adjustments and Institutional Arrangements for the Urban Flood Hazard: Grand River Watershed*, Waterloo, Ontario: Department of Geography Publication Series No. 13.

Parry, C. (1989) "Focusing on Enforcement," in *Coastal Zone '89*, Vol. 5, Ed. by O.T. Magon et al, New York: American Society of Civil Engineers.

Rosenbaum, N. (1981) "Statutory Structure and Policy Implementation: The Case of Wetlands Regulation," In *Effective Policy Implementation*, Ed. by Daniel A. Mazmanian and Paul A. Sabatier. Lexington, Massachusetts: Lexington Books.

Rutman, L. (1977) "Planning an Evaluation Study," in L. Rutman (ed.), *Evaluation Research Methods: A Basic Guide*, Beverly Hills, California: Sage Publications, Inc, 15-38.

Sabatier, P.A. (1977) "Regulatory Policy-Making: Toward a Framework of Analysis." *Natural Resources Journal*, 17(3), 416-459.

Slaats, M.J. and R.D. Kreutzwiser (1993) "Shoreline Development Regulations: Do They Work." *Journal of Soil and Water Conservation*, May/June, 1993, 158-165.

The Kettle Creek Conservation Authority Shoreline Management Plan

JIM McCOOB
Kettle Creek Conservation Authority
St. Thomas, Ontario

Introduction

The Kettle Creek Conservation Authority (KCCA) was one of the first conservation authorities in Ontario to complete its shoreline management plan. The plan was prepared by Philpott Associates Coastal Engineers Limited and was completed in December of 1989. It was circulated to the shoreline member municipalities in early 1990, reviewed with the public and affected landowners, and has been adopted or approved in principle by the Councils of Yarmouth and Southwold Townships and the Village of Port Stanley.

The KCCA is in a somewhat unique position of having a completed Plan available for the purposes of plan input and review and hazard land management. The document in itself is a valuable source of information regarding: the processes along our shoreline; the hazards to development that those processes present; alternative management scenarios; environmental considerations; and recommendations for public awareness and information. The Plan represents an approach towards integrated resources management with input from all related resource management agencies on a platform of holistic environmental planning.

The KCCA Shoreline

The KCCA has approximately 27 kilometres of shoreline, centrally located on the north shore of Lake Erie. It is located on the western side of Littoral Cell E8 as defined by the Ministry of Natural Resources, a cell that extends from Port Glascow in the west to Long Point in the east (Figure 1). The KCCA's shoreline consists mainly of high bluff with the exception of about 3 kilometres that is within the Village of Port Stanley.

Figure 1.

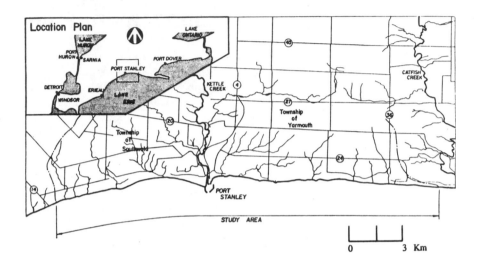

From Kettle Creek Conservation Authority Shoreline Management Plan, 1989

Within the Village there are 2 kilometres of fillet beach and approximately one kilometre of low bluff.

The high bluffs that predominate the shoreline vary in height from 37 to 40 metres. They are composed largely of Port Stanley glacial till that is a hard to very hard, silty clay and clayey silt deposit. A 3 to 4 metre layer of lacustrine clay overtops the Port Stanley till and this is overlain again by a fine sand layer that varies in thickness between 15 to 20 metres. The physiography of the bluffs is typical of cohesive bluff shorelines experiencing active erosional forces. The toe of the bluff exhibits undercutting and there are numerous, deep seated rotational slumps and gullies that may be observed at various stages of development.

Bluff recession rates along the KCCA shoreline are among the highest in the Great lakes. According to information taken from the Port Burwell litigation case and used within the KCCA Shoreline Management Plan, long term average recession rates for high bluffs located within the KCCA shoreline area range from as low as 0.65 m/yr. to a high of 4.45 m/yr. With the exception of a small (1/2 kilometre) stretch of cottages west of Port Stanley, the tablelands above the bluffs are used for agriculture or open space with no strong development pressures anticipated. The preferred management alternative of setbacks equalling 100 times the average annual recession rate plus a stable slope allowance of 3 1/2 times the bluff height, was accepted by both Yarmouth and Southwold Township councils. In fact, both townships had previously recognized the hazard faced by bluff erosion and had designated a large buffer along the bluffs, very nearly equal to the proposed setback area, as Hazard Land within their Official Plans.

The fillet beach in Port Stanley has developed as a result of the construction and extension of successive breakwaters at the mouth of the federal harbour. The beach is accreting over time, although that growth is tempered by losses of sand due mainly to severe storm activity. The influence of the breakwaters in developing the fillet beach extends to the far western end of the Village, offering an excellent recreational amenity and lure to developers. Dune growth on the beach is moderate to nonexisting and much of the beach area is subject to wave uprush flooding. Since much of the eastern portion of the beach has been historically developed and continues to be under significant development pressure, the need for realistic management options was a key theme in the development of the management plan.

The short bluff area of Port Stanley is located east of the federal harbour and is known locally as Orchard Beach. Generally the height of bluff is about 4 to 6 metres in this area. Almost the entire area is protected by various means (mostly concrete blocks and rubble) through projects completed by the owners over the years. The Shoreline Management Plan indicates that the recession rate of the low bluff area has been effectively reduced to zero as a result of the protection placed by residents. Maintenance of the existing protection is required, however, if the owners wish the protection works to continue to be effective. Further, the engineers who prepared the Plan cautioned that lowering of the nearshore lake bottom as caused by wave action could put the protection at risk by worsening the impacts of design storm conditions in this area.

Developing a Local Perspective

When the KCCA Shoreline Management Plan was developed, the Authority wanted to ensure the inclusion of a local perspective. The representatives of the three shoreline municipalities made it clear to the steering committee that while they recognized the Province's desire to have the Plan conform to the then unreleased Provincial Shoreline Policy, it also had to be sensitive to local needs and desires. If it did not, then it likely would not be supported by their Councils and the majority of the specific recommendations of the plan could never be implemented without local approval.

This position was certainly understandable to the staff of the KCCA. We recognized that while the municipalities wanted to do their share to avoid the potential property damage and threat to lives that occurred during the 1985-86 high water period, they did not want to see overly restrictive policies that would effectively sterilize land from development and cause losses in assessment. While this was true of all three shoreline municipalities, it was particularly the case for the Village of Port Stanley, which in many ways is dependent upon the beach area for much of it's economic well being. The two townships quickly recognized that effective protection of the bluff areas from erosion was neither practical nor economically feasible. The best management alternative for them was that of establishing defendable setback criteria, as they had already done within their Official Plans, and to inform landowners of the risks that were present.

Port Stanley, however, presented a very different set of management issues. First, there were two different shoreline types to look at, fillet beach and low bluff, with different management considerations for each. Criteria for new development had to be established, or a decision made on whether new development was going to be allowed at all. Then there was the multitude of existing developments and the maintenance and alterations thereof. Most existing development was older cottages, many of them built on pile foundations and likely going to require repair or replacement in the near future. Many residents were also wanting to upgrade their cottages from seasonal residences into principal residences.

In developing preferred and alternative management options for the Port Stanley area, it became increasingly clear to our steering committee that a local perspective priority had to be established if shoreline management planning was going to be implemented effectively. As a result, many of the specific recommendations within the Plan were conceived in response to local needs while still remaining sensitive to the concerns of the Province and the pending shoreline policy. I would like to present some of the ways in which these recommendations are being implemented and what the KCCA will be doing in the future to implement further recommendations of the Shoreline Management Plan.

Implementing the Plan Through Plan Input and Review

One of the first ways in which the KCCA started using the Shoreline Management Plan was in conjunction with our plan input and review responsibilities. In 1987, the Minister of Natural Resources designated conservation authorities as the lead implementing agency for delivering provincial shoreline management programs, including hazard land mapping, shoreline planning and plan input and review on matters relating to shoreline flood and erosion hazard concerns. Until the completion of the Plan, the information that was available to the Authority to draw from in responding to planning matters was limited. The KCCA had prepared the Port Stanley Protection Plan in 1986 by F.J. Reinders and Associates, but that document focused on options of structural protection, their costs, benefits and impacts, and not on the preventative options available.

With the completion of the Shoreline Management Plan in 1989, the Authority now has a comprehensive source of information on shoreline management alternatives, including various options under the preventative and protective approaches, with environmental considerations. By having that information, along with the accumulated recession rates and flood uprush data also contained in the Plan, KCCA staff now have a strong basis upon which to formulate informed, logical and realistic responses to planning proposals.

Equally important though, and significant to the overall objective of shoreline management planning, is how the Plan, and the local perspective upon which it was based, has influenced the shoreline municipalities. Since it's completion, they have included policies within their Official Plans and Zoning By-Laws which recognize setback criteria, floodproofing standards, and the requirement for the Conservation Authority to review and approve all building plans. It is our belief that without the strong local involvement and commitment by the Authority to developing a Plan with a local perspective, such policies would not be approved.

Related to the plan input and review functions of the Authority, another recommendation in the Shoreline Management Plan was the requirement for an impact statement to be prepared by proponents of new development within the regulatory shoreland zone. The impact statement is a document that addresses all aspects of the project and is circulated by the Authority to the other reviewing agencies. It is intended to address, as applicable, issues of site location; site description including environmentally significant features; coastal conditions (design parameters); description of proposed works; design calculations;

construction schedule; maintenance requirements; access; and, impacts on littoral transport and the environment.

The impact statement is required to demonstrate three things. First, that there will be no increase in the long term recession rate on neighbouring properties caused by the proposed works. Second, that the proposed works will not cause damage, directly or indirectly, to adjacent structures. And third, that the proposed works will in no way have any detrimental effects on the environment. Impact statements must be prepared by a recognized expert in coastal processes, preferably an engineer.

To date, only one complete impact statement has been prepared by a developer who has proposed a series of six cottages on Edith Cavell Boulevard at the main beach of Port Stanley. The statement was prepared by Sandwell Inc. and proved to be a useful exercise as it did identify a number of issues that otherwise may have gone undetected if the development had been reviewed by someone with a lesser knowledge of coastal processes. Such things as the footing depth and design for the foundations, lot grading requirements for the development site, vegetative requirements to minimize sand depletion, and the need for a protective sand berm to break incoming waves during more severe storms were all identified. Although the developer has not as yet addressed the identified issues and is presently studying other options for the property, the Authority will retain the impact statement for future reference should the developer wish to reactivate his interest in the property.

The Authority is somewhat discretionary in it's requirements for an impact statement and the degree of study. For example, when we review a property at the initial contact stage, we will first determine if it is affected by flood uprush, as not all properties along the beach areas are within the limits of the uprush. A property that is not affected by flooding will certainly not have to undergo the more rigorous review that a property located within the uprush limit would have to, as there is no concern for potential flood damages or impacts to littoral drift. In such cases, an impact brief prepared by a geotechnical engineer that addresses such things as the stability of footings and foundations in the unconsolidated beach deposit could be acceptable.

The Orchard Beach Nearshore Survey

One of the six key components of any Shoreline Management Plan is that of monitoring flooding and erosion. Specifically, it involves the identification of methods to monitor local conditions affecting shoreline management. The KCCA Shoreline Management Plan proposed a monitoring program to include such things as: updating bluff erosion rates using digital mapping currently being prepared, and again every ten years; including monitoring plans within a dune management program; surveying wave uprush and flood levels experienced during severe storms; conducting an annual examination of the protection structures within the Little Beach and Orchard Beach areas of Port Stanley; and, monitoring downcutting of the nearshore profile in front of the Little Beach and Orchard Beach areas every 5 years.

The nearshore profile component of the monitoring program was implemented by the KCCA in 1991/92 when seven base profiles of the nearshore area in and around Port Stanley were finished. Four of the profiles were taken at Orchard Beach and Little Beach, east of the federal harbour in Port Stanley. Two were established at the main beach to the west of the harbour and one was taken at Hawk Cliff, approximately four kilometres east of the Village.

The engineers who developed the Shoreline Management Plan had determined that the recession rates at Orchard Beach had been reduced to near zero as a result of the protection efforts of the shoreline residents, who had constructed various concrete rubble and concrete block revetments along the low, 3 to 4 metre bluff that runs the length of the subreach. The engineers qualified these comments by stating that the properties were not at risk at **present water levels**. If the nearshore water depths were to increase, however, design storm conditions in the nearshore area would worsen and the potential for damage to the protective revetment and the properties behind them would increase.

The engineers suggested that two management alternatives that could be implemented to ensure the long term viability of the protective works. First they recommended that the residents be encouraged to maintain the protection, at their cost, and to make certain modifications including the use of filter fabric under the revetment. They also suggested that although the Authority was unable to affect such things as the rise and fall of static water levels in the lake, we could establish a program to monitor nearshore bottom elevations and determine if there was any lowering through wave action.

In order for the Authority to monitor the nearshore lake levels effectively, four monitoring stations were established between Little Beach and the east end of the Orchard Beach area. An Ontario Land Surveyor was hired to establish the benchmarks for each station based upon Geodetic Survey of Canada datum, and then plot the base profiles for each to a bottom elevation of 169.0 meters GSC. Each profile could then be re-established at approximately five year intervals and an assessment made to determine if the bottom level is lowering. If it is, then arrangements can be made between the Authority and the municipality to replenish the sand levels with, for example, sand dredgate approved by MOE and obtained from periodic dredging of the federal harbour. Also, shoreline landowners can be forewarned of increased protection needs and take appropriate actions with approval of the Authority and MNR.

The two profiles that were taken at the main beach west of the harbour were done so as to provide base data to monitor not only the nearshore lake bottom levels, but also the levels of the low dunes in the foreshore area of the beach. This would give the Authority some indication of the potential impacts a design storm could have on the beach area in terms of flooding and wave damage. Furthermore, over the long term we may be able to better determine the rate of accretion of the fillet beach.

The profile at Hawk Cliff was done to establish an erosion monitoring station for this popular raptor viewing area. Recent gully erosion at the end of the road allowance that serves as an access to Hawk Cliff has become severe, and a number of massive slumps occurred there between 1990 and 1992. The worst of these was the loss of a 40 foot wide by 100 foot long piece of the tableland in one location.

Flood Uprush Lookup Tables

Another project that was recommended in the KCCA Shoreline Management Plan was to prepare a lookup table of wind speeds and directions along with the potential storm surge and wave uprush levels that could be generated. This project was designed to expand the Authority's flood forecasting and warning capabilities beyond the riverine to include the lakeshore area. This project was felt to be particularly important since Port Stanley has a strong record of lakeshore flooding with little or no warning capabilities.

When the project was first introduced to MNR and some of the neighbouring CA's, it received mixed reviews. MNR felt that such forecasting could be done more cost effectively on a lake wide basis with information disseminating from a central clearing house such as the flood forecast centre or similar agency. An ad-hoc committee of representatives of the other Lake Erie CA's was created to explore this option. However, the majority of the other CA's felt that they could probably calculate their own surge and uprush levels, to a satisfactory level of accuracy of ≈ 2 feet in vertical elevation, by using computer programs made available from Environment Canada and wind speed and direction data taken from gauges set up in many local areas.

The KCCA didn't disagree with these suggestions. We felt that we had good reasons to follow through on the lookup table approach. First, we wanted the predictions to be as accurate as possible. Due to the very flat topography of the fillet beach, a vertical accuracy of $\approx$ 2 feet could mean a difference of tens of metres horizontally. With approximately 200 properties located within the flood risk area, the Authority needed a higher degree of accuracy to determine exactly which properties would be affected under given storm conditions.

The second reason for wanting to proceed with the lookup tables approach reflected an internal, administrative consideration. Being a small Authority with few staff, everyone shares in the flood forecasting and monitoring duties. We had to have a system in place that any staff member could use with a minimal amount of instruction. Although the consultant will provide the final product as a user friendly computer model, the terms of reference require the preparation of tables that will be useable by those staff who are not familiar or comfortable with the use of the computers.

The lookup tables are currently being prepared by Milo Sturm at Shoreplan Engineering. After calibrating the surge and uprush models to reflect more realistically nearshore conditions in Port Stanley, the consultant will prepare a table quite similar to that of a mileage chart showing distances between cities. In this case, however, the chart will cross reference the variables of wind speed on one axis and wind direction on the other. It will then provide a prediction, accurate to within $\approx$ 1", of the possible uprush elevation that can be experienced if those speeds and directions are sustained. In addition, we have asked the consultant to provide hard copy maps and corresponding digital files showing graphically the extent of flooding under selected design storms (i.e.. 1:5, 1:10, 1:20, 1:50, 1:75,1:100). We will tie the digital information into the Authority's GIS for future flood forecasting use. The project itself is due to be completed by the end of 1992 and we will be using the lookup tables as an intrinsic part of our flood forecasting and warning system.

Public Information

Public interest in shoreline management, as many of you will know, rises and falls with the level of the lakes. In times of high water, when the lake is washing away coastline and flooding out summer homes, the public will demand assistance to protect properties and legislation to prevent similar disasters from happening again. Yet when the lake levels are low, as they are now, there is as strong a cry for less government interference with property rights and less regulation.

Municipalities even forget the mistakes of the past in favour of the higher financial assessment generated by large scale, commercial and residential shoreline development.

During the preparation of the Management Plan, a questionnaire was distributed to all of the shoreline residents within the study area, to determine the level of knowledge of shoreline processes and the perceived causes. Based upon the responses received, it was apparent that the KCCA will have to continue to promote awareness of shoreline issues, the management plan, and the role that the KCCA plays in shoreline management under Provincial Policy.

The KCCA Shoreline Management Plan recognized the need for continued public awareness and recommended that a shoreline bulletin be prepared on a yearly basis to be sent to all shoreline municipalities and residents. It was suggested that the bulletin would be a part of the public information component of the Plan, intended to maintain public awareness of shoreline processes and the hazards those processes can present to the unwary property owner.

The KCCA acknowledged the recommendations of the consultants that more information was required to be delivered to shoreline residents. However, the way in which this recommendation has been implemented has differed initially from that suggested by the consultant. The KCCA is in a somewhat unique position in that we prepare our annual report in a newspaper format, with the articles being short synopses of projects that were completed during the year, summaries of the various program activities, financial statements, and so forth. The annual report is distributed to every household within the watershed so that everyone will be aware of the activities of the KCCA and it's contributions to conservation and environmental management during the past year.

For the past two years, the KCCA has included articles within it's annual report specific to the shoreline management program. The timing of the annual report's release has been ideal since it is in the spring when most people are gearing up for summer projects. The articles within the annual report have typically contained information such as:

- a reminder of the existence of the shoreline management plan and the role of the Authority in shoreline management;
- a reminder of the approvals required for work along the shoreline;
- water level forecasts (from the monthly Water Level Bulletin) for the upcoming summer;
- any new developments in the implementation of the shoreline management plan such as the nearshore survey; and

- articles dealing with recent developments in shoreline management on the Great Lakes such as research results, IJC studies and findings, major shoreline development proposals, etc.

The KCCA has found the annual report to be a very effective means of distributing information to the public on all of it's programs. Inevitably, each year after it's distribution I will receive at least a dozen telephone calls from interested landowners wanting more information. Some of these people do not even own shoreline property but are simply curious about the management program and the plan.

Continuing to Make it Work

To summarize, I hope that I have demonstrated some of the ways in which the KCCA is implementing the many recommendations of our Shoreline Management Plan under a number of it's components, including:

Prevention: through plan input and review using information contained within the Plan, and through implementation of the impact statement process;
Monitoring: through the nearshore survey in Orchard Beach and other areas around Port Stanley;
Emergency Response: through the preparation of the lakeshore flooding lookup tables; and
Public Information: through the use of the KCCA Annual Report to provide watershed residents with information on shoreline management issues.

The Kettle Creek Conservation Authority will continue to implement the Plan and it's recommendations where appropriate. For example, with the completion of our shoreline digital mapping, we will be using the SPANS GIS technology for plan input and review, combining our existing planning database with the information contained within the plan to make the preferred preventative management options that much easier to implement. Other programs, such as a dune management demonstration area on beach lands owned by the Authority, will show residents how to encourage low dune growth to provide some protection from lake flooding.

The KCCA is proud of this program and proud of the contributions that an authority of it's size has made to shoreline management. The success that we have had in implementing the Plan can be attributed to our desire to be sensitive to Provincial concerns and yet maintain a local perspective. Combine that with the ability to draw from a $10 million dollar database of shoreline processes information (developed for the Port Burwell litigation) and you have the makings of a successful program. We encourage the Province to consider this in it's development of the Shoreline Policy Statement so that this success is not jeopardized by the final policy and that we as conservation authorities can make the policy work for the betterment of shoreline management.

REFERENCE

Philpott Associates Ltd. (1989) *Kettle Creek Conservation Authority Shoreline Management Plan*, St. Thomas, Ontario.

Preparation and Implementation of Shoreline Management Plans: The Sault Ste. Marie District, Ontario

PETER J. BURTCH
Sault Ste. Marie District, Ministry of Natural Resources
Sault Ste. Marie, Ontario

Forward

Managing shoreline, whether on the Great Lakes, inland lakes and rivers or on an ocean is a major blend of matching the natural elements of energy distribution, natural processes, and ecological values with man's ever-increasing desire to change it. Managing for the future, today, requires a great deal of knowledge, understanding, common sense and above all a will to succeed, to ensure that our shorelines are managed in a sustainable way which will ensure that our heirs receive a product that is better than that which we inherited. One tool that we have found to aid us greatly in not only the day-to-day management but in long-term direction is having and using a Shoreline Management Plan. This can be shown by describing the development of the Sault Ste. Marie District Shoreline Management Plan and how its implementation helps our daily workload.

"Old" Sault Ste. Marie District Profile

The area covered by the old Sault District prior to our recent re-organization contained about 500 kilometres of Great Lakes shoreline on Lake Superior, Lake Huron, and the St. Marys River (Figure 1). It now encompasses many more kilometres, and offers a great variety of shore types and values. Approximately 97 percent of the area's shore is patented land, of which 50 per cent is subdivided. We estimate that we have a client base of 4,000 riparian owners. With that type of base and many different shore types, it soon became evident that some sort of

Figure 1. Sault Ste. Marie District

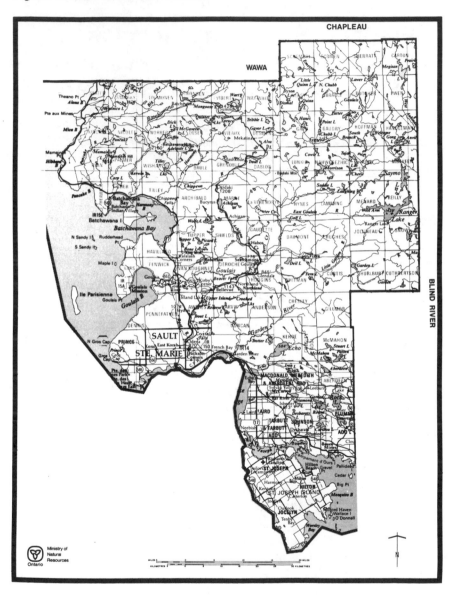

direction was needed to help our limited staff control the unregulated development which was occurring, and had resulted in the establishment of many bad habits. In many areas human actions had damaged the coastal ecology.

Why Develop a SMP?

As mentioned above, people within the planning area have been occupying the shoreline for over a century and have developed many unfortunate habits. It was strongly agreed by our staff and the general public that some sort of direction was needed. Shoreline Management in Sault St. Marie had its roots in the old Lands office in the late 70's. During the high Water levels of 1985/86 we offered a program of free technical advice for which we received over 300 requests. We saw the release of the "Guidelines for the Development of Shoreline Management Plans" by Lands and Waters Policy Branch and the subsequent funding to produce our plan as a good sign.

Like all other jurisdictions along the Great Lakes we also had many of the "standard" reasons for a plan, such as fluctuating water levels, unplanned development, poor practices, lack of understanding, and so forth. In a "nutshell" we had a lot of development pressure in an area where the public seemed receptive. We had funding and the support of our Regional and Main Offices, so we began the task of developing our plan.

The Major Components of the Sault Ste. Marie SMP

When the "Guidelines for the Development of Shoreline Management Plans" was first released our staff had small problems with the components. They could not see this document strictly as a plan identifying "Prevention, Protection and Emergency Response". It was agreed that they were very important but we felt that if we were going to produce a document that would aid our efforts in managing our coastal resource, then it had to go beyond engineering to include all of the ecological values as well. In a small sense we were "Panasonic", or just slightly ahead of our time, because it wasn't long after, that the direction of resource management in general began to stress ecological values and sustainability. Therefore, the major components of the Sault Ste. Marie District Shoreline Management Plan were: Environmental Conservation,

Prevention, Protection, Emergency Response, Public Information and Monitoring and Development Control.

The Shoreline Planning Process Production

The first step was to inventory the resource. A videotape was taken by helicopter in September of 1988. That tape, 1981 air photos and a wealth of field experience were used to break up the planning area into 39 reaches. The basis for the reach delineation was physiography, development, MNR values and past history. As the plan progressed, after well-attended public meetings, prescriptions were produced for each reach. The prescriptions addressed Protection Structures, Recreational Structures and Infrastructure. Prescriptions indicate whether a proposal is Recommended; Not Recommended; Restricted, or Prohibited.

To further help explain the prescriptions we have included a section in the plan which is referred to as "Structural Standards". This part of the plan makes it different from most resource managements plans which do not contain an educational section. We felt quite strongly that the average understanding of the complex environment along the shoreline was very limited and it was imperative that this plan provide an avenue to improve that lack of understanding. As an example, groynes are prohibited throughout the entire planning area. If our clients don't know what a groyne is, or how it affects littoral drift then we have an immediate communication problem due to no fault of the client. In addition to the Structural Standards we have also included a glossary.

Another first for this plan was the establishment of "Shoreline Environmental Protection Areas" or SEPA's as they are referred to. The SEPA acronym has been agreed to by the Ministry of Municipal Affairs. SEPA's are mostly wetlands and were introduced at a time when a Wetland Policy Statement and evaluation system was a long way from availability. Direction's 90 has since fully supported our approach to ecosystem management. The SEPA designation to date has worked very well for reviewing work permit applications, plan review and plan input. SEPA's have been included in several Municipal Official Plans within the planning area. Although SEPA's are general in nature they provide our staff, municipal staff and the public, with an upfront indication that resource values contrary to development exist in that location.

Public Participation in the Planning Process

Public consultation in the plan took place as required by the MNR planning process for the preparation of resource management plans. Public meetings at the information gathering stage, draft plan stage and the final stage occurred in three locations: Sault Ste. Marie, Desbarats, and Goulais River. They were held in these three locations in an attempt to take the plan to the people. The Draft and Final Plan meetings were purposely held during the summer months to be available to both our resident population, and our substantial non-resident population. All sessions were extremely well attended and well received. Comments such as "You should have done this years ago" were common. Our staff took advantage of the opportunity to meet the large number of shoreline owners and produced educational displays and video shows to help explain the shoreline plan and overall shoreline management. One of the most successful displays was our shoreline video. We used the videotape to show people their own property from the air, a view that many rarely see and all enjoy. In addition to the plan, we presently use our videotape almost daily to help in resource management decisions and to communicate with the public.

In addition to the public open house meetings, our staff made presentations to all organized municipalities in the planning area. The plan was discussed, a videotape of the shoreline in their municipality viewed, and the role of the municipality in shoreline management and planning was discussed.

Another major part of the public consultation effort was the establishment of the Shoreline Management Plan Public Advisory committee. Requests were sent out to local private and public organizations to nominate a representative to sit on the advisory committee. The organization included: the Ontario Federation of Anglers and Hunters, the Sault Naturalists representing the Federation of Ontario Naturalists, the Lake Superior North Shore Lake Huron Property Coalition, the Sault Ste. Marie Real Estate Association, the Sault Ste. Marie Construction Assoc., the Sault North Planning Board (representing the unorganized townships north of Sault Ste. Marie), the Sault Ste. Marie Region Conservation Authority, and the Ministries of Environment, Tourism and Recreation, and Municipal Affairs. The meetings were held every Wednesday evening for eleven weeks in which time the entire shoreline of the planning area was reviewed and prescriptions for sustainable development agreed to.

As you can see, a great deal of effort went into public consultation. The benefits of that effort are just now being realized. The occurrences of the public informing our staff that they "didn't know they needed a permit" is on the decline. The quality of applications is improved and the public's acceptance of our direction is improving. We feel this is strong evidence that the battle to manage the shore properly will not be won through legislation and enforcement — although this definitely has it's place — but will be won through education, co-operation and a realistic sustainable direction.

Public Reaction to the SMP

Three sets of public open houses took place in three locations during each phase of the plan. Overall, we had over three hundred attend the first set of Background Information sessions. Over three hundred and fifty attended the second Draft Plan sessions. Over four hundred and twenty attended the Final Plan sessions. All forms of media were utilized, including news spots on the local television and radio stations.

The public reaction was overwhelmingly supportive. Many wanted to see a similar approach for inland lakes. We received, and continue to receive, many positive comments on how well the plan is put together, in that it is easy to understand and provides an excellent educational section in the form of the "Structural Standards". Local contractors use the plan prior to committing to a job. Local Realtors inform potential buyers of shore reach prescriptions, in order to avoid customer disappointments. Municipal staff were also given a copy, and now use it to inform their clients of our direction.

Overall the plan has been well received. We still have a lot of work to do, and a lot of issues to resolve, but by having the plan in place we have a sound base to stand on, and a definite direction to follow.

Current Plan Implementation

The plan has now been completed and in use for two years. It has provided our staff with the direction it was intended to. The main avenue followed in implementation on a one-to-one basis is the issuance of Work Permits under the Public Lands Act, RSO 1990. We are finding the SMP "dove-tails" very well with the manner in which work permits have conditions applied to them, and in situations when a work permit must be declined or modified. The SMP provides a platform for consistent and fair decisions. It has saved staff travel time and helped speed up the processing time of work permits and/or replies. It is used actively as an educational tool.

The SMP also complements other resource management plans, such as the Sault Ste. Marie District Fisheries Plan, and is a great asset to the plan input/review program. As mentioned above, contractors, realtors, developers, municipal officials, and landowners in general can now benefit from the information contained in the plan. In short, it has made shoreline management consistent, fair and organized, which has made our job a lot easier and a lot more effective.

The Sault Ste. Marie District Shoreline Management Plan

In summary I'd like to emphasize that the Sault Ste. Marie District Shoreline Management Plan is a resource management plan which integrates the principles of ecological management, fisheries, engineering and land disposition. The document does not follow the "standard" methodology for resource management plans, and as a result, is user-friendly and effective. It has been well received by the public and our business partners. Including "Structural Standards" as part of the text has helped many to understand their projects better. The plan is easily expandable. Our next expansion is to the east to do the new "North Channel Area" of the revised Sault District (due to the recent re-organization of the MNR). Only the reaches and prescriptions will need to be produced.

Daily Workload Implementation

We in Sault Ste. Marie are a typical MNR office in that we suffer the same financial constraints and staff needs as is common in all of our field offices. With respect to shoreline we do differ slightly and in fact could be considered to be on the "leading edge" of front line (one-on-one) shoreline program delivery in Ontario. So how do we do it?

We start with a staff position with a job specification as a "Shoreline Technician". Responsibility in that position is for the planning, organizing and implementation of the shoreline program in three Areas in the Sault Ste. Marie District. That covers an area from just south of Wawa on Lake Superior to just west of Spanish on Lake Huron which represents quite a sizeable section of the coastline for one person. The Shoreline Technician works with the Superintendent of Lake Superior Provincial Park regarding shore related matters and the Lake Superior Provincial Park regarding shore related matters. The Lake Superior Park Master Plan sets the overall direction for the natural Environment theme.

Looking south from Lake Superior Park to the City of Sault Ste. Marie, the existing Sault Ste. Marie District Shoreline Management Plan is in place to guide decision making and assist in education. The SMP is also in place along the St. Marys River and on the Lake Huron shore east to Bruce Mines. The Sault Ste. Marie Region Conservation Authority also has a SMP and administers it within their boundary, namely the

boundary of the City of Sault Ste. Marie. The Spanish area has traditionally been administered by the Blind River Office of MNR. No SMP
exists at present for this area. The Shoreline Technician will visit the
area on a required basis, and deal with the workload with appropriate
Area staff. It is hoped that the existing Sault Ste. Marie District
Shoreline Management Plan will eventually be expanded to include the
North Channel Area of the new Sault Ste. Marie District.

Having given the overall picture we can now turn to detail. We, in
MNR collectively use Section 14 of the Public Lands Act RSO 1990 to
issue a Work Permit to authorize work on shorelines anywhere in
Ontario. This requirement fits well with the administration of a SMP.
Presently in the Sault Ste. Marie District, both in Blind River and in Sault
Ste. Marie, Work Permit Review Teams exist to review and make recommendations on all work permits including logging, bridge and culvert
installations, building construction, plan review, and so forth. These
teams, made up of staff from many program areas, are required to meet
weekly. Most applications for shoreline work are taken to the weekly
meetings by the Shoreline Technician who brings the field to the meeting via video tape. A decision is made upon receipt of an application as
to whether a field visit is required. If so, the Shoreline Technician sets
his own schedule according to work area. That is usually one day a
week north and one or two days east. A typical day out would have
anywhere from six to fifteen sites to visit.

Proposals are then reviewed by the Shoreline Technician for small
minor projects. The review team, in conjunction with the prescriptions
in the SMP for that particular reach and in consideration of other values
such as fisheries, will render its decision on the larger, more complex
projects. Should the proposal be approved conditions are developed at
that time and documented. The permit is then formalized by our clerical
staff and returned to the Technician for a final review. It is then signed
by the Technician who is an Officer under the Public Lands Act and can
authorize work.

The key to success is to keep the process flowing, to keep the lines of
communication open and to be ready to attend the weekly meetings in
an organized manner. The use of a video camera has been the greatest
tool to bring the field into the office to assist resource management decisions and to accumulate a valuable record data base. The team
approach, the SMP, and the technology of the video camera have been
the three main driving mechanisms to help the Sault Ste. Marie District
run a shoreline program over such a large and diverse area. That
approach has also enabled staff to turn most work permits around in
less then 10 working days.

Enforcement and monitoring occur as required by the individual situation. This is accomplished jointly between the Shoreline Technician and the Conservation Officer in the Area. The use of a video camera also assists greatly in keeping honesty in the client's mind. Aerial video tape taken in 1988 and in 1991 are also useful in identifying unauthorized work, physical changes (natural and man caused), offshore effects, habitat, building locations, and other changes.

Education, at the present is by the use of individual copies of the shoreline reach prescriptions and copies of pertinent structural standards sheets, along with other MNR produced brochures. One of the best one-on-one teachers is to have the applicant on site at the time of inspection or have the applicant drop by our office and review a video tape of his/her property taken on site or from the air inventory record with the Shoreline Technician.

Other ways of getting the work out include visits to Municipal Council Meetings, attending as guest speakers at conferences and evening meetings of interest groups, lecturing at Sault College to third year forestry and water resources students and developing a working relationship with contractors, developers and realtors. A news letter and video taped information packages are planned for the future. Staff have been successful in the past in getting on local and regional television shows promoting shoreline management. The latest will air December 5, 1992 on the MCTV-CTV program "Down to Earth: dealing with wetlands and how they fit into the ecology of the shoreline, expanded to give reasons why individual property owners have biological responsibility to the environment in front of their property. In short it's very much education at each and every opportunity.

Shoreline Management Futures

A lot of what is possible in the future relates directly to funding. We are currently setting up an Oracle based Work Permit system that should enable more staff to access and produce Work Permits. The program will store and retrieve data, increasing the efficiency of the program. We dream of the day when all of our data in the SMP can be brought together with the Oracle program into a GIS capable of displaying all that needs to be known of a particular site quickly and accurately. If that does not happen, life will go on. We all hope that having a program directed by a SMP will make it possible for us to be the "stewards" of the land and have a positive effect on the future for our children and our children's children.

REFERENCE

Ontario Ministry of Natural Resources (1991) *Shoreline Management Plan Sault Ste. Marie District*, Sault Ste. Marie, Ontario.

Development of the Ausable-Bayfield Conservation Authority Shoreline Management Plan

PATRICK DONNELLY
Ausable-Bayfield Conservation Authority
Exeter, Ontario

Background

Observations of the Great Lakes shorelines made over a number of years clearly demonstrate two phenomena that are of considerable concern to land owners and organizations with land use planning responsibilities. They are that the shoreline at many locations continues to change slowly through a process of erosion or accretion, and that during storms, particularly those occurring during periods of high water level, considerable damage occurs at the shoreline.

In response to these issues, and particularly the latter issue of storm damage and flooding, the Ministry of Natural Resources (MNR) developed guidelines for the preparation of Great Lakes shoreline management plans that have the objective of preventing reoccurrence of the damage at the shoreline that has occurred in the past. The responsibility for the implementation of these guidelines was given to the Conservation Authorities. This recognized the local knowledge, interests, and concerns of each Conservation Authority along the different shorelines of the Great Lakes. It also recognized the close involvement of the municipalities with the Conservation Authorities.

The Shoreline Management Plan (SMP) developed by the Ausable Bayfield Conservation Authority for the section of the Lake Huron shoreline over which we have jurisdiction (Figure 1) is discussed in this paper along with the purpose for which the plan is intended. This includes the information that is available through the plan to assist municipalities, lakeshore stakeholders and existing and prospective landowners to utilize wisely the valuable resource which we describe as the shoreline.

Figure 1. Location of the Ausable Bayfield C.A. Shoreline

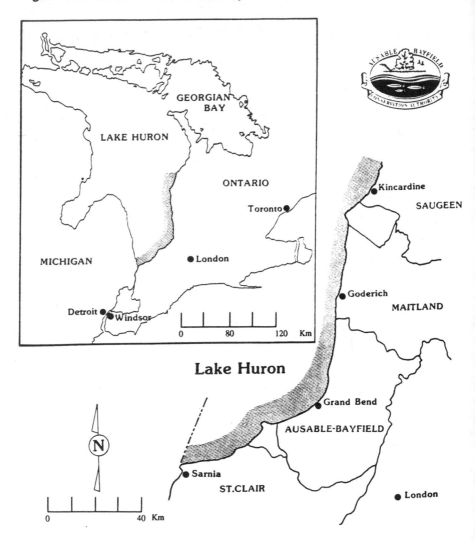

The principal objective of a SMP is to reduce or eliminate damage that may occur to existing development at the shoreline during severe storms in periods of high water and prevent new development from occurring in areas where hazards are present. To respond to this objective, a SMP will typically identify high risk areas associated with flooding, erosion and moving sand, establish setbacks from the shoreline for new development, and will identify shoreline protection considerations for existing development in high risk areas.

In February of 1988, the Ausable Bayfield Conservation Authority (ABCA) became the lead agency for planning matters along the 60 kilometre stretch of the Lake Huron shoreline over which we have jurisdiction. This encompasses the area stretching from the north limit in Lot 30, Concession 1 in Goderich Township south through the Village of Bayfield, Townships of Stanley, Hay, Stephen, and the Village of Grand Bend, to the southerly limit in Bosanquet Township at the community of Port Franks. The ABCA was directed to prepare a Shoreline Management Plan to include the shoreline of these seven municipalities.

The main objective of this specific shoreline management plan is to represent the MNR guidelines while considering the unique characteristics of the shoreline, the requirements of the community, and the responsibilities of the ABCA.

The ABCA Shoreline Management Plan has four overall objectives:

1) to prevent storm related damage adjacent to the shoreline by a) designating a hazard area and by implementing a policy that prevents development and significant reconstruction in this area; and by b) providing guidelines for the design of well engineered shore protection structures to be built in relation to existing development only and that fully reflect the dynamic nature of the shoreline;

2) to improve the environment and quality of life in the area adjacent to the shoreline by designating environmentally important areas and by encouraging and supporting the implementation of existing regulations designed to conserve the natural environment;

3) to provide a basis for continuing economic development of the region through effective planning that maintains the high quality of the environment of the region;

4) to provide a plan for the future such that future generations can enjoy an improved quality of life in the region.

Plan Development

At an early stage in the program it was agreed that effective representation from both counties, all seven municipalities, Ministry of Natural Resources (MNR) offices, and a selected number of cottage associations would be needed to provide the views and concerns of the lakeshore stakeholders.

A steering committee was formed to oversee the project and to provide direction. This committee was made up of two groups; the Project Committee and the Technical Committee. The Project Committee had representation from each of the seven municipalities, four cottage associations, and the Pinery Provincial Park (MNR). The Technical Committee represented the regulatory bodies along the lakeshore: Huron County Planning Department, Lambton County Planning Department, Public Health Department, MNR (Wingham and Chatham District Offices and the Lands and Water Policy Section in Toronto), and the two neighbouring Conservation Authorities being the Maitland Valley and St. Clair Region. A coastal consultant also provided technical input and direction to the committees. The wide representation on the committees was intended to provide a diverse background for comments on the creation of the plan. Both committees were involved from the beginning of the process and will likely continue in some form after the Plan is adopted. It is hoped that their participation will increase the effectiveness and acceptance of the Plan.

A first step was to identify the principal concerns of the community that relate to the shoreline, as well as opportunities where a shoreline management plan could provide insight into a variety of issues, recognizing that the principal thrust of the plan was to be the prevention of damage through proper management. This was accomplished through a polling of landowners and interested persons who attended two Public Meetings in the summer of 1990 and 1991 on the topic of shoreline management. This was a valuable exercise that indicated to us the concern which existed for shoreline stabilization and storm damage protection; the environment; water dependent activities; improved public space and economic development.

The Steering Committee ranked these issues according to high, medium and low priority. Although the scope of the SMP was broadened as much as feasible to include the issues relevant to this specific Lake Huron shoreline, priorities were necessary to reflect the mandate of the ABCA and limitations in project funding.

The issues were ranked as follows:

High Priority: Storm damage reduction
                           Shoreline stabilization

Medium Priority: Environmental protection
                           Water quality
                           Development pressure
                           Public access to the shoreline

Low Priority: Water dependent activities
                           Improvement of "green space"
                           Economic development

The second step was to describe and quantify the movement of sand and rate of erosion in order to provide a technical basis for the plan. The shoreline is dynamic. Many thousands of cubic metres of sand are transported along the shoreline to the south each year with some sections of the shoreline eroding at rates of greater than one metre per year.

The ABCA shoreline is contained within one littoral cell with a "J" shape. The cell northerly boundary begins at the harbour structure in the Town of Goderich and ends at the natural barrier formed by Kettle Point to the south (Figure 2). The source of material which moves along the littoral zone and forms the beaches is derived predominantly from erosion of the bluffs north of Grand Bend, while deposition occurs in the dune and beach region south of Grand Bend.

From this you can see that the landowners have very different concerns. The landowners in the south rely on sand to maintain their dunes. The source of this sand is the eroding bluffs in the northerly section of the shoreline. If the landowners in the north stop the bluff erosion, the dunes in the south will not receive the necessary supply of sand.

After the shore processes were understood, the next step was to define hazard areas on which new development should not occur and where redevelopment of existing structures should be limited. To determine these hazardous areas for future development, we looked to the past, using a historical 1935 survey and recent photogrammetric mapping (Figure 3). Lines were drawn on 1:2000 scale maps to indicate the probable future shoreline position in 100 years and the location of the top of the bluff, considering the unstable slope of many of the bluffs. With this information, the basis of a policy was developed to control development along the shoreline, in order to prevent future damage during storms and recognizing the long term erosion of the shorelines.

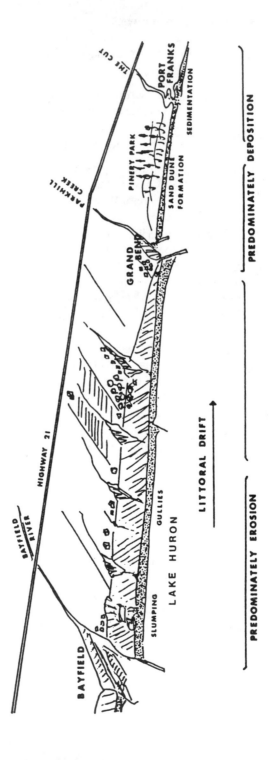

Figure 2. Stylized Diagram of Lake Huron Shoreline (Bayfield to Port Franks)

Figure 3. Example of Shoreline Change Comparison

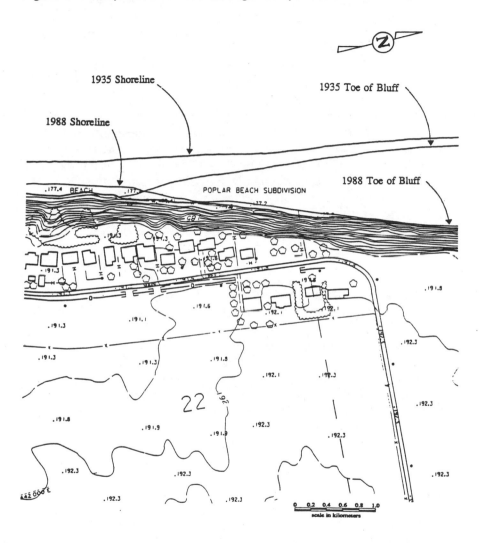

Some of the dilemmas and issues to be faced in the development of a shoreline management plan became clear. These included the following:

- The shoreline in many areas is naturally eroding. However individual property owners want to maintain their property by attempting to stop this process.
- Erosion of the bluffs provides the sand that makes up the narrow beach at the base of the bluff and provides the sand that maintains the extensive beaches between Grand Bend and Kettle Point.
- Even if the shoreline (above water) was effectively stabilized at one location, the nearshore lake bottom would continue to erode.
- The land adjacent to the shoreline is a hazard area where there is a risk of flooding and damage by storms. Along much of the shoreline, buildings have already been built in these hazard areas.
- Ownership of the shoreline/beach has come into question and requires verification to ensure that actions, such as the construction of protection, are not subject to encroachment.
- Groynes are shoreline structures that have been extensively used in some areas either to provide a beach for recreation or as shore protection. In some cases these structures have had success; however, in other areas they have been the cause of erosion to adjacent properties and litigation has resulted "pitting" cottage area against cottage area.

Given the continuing concern of shoreline owners with stabilization of the shoreline or prevention of damage during storms, shore protection guidelines were also prepared as part of this shoreline management plan. These guidelines describe the shoreline process to be considered in designing structures, and demonstrate that structures designed to stabilize the shoreline in areas where significant erosion is taking place will be extremely costly and it is unlikely that they will ever be built given the present political and economic climate. For these reasons, the most effective response to mitigating shoreline hazards is the relocation of the residence away from the shoreline.

In addition, the guidelines provide design considerations for specific shore structures. It is noted that continuing erosion of the shoreline is controlled by erosion of the nearshore lake bottom and, as very little is known about the lake bottom in terms of erosion rates or its composition, this should be further investigated. This fact further substantiates the recommendation of residence relocation rather than relying on the short term benefits of shore protection.

A draft Shoreline Management Plan has been prepared for review and provides a detailed description of the shoreline and presents maps with lines that denote flood limits, future erosion limits, stable slope allowances, and areas effected by dynamic beaches. These limits form the basis for a policy to manage existing development and control new development in order to prevent future storm related damage. This policy is introduced within the shoreline management plan and is likely the most controversial aspect and most commonly quoted portion of the entire Plan.

The shoreline management plan contains the following:

- detailed description of the shoreline and shoreline processes,
- 1:2000 scale maps showing flood limits, erosion limits, stable slope allowances (for bluffs), and
  dynamic beach limits (for sand dune areas),
- policy that controls development within the defined hazard areas,
- guidelines for the design of shore protection structures,
- designation of environmentally significant areas,
- emergency response procedures, and
- recommendations for future monitoring of the shoreline.

Municipal and Public Involvement in the Plan

As mentioned previously, from the onset of the development of the Plan, it was evident that the plan would require a significant amount of public and municipal input. We required the expertise of technical people as well as the knowledge of long-time residents of the shoreline. Of equal importance was the need for a plan that would be effective in its implementation and accepted by the lakeshore users, something that would be aided by extensive public involvement. Therefore, we began involving residents in the fall of 1989.

Five methods were used to receive input:

1. Steering Committee (Technical Committee and Project Committee)
2. Public Meetings
3. Publications
4. Open Houses
5. Personal Communications

Each method had its own purpose and degree of success. Some of the various communication challenges which we encountered are outlined below.

There are approximately 2,750 landowners in the area affected by the Plan, or about 5,000 residents. There are approximately 60 cottage areas with only half that number having organized cottage associations. As an extra challenge, the majority are seasonal residents with permanent residents elsewhere in Canada, the United States, and in a few cases, on other continents. With these varied residences, backgrounds and interests in the shoreline, the traditional local newspapers and media were not effective means to reach a significant number of affected landowners.

For this reason an information bulletin was mailed directly to all landowners in May, 1992. The bulletin informed them about the Shoreline Management Plan and encouraged them to attend the Open Houses planned throughout the summer or visit our office to learn more about the Plan and give input to the Draft document. This direct mailing eliminated the need for paid advertising of the draft plan and ensured that the information about the draft plan and direction as to where to go to obtain more information had reached all landowners.

Because of the long time span of the project (1989 - 1992) it was difficult to keep the attention of the public on the issue of shoreline management. The plan development was significantly delayed by delays in the production of the 1:2000 maps. Interest was high at the first public meeting in 1990, but interest and patience with the process waned by the second public meeting in 1991. Common remarks after the second public meeting were "don't call another meeting until you can give us more details".

Perhaps the greatest challenge was to keep all landowners apprised of the correct information. In June of 1992, unsubstantiated rumors existed and were spread among the lakeshore landowners. The benefit of this was that it got the attention of the landowners and started a great deal of discussion about shoreline management. The disadvantage of this was that much staff time was spent dispelling the rumors with correct information.

Five open houses were hosted by the ABCA at various lakeshore municipalities on Saturdays in 1992. This presented the draft plan and associated mapping to the public through displays. Staff and committee members answered questions and received comments. The open houses along with one-to-one dialogue helped to clear up much of the misinformation. Only 20 people attended the first open house, but 300 attended one later in August primarily as a direct result of the spread of erroneous information. The overall attendance was well over 500 people to the open houses.

The direction of the Technical and Project Committees was a key part of the process of developing the SMP. Both committees acted as liaisons between their respective agencies/associations and the authors of the plan. They provided local knowledge, expertise, direction and guidance.

They were involved from the beginning of the process and will likely continue in some form after the Plan is adopted. The numerous meetings required a significant time commitment without financial reimbursement. Beneficial dialogue and results occurred from having cottage association representatives sitting at the same table as municipal councillors. Unfortunately, with only four cottage representatives, it was difficult to maintain a significant liaison with the lakeshore landowners.

Occasional use of news releases at the start of the plan development was used to keep the general public up to date on the project. This was increased in intensity in May 1992 as the draft was being completed. Fact sheets were produced to complement the 1992 news releases. Personal communications involved onsite visits as well as landowner visits to our office. Staff attended municipal council and cottage association meetings to keep them apprised of the plan's development. The one-to-one communication was invaluable in addressing site specific concerns.

Because so many comments have been received, some substantial revisions may be undertaken. Of prime concern to the landowners is the effect that the plan will have on property values. The underlying theme is that the plan is a good idea for the lakeshore, but not for individual properties (especially if it's my property) and we were exposed to a variation of the NIMBY (not in my backyard) syndrome, i.e. the NAMLS (not at my lakeshore). We have found, however, that once landowners have an opportunity to read and understand what it is that the Plan is attempting to achieve, they certainly agree in principle to shoreline management.

Implementation of the ABCA Shoreline Management Plan

The implementation of the ABCA's SMP will be achieved with the overall support of the groups and agencies involved in its preparation, including;

a) the adoption of the plan by each of the seven municipalities which share lakeshore frontage;
b) the consensus of the individuals who represent the shoreline community on the steering committee;
c) the adoption of the plan by the Lambton and Huron County Planning Departments who will, with the cooperation of the municipalities, incorporate the recommendations of the SMP into the lakeshore municipality's planning documents (i.e. zoning bylaws, secondary plans, and official plans);
d) the support of the various government agencies who have an interest in the shoreline through legislation or regulations; and
e) the acceptance of the plan by the general public through the use of

open houses, news releases, and bulletins during the spring and summer, 1992 and possibly 1993.

Summary

The Shoreline Management Plan is presently in draft form with a second draft intended for release in April, 1993. Upon completion of the plan scheduled for December, 1993, it will not be a static document. It is intended to evolve to reflect the changing demands which will occur in the future. However it does set the groundwork and raise the level of awareness of basic shoreline information in a comprehensive manner and on a shoreline reach basis. This will allow landowners, land use planners, and municipalities to better understand the shoreline and how increasing changes and demands which are progressively impacting the shoreline need to be directed, altered, or changed.

The shoreline management plan is based on a vision for the future where the occurrence of severe storms is not accompanied by losses and hardships to shoreline property owners, where beaches exist along the shoreline, where access to the lake can be achieved by residents and visitors alike, and where the environment and natural landscape of the shoreline continuously improves. The shoreline is a unique resource where management is a major concern to a number of diverse user groups. It is worthy of special attention.

Developing a Shoreline Management Plan for the Saugeen Valley Conservation Authority

GEOFF PEACH
Saugeen Valley Conservation Authority
Hanover, Ontario

Introduction

The Provincial Great Lakes Shoreline Management program has, to date, focused on hazard land management, where the aim is to prevent development from locating in areas susceptible to flooding and/or erosion along the shoreline. In developing a Shoreline Management Plan for its jurisdiction along the Lake Huron shoreline, the Saugeen Valley Conservation Authority felt that a more holistic approach was required, particularly considering the sensitive nature of this section of shoreline from both a physical and a biological standpoint. The aim was to look beyond protecting development from the natural processes of the coastal environment (i.e. flooding and erosion) and include protecting the coastal environment from the negative impacts of development.

A resource survey of the study area was undertaken using the ABC Resource Survey Approach, developed at the University of Waterloo. The study identified the main abiotic, biotic and cultural features and processes of this coastal area. The information derived from this study will form the basis for the development of a Shoreline Management Plan which will attempt to maintain, preserve, restore and enhance the coastal ecology of the study area.

Shoreline Management is a relatively new undertaking of Conservation Authorities in Ontario, which have historically been involved in riverine management. In 1986, during a period of record high water levels on the Great Lakes, the Minister of Natural Resources appointed the Shoreline Management Review Committee to study and provide recommendations for the long term management of Ontario's Great Lakes shorelines. The Committee reported that in 20 southern Ontario municipalities, new construction in hazardous lands increased by

40 percent in the ten years following the last high water levels experienced in the 1970's. The Committee identified that prevention of future development in areas subject to flooding and erosion should be one of the priorities for Shoreline Management in Ontario.

The Minister subsequently announced that Conservation Authorities would fulfil this role and in 1987 the Ministry released its "Guidelines for the Development of Shoreline Management Plans", suggesting that Conservation Authorities have regard for six components:

1. prevention
2. protection
3. emergency response
4. communications
5. environment
6. monitoring

While the guidelines were somewhat vague, they did recognize that local ecological conditions vary from one reach of shoreline to another and, accordingly, responsibility for initiating Shoreline Management Plans rests at the local Conservation Authority level, and Shoreline Management Plans would be specifically tailored for each section of shoreline. The Shoreline Management Plan would be a document designed to assist and guide agencies — including the Conservation Authority — municipalities and the public in the conservation and management of coastal areas.

Given the nature of the Saugeen Valley Conservation Authority's shoreline, it was felt that while hazard land management was an important consideration, there were many other equally important considerations required in order to adequately conserve and manage the shoreline. For instance, forest fragmentation and habitat loss, destruction of sand dune ecosystems, alterations to coastal wetlands, water quality and all development-related impacts should be addressed in a shoreline management plan.

To address these issues, the Saugeen Valley Conservation Authority's approach to the development of a shoreline management plan proposes to take an ecosystem perspective. Vallentyne and Beeton (1988) have described an ecosystem approach as "an integrated set of policies and management practices that relate people to ecosystems of which they are a part rather than to external resources or environments with which they interact. Actions are ecological, anticipatory and ethical in respect to other systems of nature."

Lake Huron Shoreline Characteristics -
Point Clark to Southampton

The Lake Huron shoreline within the jurisdiction of the Saugeen Valley Conservation Authority spans approximately 82 kilometres, from Point Clark to Southampton (Figure 1). The Authority's jurisdiction extends five kilometres offshore into Lake Huron. Onshore, the coastal planning area extends inland and follows the physiographic region known as the Huron Fringe (Chapman & Putnam, 1966). This region comprises the wave cut terraces of glacial Lake Algonquin (c 10,000 years B.P.) and Lake Nipissing (c 6,000 years B.P.), with their boulders, gravel bars, relic beaches and sand dunes (Figure 2). The Lake Algonquin shorebluff is a very discernable feature within the area and acts as a convenient easterly boundary. Most of the coastal development is concentrated between the Algonquin shoreline and present Lake Huron shoreline.

The physical characteristics of the Saugeen shoreline differ markedly from the cohesive shorelines of southern Lake Huron and the Lower Great Lakes, and the management concerns and priorities are different as well. Unlike the high clay bluffs to the south, the Saugeen shoreline consists of a low lying coastal plain consisting primarily of sand and gravel deposits of former lakes. The shoreline is predominantly bedrock in the north and protected by extensive nearshore lag deposits in the south. Relic sand dunes, large sandy beaches, small "pocket" beaches, and coastal wetlands are the predominant features of this shoreline. From a hazard land perspective, flooding is the primary concern, while erosion is localized.

Biologically, the Saugeen coastal area is diverse (Figure 3). A large continuous forest corridor exists between MacGregor Point and Inverhuron Bay (Figure 4). This forested area, commonly referred to as Huron Fringe Forest, contains a mosaic of coniferous, deciduous and mixed forest communities. The corridor represents a major ecological link to the Bruce Peninsula (Parker, personal communication, 1991). South of this large forest corridor, the Huron Fringe Forest has been reduced and fragmented, largely a function of increases in development. These forest fragments to the south lack the connectivity and ecological diversity of the Huron Fringe Forest to the north.

Swamps, marshes, fens and wet beach strands are represented in isolation and in complexes within this coastal area. A series of wetlands which exist parallel to the shore between MacGregor Point, south to Baie du Dore, form a successional gradient from open water, through sedge dominated marshes and shrub phases to closed deciduous swamps (Hilts & Parker, 1980). Development pressure is beginning to threaten the eco-

Figure 1. Lake Huron Coast Study Area

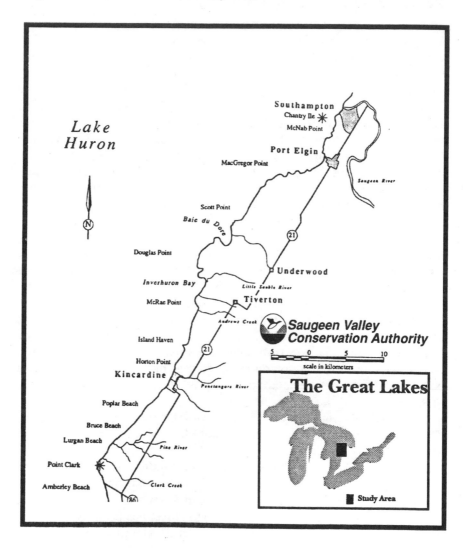

Figure 2. Lake Huron Coast Quaternary Geology

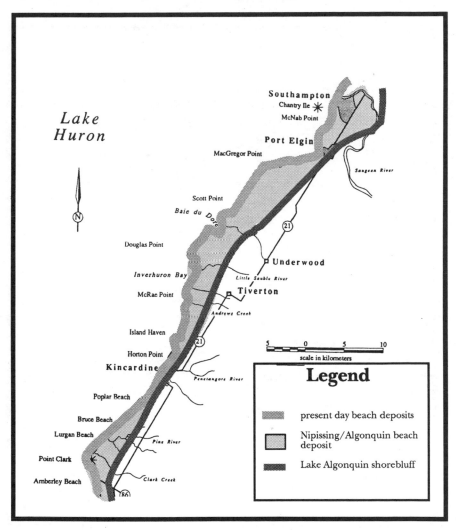

Figure 3. Areas of Biological Significance

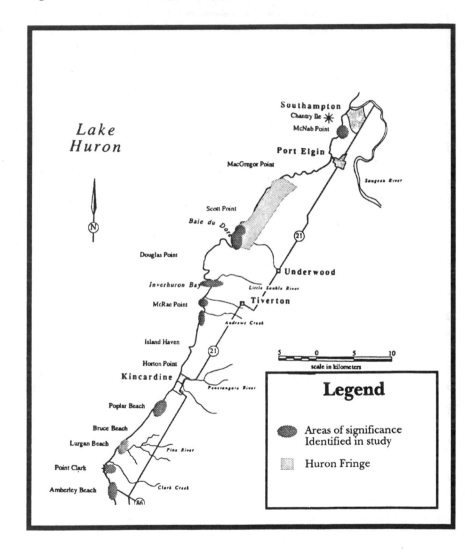

Figure 4. Forest

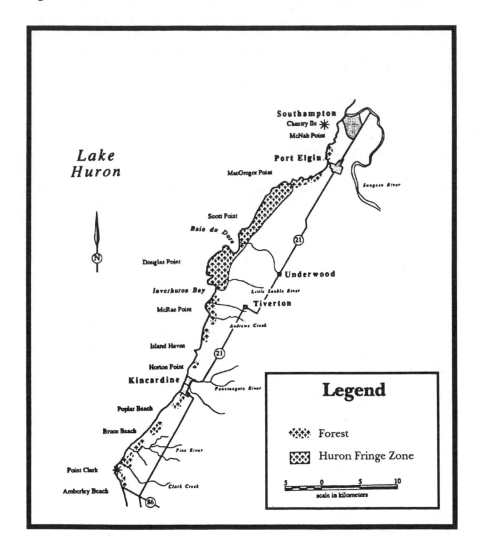

logical function and balance of many of these wetlands.Sand dune areas, in various stages of successional development, occur in a number of locations in the Saugeen coastal area. A number of Provincially rare vascular plants have been identified in these areas. Most of the dunes are being disturbed or altered from human activity, and will require management initiatives to protect them. Finally, mammal, herpetofaunal and fisheries inventories conducted in the area emphasize the importance of the Saugeen coastal zone for a variety of habitat.

ABC Resource Survey

In developing a Shoreline Management Plan, the Saugeen Valley Conservation Authority felt that a holistic or ecological approach would be necessary, given the nature of the shoreline within its jurisdiction. As a first step, it was considered necessary to prepare a background study that would be comprehensive in looking at the coastal environment. A literature review of holistic resource management studies and surveys revealed that the Heritage Resources Centre, at the University of Waterloo, had been developing an approach known as the ABC Resource Survey. This approach focused on abiotic, biotic and cultural resources (hence, ABC) from both their function and process, allowing one to look at the general ecological characteristics of a study area for purposes of planning and management.

One of the key aspects which made the ABC approach attractive to the Saugeen Valley Conservation Authority was that all of the information gathered and analyzed during the study process was mapped, so that the information would be very visual. Since the Authority's Shoreline Management Plan would involve public consultation at various levels, it was felt that this visual aspect could be very helpful in conveying information and ideas.

The Heritage Resources Centre was contracted to assist the Saugeen Valley Conservation Authority in carrying out an ABC Resource Survey of its coastal area. The HRC would contribute two research interns, while the Saugeen Valley Conservation Authority would contribute two summer staff hired under the federal Environmental Youth Corps program. The Project Management Team included Dr. Gordon Nelson, Dr. Rafal Serafin, Patrick Lawrence of the HRC, and the author, representing the Saugeen Valley Conservation Authority.

During our initial meetings, it was felt that, given the scope and magnitude of the project, the study could benefit greatly from public input at the very outset, and so this was incorporated into the Terms of

Reference. Initial themes for mapping by the ABC were identified by the Study Team, and listed for further consideration by agencies, municipalities, and the public. A meeting of public agencies and interest groups was first held to get some initial input and reaction. This was followed by a public meeting to present an overview of the project and present the first set of draft maps. The public was asked for their input to help the Study Team ensure that the information being collected was accurate, and that none of the important information was being omitted. A second public meeting was held four months later to present the draft report. This was another attempt to get comments, information and suggestions before the final report was to be prepared. Comments received from the public through this process showed that they were quite receptive to this public involvement approach.

Towards a Shoreline Management Plan - Discussion

The final report was presented to the Saugeen Valley Conservation Authority by the Heritage Resources Centre in the spring of 1992. With the completion of this comprehensive study, the next phase involves taking the findings and recommendations from this report and develop a Management Plan that will be functional, and not just another report for the bookshelf. The Plan should be action-oriented, with time horizons for achieving tasks. The Shoreline Management Plan will articulate the Saugeen Valley Conservation Authority's direction as to how it intends to address issues within its mandate and sphere of influence over the next 20 years.

The Plan will set out strategies for carrying out work in the four main areas of Conservation Authority work:

1. Information and Education - informing and educating local municipalities, agencies, special interest groups, and the general public about shoreline management issues,
2. Land Use Planning and Regulations - plan input and review functions under The Planning Act, establishing and enforcing Regulations under the Conservation Authorities Act,
3. Research and Monitoring - collecting information necessary to gain a better understanding of the coastal ecosystem, in order that appropriate policies can be developed based on the best information available. Monitoring changes in the coastal landscape will be critical to ensure that policies and strategies are relevant,

4.   Extension - includes community environmental projects, land acquisition, capital works, landowner advisory service, landscape restoration projects.

Where issues identified in the SMP are beyond the Authority's mandate, the Authority will encourage agencies and interest groups to respond to the issues in a manner that would be consistent with the goals and objectives of the SMP, and try to establish some form of commitment as to what action they would be prepared to take. To achieve that, the Authority would look at doing a number of things:

(i)   ensure that the roles with respect to the shoreline are clarified amongst agencies;
(ii)   minimize overlap in the way various agencies with a role in shoreline management operate;
(iii)   act as a catalyst in encouraging research initiatives (e.g. water quality studies, habitat research, forest ecology studies, etc.);
(iv)   form partnerships with other groups and agencies in areas of communication, strategic planning and extension work.

Overseeing the preparation of the SMP will be a Steering Committee comprised of members of the Authority's Board of Directors, a representative from the Ministry of Natural Resources, County Planning Department and the Heritage Resources Centre. In addition, three "Task Groups" are proposed to prioritize the issues and look at alternatives for dealing with each of the issues. The three Task Groups reflect three key components stressed in the ABC report—Environment, Communications and Land Use Planning. The Task Groups will be represented by landowners, cottage association representatives, naturalist groups, as well as technical specialists and municipal representatives. The public-at-large will be consulted through a "Coastal Forum", which will act to inform people interested in shoreline management and solicit their input into the process.

A formidable challenge lies ahead to develop an effective, proactive management plan which, as it is intended, will involve implementing an ecosystem approach to shoreline management. Many have advanced the idea of Great Lakes Ecosystem Management (e.g. Rawson Academy, 1989, I.J.C., 1990, Crombie Commission, 1992), and it is, in the author's views, the appropriate course to follow. The ABC Resource Survey will be a key starting point to achieving these ends.

REFERENCES

Chapman, L and Putnam (1984) *The Physiography of Southern Ontario*, 3rd Edition, University of Toronto Press.

Crombie Commission (1992) *Regeneration - Toronto's Waterfront and the Sustainable City: Final Report*, Royal Commission on the Future of the Toronto Waterfront, Queen's Printer.

Hilts, S. and M. Parker (1980) *Environmentally Sensitive Areas of Southern Bruce County*, unpublished report to the Ministry of Natural Resources.

International Joint Commission (1989) *Living with the Lakes: Challenges and Opportunities*, progress report to the IJC from the Project Management Team, Levels Reference Study

Lawrence, P.L. and J. G. Nelson (1992) *Preparing for a Shoreline Management Plan for the Saugeen Valley Conservation Authority*, Heritage Resources Centre publication, University of Waterloo, Waterloo, Ontario.

Lawrence, P.L., J. Chisholm, M. Healy, and M. Quinn (1992) *Resource Survey of the Lake Huron Coast: Technical Notes*, Heritage Resources Centre publication, University of Waterloo, Waterloo, Ontario.

Ontario Ministry of Natural Resources (1987) *Guidelines for Developing Great Lakes Shoreline Management Plans*, Conservation Authorities and Water Management, Ministry of Natural Resources.

Rawson Academy of Aquatic Science (1989) *Towards an Ecosystem Charter for the Great Lakes - St. Lawrence*, Rawson Occasional Paper No. 1, Ottawa, Canada.

Vallentyne, J.R. and A.M. Beeton (1988) "The Ecosystems Approach to Managing Human Uses and Abuses of Natural Resources in the Great Lakes Basin." *Environmental Conservation*, 15(1), 57-62.

Panel Discussion

Panel: Peter Burtch, Sault Ste Marie Ministry of Natural Resources
         Jim McCoob, Kettle Creek Conservation Authority
         Pat Donnelly, Ausable-Bayfield Conservation Authority
         Geoff Peach, Saugeen Valley Conservation Authority

Moderator: Reid Kreutzwiser, University of Guelph

Kreutzwiser: We have time to have questions of the presenters and perhaps discuss some significant issues.

What is the cost, per kilometer for the plans, and how you are you funding the local portion of the cost ?.

Peach: In our particular situation the plan is funded locally at 85% for our particular area. 50% of this is raised with levees to the seven municipalities. The Heritage Resources Centre project which we completed last year was done at a cost of $15,000, and the greater part of our funding is used for public participation. The plan itself will be done in-house.

Would you care to comment on whether you're planning provides for some degree of uncertainty

Donnelly: The one thing that we did highlight in the plan is something that I think will be coming out of the IJC Levels Reference Study. The lakeshore bottom continues to erode regardless of what lake level you are talking about. There is an erosion component there and to some degree the lake bottom erosion is the controlling factor for bluff recession. For that reason an attempt is being made to raise local awareness that protection structures are effective as long as they are properly designed and maintained.

Kreutzwiser: Further to that question, I think we have the capacity now to identify which areas of Great Lakes shore might be sensitive to a lowering of water levels due to climate warming. It certainly is a concern of mine that possible changes in shore ice might effect shore erosion.

Nelson: In the Saugeen Valley Conservation Authority public meetings, we raised the question of climate change in public meetings several times, no one responded. That is one reason why that doesn't appear in the documentation that we've prepared. That in turn raises the kind of fundamental question of how you deal with an issue like that when people don't really respond to it in any way.

Peach: The shoreline management plan is a twenty year time horizon. I am not sure that any lowering of the water levels due to climate change is going to occur in the time frame that we are talking about here.

Kreutzwiser: I think that Marie Sanderson is thinking of a slightly longer term, but I think the issue is more one of uncertainty and how we can plan for it.

Are the Conservation Authorities based on watersheds ?

Donnelly: Yes

Is their sole focus on shoreline management ? And if so what do you do with the rest of the watershed ?

Donnelly: Conservation Authorities have been involved in protecting and enhancing natural resources of the watershed on a riverine basis, that has been the focus of most conservation authorities. Some, like the Essex, which is surrounded by three shorelines, have focussed on shorelines. Shoreline management is a new program started in 1987, with the transfer of responsibilities to the Conservation Authorities, so it is fairly recent. The rest of the programs of the Conservation Authorities focus on protection of properties from flooding in riverine situations as well as water quality, and other issues such as conservation, recreation and land.

Who is it that defines the characteristics of the shoreline, the things that are going to be dealt with there ?

Kreutzwiser: It is my understanding that the 1987 guidelines offer some initial guidance, but again I think this is something that is likely to be interpreted differently depending on who you may ask. You may get three or four different responses.

I have heard George Penfold discuss the work of the Sewell Commission, and he seemed very optimistic that once provincial policy is in place, municipalities in Ontario will have responsibility for land use planning . What I have heard today is that the conservation authorities are developing plans. How do you see the Sewell Commission having an effect on shoreline management ?

Donnelly: I don't think that what the Sewell Commission is suggesting goes along the lines of what we are already doing in terms of watershed planning.

Kreutzwiser: There is a fundamental question here that has been a concern to me. I don't see that these Conservation Authority shoreline management plans have any legal basis. They are guiding documents and I am not at all clear what the relationship between these plans and official plan documents really is. In other words will anything else be done under the Planning Act? I appreciate that the elements of the plan — at least the regulatory functions of the authorities — will get a boost when we have this provincial policy under Section 3 of the Planning Act. But in terms of the documents themselves, the plans that the CA's have been working on for awhile, some of which are finished in the case of Kettle Creek, with Sault Ste Marie and others, how do these fit with what municipalities are doing ?

Lawrence: In regard to the Sewell Commission, a major concern of mine is that they are promoting the idea that municipalities do watershed planning and they are downplaying the role of the Conservation Authorities. In fact I was surprised to note little enthusiasm in the commission for the role of CA's in watershed planning and I have not seen anything in regards to shoreline planning whatsoever. In terms of the shoreline management plans, it appears that without the solid support of the provincial policy statement, the plans will be used as tools for education, communication, public awareness. They are excellent information documents for discussing the issues related to the shoreline, and can be used very effectively as a tool. But how does that fit into the planning process, whether that be municipal or watershed plans of the conservation authorities?

Donnelly: From a Huron County perspective, we envision the CA shoreline management plan as a background document. In other words, the zoning and other planning documents are put in place by the municipalities for the shoreline areas. There will be more information through the plans to provide direction to the municipalities to make changes, revise the zoning by-laws and setbacks.

Nelson: If the plans are thought of as a strategic document then it could influence the way people make public investment. Infrastructure, sewer lines, parks, and so on are all decisions that could be made based on what is in the plan. Those are much more fundamental decisions in terms of deciding what is going to happen along the shore. Plans are also broadly educational. Lots of people don't really understand the coastal situation very well. They don't have an overview even of the area they live in, as to what is happening in one area as opposed to another. So in that sense they will have a better appreciation of what is happening and they are better informed and more likely to participate in the process of developing the plans and their implementations.

Two points of clarification. In reference to the role of the shoreline management plans in the municipal planning process, the shoreline management plans once adopted by the municipalities will become the policy of the authority. Municipalities have the option of using that information when they update their zoning and planning documents. The authorities also have the option, as has been done in a couple of authorities, of securing provincial regulations which would then allow the authority to enforce what the shoreline management plan says.

Regarding the Sewell Commission in terms of watershed planning, their concern is that they do not want the Conservation Authority watershed plans to supersede the municipal planning documents. The Commission is suggesting that the watershed plans become an integral part of the planning process, but they are not a document above the planning documents.

I have found it very exciting this morning to see the range of things that the various conservation authorities are trying. Has someone approved these, for example the plan for the Long Point area.

Kreutzwiser: There is really no provision for approval of these plans. That is a real concern that I have had for a long time.

These very comprehensive plans, for example the Saugeen, are really impressive documents, but who is seeing that these things fit together, I have always been concerned about the destruction of the environment and I did not have any sense from what you are saying that these things are going to fit together as a package. Is there someone looking at the whole package ?

Kreutzwiser: The provincial committee that drafted the basis for the provincial shoreline management program envisioned that the planning process should be a more centralized effort. The Ministry of Natural Resources would be preparing these plans, perhaps on a lake wide basis. The Ministry accepted the notion of the preparation of the plans but opted instead to give the responsibility to the Conservation Authorities and there is some merit in that. I can see that the conditions on Lake Erie or Lake Huron vary considerably and that there should be opportunities for local initiatives. But, the tradeoff is the possibility of not having consistency and coordination. The plans are largely being done independently with a few exceptions. Four Lake Huron conservation authorities have decided to cooperate. But there is nothing that forces or strongly encourages cooperation. There is no mechanism that I am aware of that specifies for example, that the Ministry must ensure that the plans meet these guidelines or goals.

Session V

SETTING THE AGENDA:
GROUP SESSIONS

Montreal River, Lake Superior
Cobble Beach/river mouth formation
(photo provided by Peter Burtch, Sault Ste Marie, MNR)

Working Group Reports

Small working group sessions were held to consider the ideas and information in the papers presented at this meeting. The following are summaries of discussions and recommendations presented by each group.

GROUP # 1   SUMMARY

Moderator: Christian J. Stewart, Environment Canada

Consistency

Consistency in the application of certain shoreline management policies and practices was identified as one concern. For example, many municipalities will enforce strict setback or elevation requirements, but others will not. Also, in the U.S., setbacks for erosion vary from state to state, some using 50 year setbacks, others using 30 year, others using 100 year. It was felt by the group that in Ontario, consistency will improve greatly once the Provincial Flood and Erosion Policy is in place.

Some in the group felt that the 100 year setback criteria for recession was too harsh and that it would be difficult to "sell" this to the public. A related comment was that it might be difficult to sell a line on a map if there is no physical basis for the line. To explain, the 100 year setback will be based on historic recession rates. It is assumed in setting the setback line, that rates of recession that have occurred in the past, will continue in the future. However, if the shore erodes back to a more stable position (a more resistant soil type), then the recession rate could change, and hence the position of the setback line would be different. In other words, we would be drawing a line based on an extrapolation of the past, without a clear knowledge of what the real future would be. It was felt that this issue needs to be addressed very clearly in the Provincial Policy and the implementation guidelines that are developed.

Shoreline Management or Coastal Zone Management?

A second issue that came to light, was related to terminology, as well as to the overall objective of Great Lakes Shoreline (zone?) Management. Are we examining shoreline management, or are we examining coastal zone management? There is a key difference. Shoreline management can be perceived as simply addressing a line along the coast, that line being the interface between land and water. Issues to be addressed along this "line" would include those that are being addressed by the Provincial Program, for example flooding, erosion, shore damages and shoreline protection. Coastal zone management on the other hand, would deal with the interface among all land based (e.g. land use) and water based (e.g. boating, industry) activities within the entire watershed.

It was felt that the Provincial Program, at this point, represents a shoreline management plan, in that it only addresses the flooding and erosion issue, but that there was a strong potential for the development of coastal zone management. Programs such as the OMNR Flood and Erosion Policy, the Remedial Action Plans (RAPS), the Great Lakes Water Quality Agreement, and other possible actions such as those related to water levels and the current Water Level Reference Study, could all be linked into an overall Great Lakes Coastal Zone Management Plan.

It was felt that no one agency would want to lead, but that a system of "linked" management should be devised, so as to permit coordination of all involved agencies, both federal and provincial. There was mention of a possible "Office of Great Lakes Coastal Zone Management" which could be formed to act as facilitator of this coordination. It was also clear that some level of coordination with federal levels of government (Environment Canada) would be needed by the Province to make the policy effective. An example of such coordination is the Flood Damage Reduction Program. It was felt that this type of coordination (or at least discussion) has been lacking to date.

What Should the OMNR Flood and Erosion Policy Address?

In light of the above concern, discussion of in the current situation, OMNR's Shore Management Program continued, with the general feeling that while it tends to be promoted as an "ecosystem" approach (i.e. a coastal zone plan), it really focuses only on issues of flooding and erosion, which may be considered too narrow a view. The Policy is simply just a series of regulations to prevent future flooding and erosion damages as opposed to being a comprehensive shoreline (zone) management plan. Mention was also made of those shore management plans already completed by some Conservation Authorities, and as to how they tended to be oriented to structural solutions. It was felt that OMNR should not promote their Program as one that addresses the whole ecosystem, but that they should make it very clear that it is only addresses a narrow range of issues within that ecosystem.

Public Education, Consultation, Involvement and Participation

The importance of involving the public in the decision making process, as opposed to simply presenting decisions for their comment, was highlighted. The example of the public participation component of the IJC Levels Reference study was given. While public involvement in the working groups of this study has sometimes been rather negative (long learning curves, breaking through their bias on certain issues), it has been primarily positive, as it gives many interest groups a chance to state their preferences for decisions before the decisions are made. It also highlights for people the complexities involved in comprehensive studies of that nature, and it better educates people as to the physical, social, environmental and economic processes that occur.

It was felt that for any shore management plan to work in the Great Lakes basin, the public needs to be involved from start to finish. The involvement of many citizens and public interest groups in the development of Conservation Authority Shore Management Plans is a good start in this regard.

Where Do We Take These Ideas?

There was some frustration as to where all the great ideas being put forth in this discussion and at this workshop will go. Many of us are not in positions to be able to make that great a difference and it was felt that there would be difficulty in communicating these ideas to the "higher-ups." There was also a feeling that those who make the decisions need to be "re-trained" to think in terms of the ecosystem approach.

Ultimately, the group felt that both a "bottom-up" and "top-down" approach needed to be taken. If those of us at the bottom continue to promote the need for comprehensive management programs to those above us, and similarly, those at the top strive to implement programs they feel can be important, then at some point there will be a "meeting of the minds" and successful programs may get off the ground.

From a federal perspective, it was felt that there could be a number of "tie-ins" for Great Lakes Shore Management (and for that matter an overall Canadian Coastal Zone Management Program) with the Greenplan initiatives currently underway.

Implementation / Communication of Shore Management Practices

The group felt that the development of shoreline management regulations on the part of Conservation Authorities was good, but that the communication of these policies to the member municipalities was often poor. This, it was felt, has led to rather poor and inconsistent enforcement of many of the regulations. For example, while the Long Point Region Conservation Authority has a Shore Management Plan completed, the municipality is still allowing construction, and reconstruction of cottages and homes on Hastings Drive, a road that was virtually wiped out by flooding and wave damage during two storms in 1985.

It was felt that Plans needed to have more "teeth" so that these types of situations could be prevented. It was also felt that more efforts need to go towards educating communities and municipalities as to the ecosystem nature of the basin. The group argued that while you could teach some the importance of ecosystem values so that they could see why certain regulations were needed, there would be difficulty in teaching others this, and as a result, tough regulations would be needed to properly manage the shoreline.

Finally, it was felt that the range of shore management practices, from educating people on ecosystem values, to enforcing tough regulation on setbacks, represented a set of shore management "tools" that a manager would have available to deal with issues on a site specific or regional basis.

GROUP #2 SUMMARY

Moderator: Andrew Skibicki, Heritage Resources Centre

Major Issues

1. There is a need for a better way to bring conservation authorities together, perhaps we need a new vehicle to accomplish this. This is also tied to the need for better co-ordination amongst C.A.'s. Authorities also vary amongst each other in physical and jurisdictional ways and we need to understand this in any further planning for the coastal zone.
2. Agencies such as C.A.'s need a better way to adapt to municipal planning and to work with these other levels of government. Problems can occur when a C.A.'s project or mandate interferes with a municipality's jurisdiction or interest.   Municipalities are very defensive about this involvement.
3. The Waterfront Regeneration Trust can serve as a good model to get C.A.'s to talk to other levels of government and to NGO groups.   A Trust may be a difficult initiative to implement in poorer areas.
4. Is there a problem with the lack of strong federal involvement? Do we need more federal guidance or funding for projects at a comparable level to what is going on in the U.S.?

How Should the Issues be Addressed?

1. Stronger provincial direction is needed. Perhaps we need to establish a shoreline agency or "pool resources" towards more effective operation and protection of the shoreline. Perhaps a financial commitment from the province is what is needed.
2. Public Education: Perhaps we could target C.A. educational programs towards shoreline property owners in a more direct manner, for example, use the landowner contact program in the Grand River watershed for Carolinian Canada sites as a model for shoreline resources. NGO's could be more active.
3. Provincial Policy Statements: These should be designed to allow for

regional variations. i.e. emphasizing what is regionally important in each coastal area. Ministry directives can be too stringent and not based on the needs of the individual C.A.'s. These need to be more flexible and adaptable to the region involved.

What Can we do? What do we want to do?

1. The Trust idea may be effective in bringing people together but can it meet all the major needs ?. Some types of provincial statements/standards must eventually be set.
2. Monitoring problems: We need standard data and collection methods. We could have a regional information network (perhaps established by a Trust) that is gathering updated and supporting data for shoreline management. Conservation Authorities have trouble getting monitoring information as they don't know where to turn for convenient data.
3. Communications: There is a need for easier data exchange between C.A.'s. Links could be made between C.A.'s and universities for better data exchange.
4. A more open policy is needed to get information from the federal-provincial to the local level. The federal government may have an easier time getting concepts in place for better shoreline management.
5. Assessing for cumulative effects is a difficult matter in coastal areas. We should look for better ways to get at this.

GROUP # 3 SUMMARY

Moderator: Ron Stenson, Heritage Resources Centre

Perceived Problems

It was generally agreed by all of those present that the greatest problem facing coastal zone management, regardless of geographical location, is a lack of coordination among "responsible agencies". It was felt that all other technical problems paled in comparison to this overwhelming shortcoming. Other problems that were named but not particularly addressed were: (i) lack of consistent guidelines at either the provincial or especially the federal level; (ii) lack of initiatives for monitoring base-line data for assessment of the few policies or plans implemented; and (iii) too much emphasis is on physical (engineering) management approaches and not enough on zoning and restrictions for development.

Promising Moments

It was pointed out that at different times over the last decade or so a few promising initiatives were completed, but that they were never followed through upon. One example of this was the 1981 document produced jointly by Fisheries and Oceans, Environment Canada, and Ontario Ministry of Natural Resources (OMNR), i.e. the Canada/Ontario Great Lakes Shore Management Guide. The document contained very good suggestions, but no mandate to follow through, implement or enforce.

Prospective Solutions

It was suggested that in light of the general lack of coordination between present agencies, a new lead agency be established and mandated to coordinate existing efforts. This agency may be modelled after the Royal Commission on the Future of the Toronto Waterfront. It would be responsible for long term, broad scale coastal planning and would establish guidelines with the existing agencies. The amount of resources wasted in "turf wars" was thought to be very high.

The agency would be relatively small and provincially funded. It would not be a licensing agency, but would act as the "hub in a wheel" where existing agencies would be "spokes" and the "rim" would be the coastline and its communities.

Examples of similar agencies which have enjoyed at least partial acceptance and success were given as: (1) Royal Commission on the Future of the Toronto Waterfront (Crombie Commission), (ii) the Niagara Escarpment Commission; and (iii) CORE, a central agency coordinating management of the Fraser River Estuary in British Columbia.

APPENDICES

Beaches Area of Metro Toronto Waterfront
(photo provided by Patrick Lawrence, University of Waterloo)

The Waterfront Regeneration Trust: From Concepts to Implementation Notes for the Evening Keynote Address

L.R.L. SYMMES
Toronto Waterfront Regeneration Trust
Toronto, Ontario

Introduction

On June 25 1992, the Ontario Legislature approved Bill 1, An Act to Establish the Waterfront Regeneration Trust. The Bill received Royal Assent the same day, establishing the Waterfront Regeneration Trust as an agency of the provincial government. The Trust will build on the work of the Royal Commission on the Future of the Toronto Waterfront by working in co-operation with all stakeholders toward implementing the Commission's recommendations.

The objects of the Waterfront Regeneration Trust are to:

- facilitate the establishment of a trail and associated green or open spaces on waterfront lands from Burlington Bay to the Trent River;
- co-ordinate programs and policies of the Government of Ontario and its agencies relating to waterfront lands;
- advise the Province on any matters relating to the use, disposition, conservation, protection, and regeneration of waterfront lands;
- serve as a resource centre and information clearinghouse for policies of the Government of Ontario relating to waterfront lands;
- consult with the public interest on the environmental integrity of waterfront lands; and
- do such other things as the Government of Ontario may direct.

At the request of the Province, the Trust is undertaking a number of priority projects, including the Lake Ontario Greenway Strategy, Garrison Common Implementation, lower Don lands Strategy, Toronto Central Waterfront Transportation Corridor Study, and the creation of Partnership Agreements.

Outline of presentation

I. Introduction

A. Who am I, Why here, Why I am pleased to have the opportunity

B. What I will talk about
1. The Royal Commission On the Future of Toronto Waterfront, and its concepts
2. The Waterfront Regeneration Trust and its mandate
    a. Projects and Product
3. Some hopes and observations for Shoreline planners

C. Opportunity for Comment, Questions, What should be done.

II. The Royal Commission on the Future of the Toronto Waterfront original mandate

The Prime Minister of Canada appointed David Crombie Commission March 30, 1988.
1. Role and mandate of Board of Toronto Harbour Commissioners
2. Future of Toronto Island Airport
3. Protection and renewal of the natural environment
4. Use of Federal lands: Olympics and Worlds Fair
5. Three year mandate

A. Added Provincial Mandate (2nd in history) after first interim report: Appointed as a Provincial Commission October 17 1989 to address:
1. Appropriate allocation of waterfront lands
2. Waterfront transportation
3. Housing and community development on waterfront
4. Employment and job opportunities
5. Initiatives to preserve and enhance the quality of the environment
6. Area expanded to the Greater Toronto Area (GTA) (Burlington to Ajax) waterfront, Niagara Escarpment north and west, and Oakridges Moraine north and east

B. Needs Identified
1. Need for Concurrent (as opposed to sequential) Planning
    a.   Time required too long

      b.   Interchange needed to link considerations, integrate decisions

2.   City and Country Connected
      a.   Where does the water come from
      b.   Where does the food come from
      c.   How do we travel, find recreation, resources such as energy

3.   Humans part of the Ecosystem, not separate from it
      a.   Planning processes sometimes separated "environment", and "people". . . as though what we did to environment could be engineered away
      b.   Mechanisms and connections must be understood to avoid
          i.   Surprises (largely unpleasant)
         ii.   Build and fix syndrome

C.   Principles: Clean, Green, Connected, Open, Accessible, Useable, Diverse and Affordable

1.   Ecosystem approach (refer to Regeneration)
      a.   The ecosystem is "a home"
      b.   Everything is connected to everything else
      c.   Sustainability
      d.   Understanding places (all the values present)
      e.   Integrating processes.

The key is to define a natural system planning envelope rather than an arbitrary boundary, and then understand and consider the links to other systems . . . For example consider a watershed rather than a municipality, . . . or a littoral cell in a lake rather than one municipal waterfront alone.

D.   Reports, Watershed, Report 13, Regeneration

E.   Recommendations with particular reference to shorelines and CA's

1.   The need for an ecosystem approach to planning northern Lake Ontario shoreline (much broader than any one municipality)

2.   The need for a coordinated plan across jurisdictions:
      a.   Protection of remaining natural areas
      b.   Rehabilitation of degraded areas
      c.   Mechanism to consider cumulative effects
      d.   Improved access and Recreation opportunities

3.   Moratorium on major new lakefill or erosion control pending that plan

4.   Public consultation

5. Practical codes for marine construction
6. Up to date guidelines for sediments in open water disposal
7. Other related matters . . .

III. The Waterfront Regeneration Trust (Bill 1 — June 1992)

A. Mandate
1. Burlington to Trent River . . . boundaries, ecosystem
2. Facilitate the establishment of a trail and associated green or open spaces on waterfront lands Burlington Bay to the Trent River
3. Coordinate programs and policies of the Government of Ontario and its agencies relating to waterfront lands
4. Advise the Province on any matters relating to the use, disposition, conservation, protection, and regeneration of waterfront lands
5. Serve as a resource centre and information clearinghouse for policies of the government of Ontario relating to waterfront lands
6. Do such other things as the Government of Ontario may direct

B. Projects
1. Lake Ontario Green way Strategy (LOGS) , Garrison Common Implementation, Lower Don Lands Strategy, Central Waterfont Transportation (Gardner)
2. LOGS is the over all "Strategy", so-called because we do not see this as a "Plan" to further complicate implementation, but rather an over all scheme that will be implemented through existing mechanisms
   a. New and existing Government Policy and Guidelines under the Planning Act
   b. Municipal and Regional Plans and zoning
   c. A coordinated coherent approval mechanism
   d. Partnership Agreements (a multi agency tool for local action/cooperation)
3. Underlogs, Subprojects, including:
   a. Waterfront Trail
   b. Shoreline Management Project
      i. Establish what tools, information needed
      ii. What exists
      iii. What significant gaps
      iv. How best to fill them

C. Products expected from Shoreline Management Work Group
1. Descriptive maps, i.e. Key Habitat, coastal processes
2. Policy options, and draft criteria for where and how lakefilling and erosion control may take place
3. Draft guidelines for lakefilling methods and construction
4. Same for erosion control measures
5. Concise Planners Guide to coastal processes, mechanisms, and their application

D. Request comment on usefulness, other needs appropriate

E. Note Public Hearings in November

F. Approach, consultative, cooperative, facilitators

IV. Comments for Shoreline Planners

A. Comment for undertaking of shoreline management planning

B. Recommend practical application of an Ecosystem Approach
1. Remember connections to the hinterland (storm water management, etc.)

C. More than just hazard land based, balance with natural, cultural, economic values

D. Partnership agreements, a tool to bridge jurisdictions/agencies

E. Pay attention to Sewell Commission and respond

V. Closing

A. Summary
1. Commend all those here for their contribution to the difficult and complex problems of shoreline management
2. The Waterfront Regeneration Trust Agency is launching into a new Implementation Role, on the ideas of the Royal Commission
3. We hope to make our contribution through clarifying the Provincial Interest in the shoreline, and coordinating the actions of Governments within the Greater Toronto Bioregion and creating new tools (like Partnership Agreements)

4.   We hope that our work on specific shoreline management issues and plans will be of benefit more generally. We are keenly interested in what others are doing in the field

B.   Newsletter as way to keep in touch with developments, public consultation, and shoreline Work Group reports

C.   Thank for opportunity to meet and speak with so many persons interested in this important field of endeavour

REFERENCES

Royal Commission on the Future of the Toronto Waterfront (1988) *Shoreline Regeneration,* Toronto, Ontario.

Royal Commission on the Future of the Toronto Waterfront (1992) *Regeneration Final Report,* Toronto, Ontario.

Managing the Great Lakes Shoreline: Experiences and Opportunities

October 22-23, 1992
University of Waterloo, Engineering 2, room 1303

WORKSHOP AGENDA

PURPOSE

Recently there has been interest and support for bringing approaches such as ecosystem and sustainability more fully into the development of coastal or shoreline management plans at the regional level. The goal of this workshop is to review and assess several recent initiatives in regional coastal management. Case studies will be presented from Vancouver and the West coast of North America, Toronto Waterfront, Michigan, and the Great Lakes. Day two will focus on the development of Shoreline Management Plans by Ontario Conservation Authorities on the Great Lakes.The workshop will strive to bring together agencies responsible for coastal management with professionals in geography, biology and planning to evaluate the current state and future trends in management of coastal resources and development. This workshop is sponsored by the Heritage Resources Centre, University of Waterloo, the Saugeen Valley Conservation Authority and the Ontario Ministry of Natural Resources, Water Policy Section.

DAY 1 THURSDAY, OCTOBER 22, 1992

8:30-9:00   Registration

9:00-9:15   Welcome   *Gordon Nelson, and Patrick Lawrence,*
            Heritage Resources Centre
            Geoff Peach, Saugeen Valley Conservation Authority

Session I: " Setting the Stage "

9:15-9:45   Canada and Coastal Management
            Larry Hildebrand, Environment Canada

9:45-10:15   Coastal Management Approaches on the
            West Coast of Canada and U.S.
            Chad Day, Simon Fraser University

10:15-10:30 Coffee Break

10:30-11:00 Coastal Zone Management in the U.S. Great
Lakes with special reference to Michigan
Penny Holt, Michigan Department of Natural Resources

11:00-12:00   Experiences and Lessons Panel *Discussion*

12:00-1:00   LUNCH

Session II: " Alternative Approaches"

1:00-1:30 Developing a Human Ecological Approach to
Coastal Management: Case Studies from the Great Lakes
*Patrick Lawrence, and Gordon Nelson Heritage
Resources Centre*

1:30-2:00 Towards a Great Lakes Biosphere Reserve:
Linking the local to the Global
*George Francis, Environment and Resource Studies,
University of Waterloo*

2:00-2:30 Conservation of Biodiversity : Comparison of
Great Lakes and Poland Coastal Management Plans
Rafal Serafin, University of Waterloo

2:30-3:00 A Sustainable Development Approach to
Great Lakes Coastal Management
Ian McKenzie, Department of Geography, UW

3:00-3:15 Coffee

Session III: " Concepts, roles and Institutions "

3:15-3:45 Great Lakes Management and the Role of the IJC
Chris Stewart , Environment Canada

3:45-4:15 Climate Change and Great Lakes Management
Marie Sanderson, Water Network, UW

4:15-4:45 Canada's Great Lakes Clean-up Fund
Griff Sherbin, Environment Canada

4:45-5:30 The Ontario Wetlands Policy and the Great Lakes
Group Discussion
We welcome interested agencies/individuals to give a paper or
poster presentation on this topic

5:30-7:30   DINNER (Make your own arrangements)

8:00-9:30   RECEPTION / KEY NOTE
              " The Waterfront Regeneration Trust:
              From Concepts to Implementation"
              Ric Symmes, Toronto Waterfront Regeneration Trust

DAY 2 FRIDAY OCTOBER 23, 1992

Session IV: " Ontario Shoreline Management Program "

9:00-9:30   A Review of the Ontario Shoreline Management
              Program
              Pearl McKeen, Ontario Ministry of Natural
              Resources, Water Policy Section

9:30-10:00   Evaluation of Ontario Conservation Authority
              Shore Development Regulations
              Reid Kreutzwiser and Jan Slaats, University of Guelph

10:00-10:15   Coffee

10:15-12:00   Case Studies of Ontario Conservation Authorities
              Shoreline Management Plans

              Speakers:

Sault Ste Marie Ministry of Natural Resources	*Peter Burtch*
Kettle Creek Conservation Authority	*Jim McCoob*
Ausable-Bayfield Conservation Authority	*Pat Donnelly*
Saugeen Valley Conservation Authority	*Geoff Peach*

              We encourage any Conservation Authorities or other agencies
              wishing to prepare posters or displays on their Shoreline
              Management Plans or programs to contact the workshop coordinator.

12:00-1:00   LUNCH

Session V: "Setting the Agenda"

1:00-3:00   Group Sessions
Themes: Planning Needs
              Information Needs
              Developing a Shoreline Hazard Policy
              Scope-Concepts-Integration
              Public Participation-Communication-Education
              Role of Management Agencies

3:00-3:15   Coffee

3:15-4:30   Discussion/Wrap-up

List of Participants

Douglas Banks
Steering Committee
Lake Huron Preservation Association
546 Leyton Crescent
London, OntarioN6G 1T3

Karen Beazley
Heritage Resources Centre
University of Waterloo
Waterloo, Ontario N2L 3G1

Leslie Benson
Water Resources Engineer
Ganaraska Region C.A.
Box 328
Port Hope, Ontario L1A 3W4

Bianca Bielski
Municipality of Metropolitan Toronto
Metropolitan Planning Department
Metro Hall, 55 John Street,
Station 1222
Toronto, Ontario M5V 2C6

Jane M. Bowes
Adjunct Professor
University of Western Ontario
R.R. #3
Thorndale, Ontario N0M 2P0

Peter Burtch
Ministry of Natural Resources
Sault Ste Marie District
P.O. Box 130
875 Queen St East
Sault Ste Marie, Ont   P6A 5L5

Terry Chapman
Ausable Bayfield CA
R.R.#3
Exeter, Ontario N0M 1S7

Colin Crance
Wilfrid Laurier University
Department of Geography
Waterloo, Ontario N2L 3C5

Cathie Cunningham
Land & Water Management Analyst
Michigan Dept. of Natural Resources
P.O. Box 30028
Lansing, MI 48909 U.S.A.

Chad Day
Natural Resources Management
Program
Simon Fraser University
Burnaby, British Columbia
V5A 1S6

Tony DiCiocco
Engineering Technologist
Essex Region CA
360 Fairview Avenue West
Essex, Ontario N8M 1Y6

Pat Donnelly
Ausable-Bayfield CA
Box 2410, 175 Thames Road West,
Exeter, Ontario   N0M 1S0

Lee Doran, President
Ecological Writings #1 Inc.
P.O. Box 973
Adelaide St. P.O.
Toronto, Ontario M5C 2K4

Joe Farwell
Design & Construction Engineer
Grand River Conservation Authority
400 Clyde Rd. Box 729
Cambridge, Ontario N1R 5W6

George Francis
Environment and Resource Studies
University of Waterloo
Waterloo, Ontario N2L 3G1

Donald Gordon
Research Officer
World Conservation Monitoring
Centre U.K.

Larry Hildebrand
Environment Canada
45 Aldernel, 15th Flr
Queens Square
Dartmouth, Nova Scotio B2Y 2N6

Penny Holt
Land & Water Management Analyst
Michigan Dept. of Natural Resources
P.O. Box 30028
Lansing, MI 48909 U.S.A.

Drew Knight
Environmental Studies
University of Waterloo
Waterloo, Ontario N2L 3G1

Mark Kolberg
Principal
Atria Engineering Hydraulics Inc.
8 Stavebank Rd. N. #301
Mississauga, Ontario L5G 2T4

Grace Koshida
Canadian Climate Centre
Environment Canada
4905 Dufferin St.
Downsview, Ontario M3H 5T4

Reid Kreutzwiser
University of Guelph
Guelph, Ontario N1G 2W1

Tom Kurtz
Director of Shoreline Management
Waterfront Regeneration Trust
Toronto,Ontario M5J1A7

Teresa Labuda
Halton Region C.A.
2596 Britannia Road West
R.R. #2Milton, Ontario L9T 2X6

Neely Law
University of Waterloo
Waterloo, Ontario N2L 3G1

Patrick Lawrence
Heritage Resources Centre
University of Waterloo
Waterloo, Ontario N2L 3G1

Laurie Ludlow
Environmental Planner
Gore & Storrie Ltd.
Environmental Planning Services Div.
20 Hobson Street
Cambridge, Ontario N1S 2M6

Rob MacGregor
Lake Erie Management Biologist
Ontario Ministry of Natural Resources
Box 5463659 Exeter Rd.
London, Ontario N6A 4L6

Steve May
University of Waterloo
Waterloo, Ontario N2L 3G1

Laurie Maynard
Canadian Wildlife Service
Environment Canada
70 Fountain St. E.
Guelph, Ontario N1H 3N6

Jim McCoob
Kettle Creek Conservation Authority
R.R. # 8
St.Thomas, Ontario N5P 3T3

Ian McKenzie
Dept. of Geography
University of Waterloo
Waterloo, Ontario N2L 3G1

Ed Mickiewicz
Municipality of Metropolitan Toronto
MetropolitanPlanning Department
Metro Hall, 55 John Street
Station 1222
Toronto, Ontario M5V 2C6

RonMoulton
Manager, Engineering
Grand River Conservation Authority
400 Clyde Rd.Box 729
Cambridge, Ontario N1R 5W6

Rob Nairn, Consultant
Coastal Processes and Engineering
316 Maple Ave.
Oakville, Ontario L6J 2H7

Gordon Nelson, Chair
Heritage Resources Centre University
of WaterlooWaterloo, Ontario N2L 3G1

Michelle Nicolson, Consultant
Environment Canada
Water Planning and Management
867 Lakeshore Road
Burlington, Ontario L7R 4A6

Pitman Patterson, Project Co-ordinator
Shoreline Management
Waterfront Regeneration Trust
207 Queen's Quay W, Suite 580
Toronto, Ontario M5J 1A7

Geoff Peach
Saugeen Valley CA
R.R. #1, Hanover, Ontario N4N 3B8

Tom Prout
Sauble-Bayfield CA
R.R.#3, Exeter, Ontario N0M 1S5

Frank Quinn
Water Policy Advisor ECB/ESED
Environment Canada
Ottawa, Ontario K1A 0H3

Mardani Ratha
Professor and Director
Udayan University
Pusat Studi LingkanganJ1. P.B.
Sudirman Denpasar, Bali Indonesia

J. Ross Raymond, MCIP
Raymond, Walton, Hunter
Professional Planning Consultants
180 John St.N.
Gravenhurst, Ontario P1P 1H2

Jim Reckahn, President
Richmond Hill Naturalists
729 Sunnypoint Dr.Newmarket,
Ontario L3Y 2Z7

Marie Sanderson
Water Network
University of Waterloo
Waterloo, Ontario N2L 3G1

David Sawyer
St. Clair Region C.A.
205 Mill Pond Crescent
Strathroy, Ontario N7G 3P9

Glenn Schmidt
Resource Technician
Prince Edward Region C.A.
P.O. Box 310Picton, Ontario K0K 2T0

Don Scott
University of Waterloo
c/o 53 McCarron Cres.
Waterloo, Ontario N2L 5M9

Rafal Serafin, Research Associate
Heritage Resources Centre
University of WaterlooWaterloo,
Ontario N2L 3G1

Griff Sherbin
Environment Canada
Great Lakes Environment
25 St.Clair Ave East
Toronto, Ontario M4T 1M2

Andy Skibicki
Heritage Resources Centre
University of Waterloo
Waterloo, Ontario N2L 3G1

Jan Slaats
University of Guelph
Guelph, Ontario N1G 2W1

James Steel
Director, Public Education
Huntsman Marine Science Centre
Brandy Cove
St. Andrews, N.B. E0G 2X0

Ron Stenson
Heritage Resources Centre
University of Waterloo
Waterloo, Ontario N2L 3G1

Chris Stewart
Coastal Resource Scientist
Environment Canada
Canada Centre for Inland Waters
867 Lakeshore Rd., P.O. Box 5050
Burlington, Ontario L7R 4A6

Judy Sullivan
Metropolitan Toronto and Region C.A.
5 Shoreham Drive
Downsview, Ontario M3N 1S4

Ric Symmes
Toronto Waterfron Regeneration Trust
207 Queen's Quay West Suite 580
Toronto, Ontario M5J 1A7

Stan Taylor
Water Management Supervisor
Essex Region Conservation Authority
360 Fairview Avenue West
Essex, Ontario N8M 1Y6

Ingrid Vanderschot
Canada-Great Lakes Environment
25 St. Clair Ave. E. 6th Floor
Toronto, Ontario M4T 1M2

Anne-Marie Watts
Ministry of Natural Resources
Box 706, Simcoe, Ontario N3Y 4T2

Valerie Welsh
Resource Technician
Lower Thames Valley C.A.
100 Thames St.
Chatham, Ontario N7L 2Y8

Jane Welsh
Municipality of Metropolitan Toronto
Metropolitan Planning Department
Metro Hall, 55 John Street,
Station 1222
Toronto, Ontario
M5V 2C6

R.C. Wolvin
Ministry of Government Services
777 Bay St., 15th Floor
Toronto, Ontario
M5G 2E5

Gloria Yeung
Development Planner
Grand River Conservation Authority
400 Clyde Rd. Box 72
Cambridge, Ontario
N1R 5W6

Ling Yeung
Heritage Resources Centre
University of Waterloo
Waterloo, Ontario
N2L 3G1